Solutions Manual

An Introduction to Management Science
Quantitative Approaches to Decision Making
ELEVENTH EDITION

David R. Anderson
University of Cincinnati

Dennis J. Sweeney
University of Cincinnati

Thomas A. Williams
Rochester Institute of Technology

THOMSON

SOUTH-WESTERN

Australia · Canada · Mexico · Singapore · Spain · United Kingdom · United States

THOMSON

SOUTH-WESTERN

Solutions Manual for An Introduction to Management Science:

Quantitative Methods to Decision Making, 11e

David R. Anderson, Dennis J. Sweeney, Thomas A. Williams

Publisher:
George Werthman

Sr. Acquisitions Editor:
Charles E. McCormick, Jr.

Sr. Developmental Editor:
Alice C. Denny

Sr. Marketing Manager:
Larry Qualls

Sr. Production Editor:
Deanna Quinn

Manufacturing Coordinator:
Diane Lohman

Technology Project Editor:
Chris Wittmer

Sr. Media Editor:
Amy Wilson

Printer:
Globus Printing

AN INTRODUCTION TO
MANAGEMENT
SCIENCE

QUANTITATIVE APPROACHES
TO DECISION MAKING

11e

ANDERSON
SWEENEY
WILLIAMS

Contents

Preface

Chapter

Preface

The purpose of *An Introduction to Management Science* is to provide students with a sound conceptual understanding of the role management science pays in the decision-making process. The text emphasizes the application of management science by using problem situations to introduce each of the management science concepts and techniques. The book has been specifically designed to meet the needs of nonmathematicians who are studying business and economics.

The Solutions Manual furnishes assistance by identifying learning objectives and providing detailed solutions for all exercises in the text.

Note: The solutions to the case problems are included in the Solutions to Case Problems Manual.

Acknowledgements

We would like to provide a special acknowledgement to Catherine J. Williams for her efforts in preparing the Solutions Manual. We are also indebted to our acquisitions editor Charles E. McCormick, Jr. and our developmental editor Alice C. Denny for their support during the preparation of this manual.

David R. Anderson
Dennis J. Sweeney
Thomas A. Williams

Chapter 1
Introduction

Learning Objectives

1. Develop a general understanding of the management science/operations research approach to decision making.

2. Realize that quantitative applications begin with a problem situation.

3. Obtain a brief introduction to quantitative techniques and their frequency of use in practice.

4. Understand that managerial problem situations have both quantitative and qualitative considerations that are important in the decision making process.

5. Learn about models in terms of what they are and why they are useful (the emphasis is on mathematical models).

6. Identify the step-by-step procedure that is used in most quantitative approaches to decision making.

7. Learn about basic models of cost, revenue, and profit and be able to compute the break-even point.

8. Obtain an introduction to microcomputer software packages and their role in quantitative approaches to decision making.

9. Understand the following terms:

model	infeasible solution
objective function	management science
constraint	operations research
deterministic model	fixed cost
stochastic model	variable cost
feasible solution	break-even point

Solutions:

1. Management science and operations research, terms used almost interchangeably, are broad disciplines that employ scientific methodology in managerial decision making or problem solving. Drawing upon a variety of disciplines (behavioral, mathematical, etc.), management science and operations research combine quantitative and qualitative considerations in order to establish policies and decisions that are in the best interest of the organization.

2. Define the problem

    Identify the alternatives

    Determine the criteria

    Evaluate the alternatives

    Choose an alternative

    For further discussion see section 1.3

3. See section 1.2.

4. A quantitative approach should be considered because the problem is large, complex, important, new and repetitive.

5. Models usually have time, cost, and risk advantages over experimenting with actual situations.

6. Model (a) may be quicker to formulate, easier to solve, and/or more easily understood.

7. Let d = distance
        m = miles per gallon
        c = cost per gallon,

    $$\therefore \text{Total Cost} = \left(\frac{2d}{m}\right)c$$

    We must be willing to treat m and c as known and not subject to variation.

8. a. Maximize $10x + 5y$
        s.t.
        $$5x + 2y \leq 40$$
        $$x \geq 0, y \geq 0$$

    b. Controllable inputs: x and y
        Uncontrollable inputs: profit (10,5), labor hours (5,2) and labor-hour availability (40)

c.

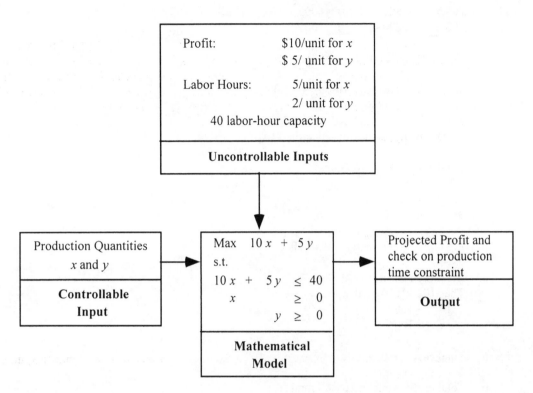

d. $x = 0$, $y = 20$ Profit = \$100
   (Solution by trial-and-error)

e. Deterministic - all uncontrollable inputs are fixed and known.

9.   If $a = 3$, $x = 13\ 1/3$ and profit = 133
        If $a = 4$, $x = 10$ and profit = 100
        If $a = 5$, $x = 8$ and profit = 80
        If $a = 6$, $x = 6\ 2/3$ and profit = 67

   Since a is unknown, the actual values of x and profit are not known with certainty.

10. a. Total Units Received = $x + y$

   b. Total Cost = $0.20x + 0.25y$

   c. $x + y = 5000$

   d. $x \le 4000$ Kansas City Constraint
       $y \le 3000$ Minneapolis Constraint

   e. Min $0.20x + 0.25y$
       s.t.

$$
\begin{array}{rcl}
x + y & = & 5000 \\
x & \le & 4000 \\
y & \le & 3000
\end{array}
$$

       $x, y \ge 0$

11. a.   at $20 $d = 800 - 10(20) = 600$
        at $70 $d = 800 - 10(70) = 100$

   b. $TR = dp = (800 - 10p)p = 800p - 10p^2$

   c.   at $30 $TR = 800(30) - 10(30)^2 = 15,000$
        at $40 $TR = 800(40) - 10(40)^2 = 16,000$
        at $50 $TR = 800(50) - 10(50)^2 = 15,000$
        Total Revenue is maximized at the $40 price.

   d. $d = 800 - 10(40) = 400$ units
        $TR = \$16,000$

12. a. $TC = 1000 + 30x$

   b. $P = 40x - (1000 + 30x) = 10x - 1000$

   c.   Breakeven when $P = 0$
        Thus $10x - 1000 = 0$
           $10x = 1000$
             $x = 100$

13. a.   Total cost $= 4800 + 60x$

   b.   Total profit $=$ total revenue - total cost
                     $= 300x - (4800 + 60x)$
                     $= 240x - 4800$

   c.   Total profit $= 240(30) - 4800 = 2400$

   d. $240x - 4800 = 0$

       $x = 4800/240 = 20$

       The breakeven point is approximately 20 students.

14. a.   Profit $=$ Revenue - Cost
               $= 20x - (80,000 + 3x)$
               $= 17x - 80,000$

       Break-even point

       $17x - 80,000 = 0$
            $17x = 80,000$
             $x = 4706$

   b.   Loss with Profit $= 17(4000) - 80,000 = -12,000$

   c.   Profit $= px - (80,000 + 3x)$
               $= 4000p - (80,000 + 3(4000)) = 0$
                              $4000p = 92,000$
                                    $p = 23$

d.   Profit = $25.95 (4000) - (80,000 + 3 (4000))
             = $11,800

Probably go ahead with the project although the $11,800 is only a 12.8% return on the total cost of $92,000.

15. a.   Profit   = $100,000x - (1,500,000 + 50,000x)$ $= 0$

$$50,000x = 1,500,000$$
$$x = 30$$

b.   Build the luxury boxes.

Profit $= 100,000 (50) - (1,500,000 + 50,000 (50))$
        $= \$1,000,000$

16. a.   Max $6x + 4y$

b. $50x + 30y \leq 80,000$
                  $50x \qquad\quad \leq 50,000$
                  $\qquad 30y \leq 45,000$
                  $x, y \geq 0$

17. a. $s_j = s_{j-1} + x_j - d_j$

or $s_j - s_{j-1} - x_j + d_j = 0$

b. $x_j \leq c_j$

c. $s_j \geq I_j$

Chapter 2
An Introduction to Linear Programming

Learning Objectives

1. Obtain an overview of the kinds of problems linear programming has been used to solve.

2. Learn how to develop linear programming models for simple problems.

3. Be able to identify the special features of a model that make it a linear programming model.

4. Learn how to solve two variable linear programming models by the graphical solution procedure.

5. Understand the importance of extreme points in obtaining the optimal solution.

6. Know the use and interpretation of slack and surplus variables.

7. Be able to interpret the computer solution of a linear programming problem.

8. Understand how alternative optimal solutions, infeasibility and unboundedness can occur in linear programming problems.

9. Understand the following terms:

problem formulation	feasible region
constraint function	slack variable
objective function	standard form
solution	redundant constraint
optimal solution	extreme point
nonnegativity constraints	surplus variable
mathematical model	alternative optimal solutions
linear program	infeasibility
linear functions	unbounded
feasible solution	

Chapter 2

Solutions:

1. a, b, and e, are acceptable linear programming relationships.

    c is not acceptable because of $-2x_2^2$

    d is not acceptable because of $3\sqrt{x_1}$

    f is not acceptable because of $1x_1x_2$

    c, d, and f could not be found in a linear programming model because they have the above nonlinear terms.

2. a.

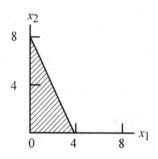

    b.

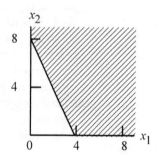

    c.

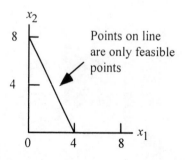

3. a.

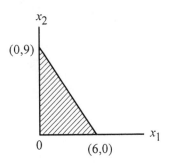

    b.

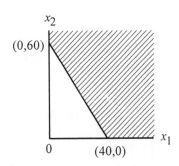

    c.

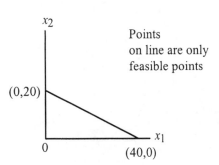

4. a.

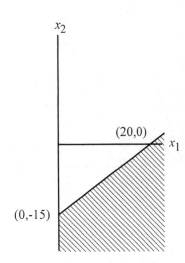

b.

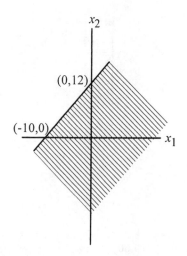

c.

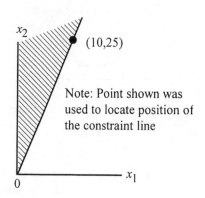

(10,25)

Note: Point shown was
used to locate position of
the constraint line

5.

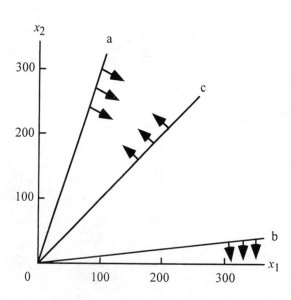

6.   For $7x_1 + 10x_2$, slope = -7/10

       For $6x_1 + 4x_2$, slope = -6/4 = -3/2

       For $z = -4x_1 + 7x_2$,   slope = 4/7

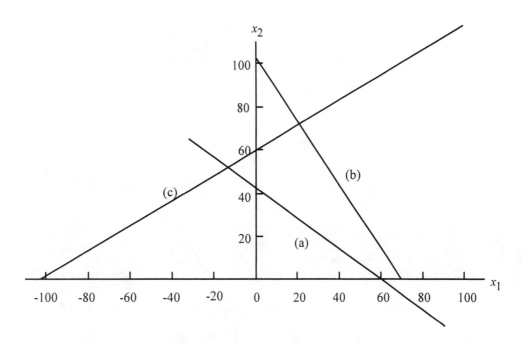

7.

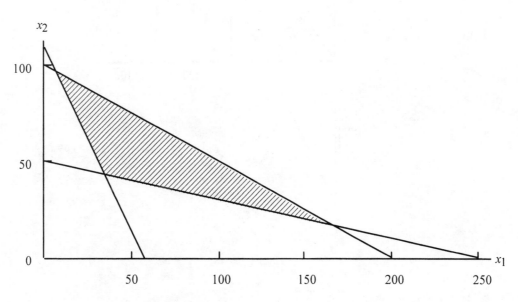

8.

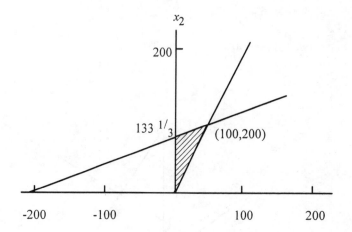

9.

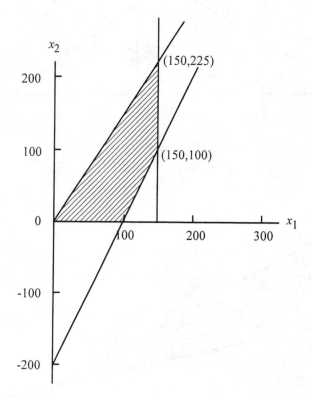

10.

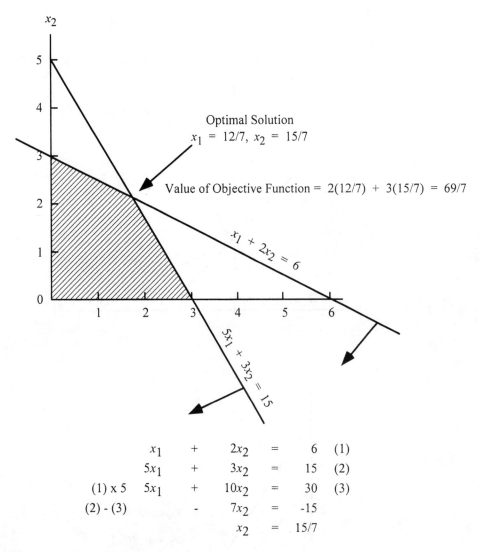

$$x_1 + 2x_2 = 6 \quad (1)$$

$$5x_1 + 3x_2 = 15 \quad (2)$$

(1) x 5 $\quad 5x_1 + 10x_2 = 30 \quad (3)$

(2) - (3) $\quad - 7x_2 = -15$

$$x_2 = 15/7$$

From (1), $x_1 = 6 - 2(15/7) = 6 - 30/7 = 12/7$

11.

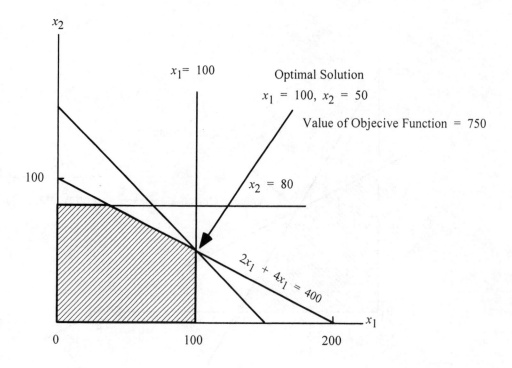

12. a.

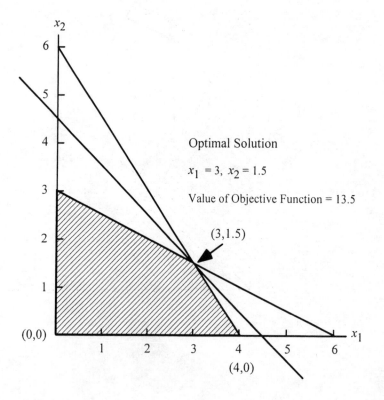

b.

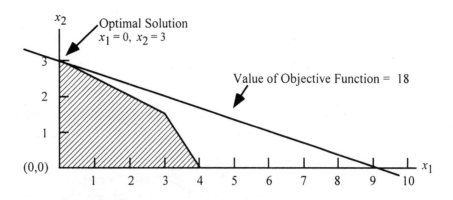

c.   There are four extreme points: (0,0), (4,0), (3,1.5), and (0,3).

13.   a.

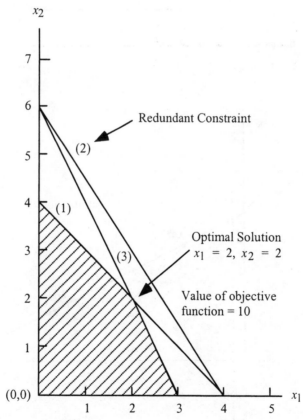

b.   Yes, constraint 2.

The solution remains $x_1 = 2$, $x_2 = 2$ if constraint 2 is removed.

14. a.

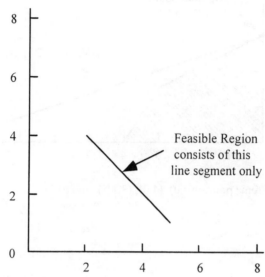

b. The extreme points are (5, 1) and (2, 4).

c.

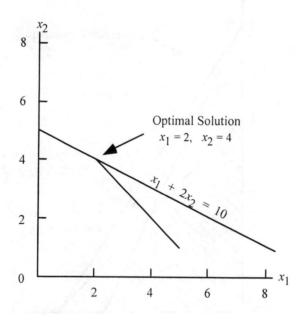

15. a.

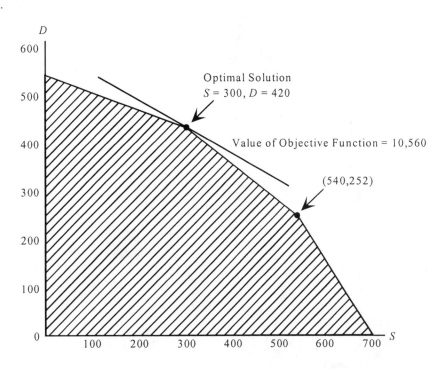

b. Similar to part (a): the same feasible region with a different objective function. The optimal solution occurs at (708, 0) with a profit of $20(708) + 9(0) = 14,160$.

c. The sewing constraint is redundant. Such a change would not change the optimal solution to the original problem.

16. a. A variety of objective functions with a slope greater than -4/10 (slope of I & P line) will make extreme point 5 the optimal solution. For example, one possibility is $3S + 9D$.

b. Optimal Solution is $S = 0$ and $D = 540$.

c.

Dept.	Hours Used	Max. Available	Slack
C & D	$1(540) = 540$	630	90
S	$5/6(540) = 450$	600	150
F	$2/3(540) = 360$	708	348
I & P	$1/4(540) = 135$	135	—

17.

$$\text{Max} \quad 5x_1 + 2x_2 + 8x_3 + 0s_1 + 0s_2 + 0s_3$$

s.t.

$$1x_1 - 2x_2 + \tfrac{1}{2}x_3 + 1s_1 = 420$$
$$2x_1 + 3x_2 - 1x_3 + 1s_2 = 610$$
$$6x_1 - 1x_2 + 3x_3 + 1s_3 = 125$$
$$x_1, \ x_2, \ x_3, \ s_1, \ s_2, \ s_3 \geq 0$$

18. a.

$$\text{Max} \quad 4x_1 \quad + \quad 1x_2 \quad + \quad 0s_1 \quad + \quad 0s_2 \quad + \quad 0s_3$$

s.t.

$$10x_1 \quad + \quad 2x_2 \quad + \quad 1s_1 \qquad\qquad\qquad = \quad 30$$
$$3x_1 \quad + \quad 2x_2 \qquad\qquad + \quad 1s_2 \qquad\qquad = \quad 12$$
$$2x_1 \quad + \quad 2x_2 \qquad\qquad\qquad\qquad + \quad 1s_3 \quad = \quad 10$$

$$x_1, \ x_2, \ s_1, \ s_2, \ s_3 \ \geq 0$$

b.

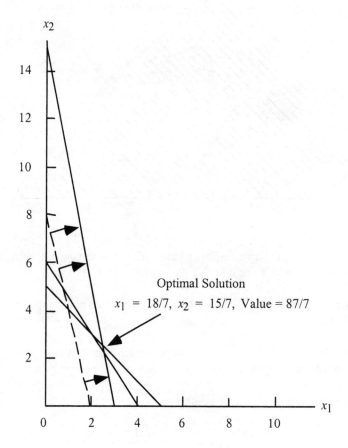

Optimal Solution
$x_1 = 18/7, \ x_2 = 15/7, \ \text{Value} = 87/7$

c. $s_1 = 0, s_2 = 0, s_3 = 4/7$

19. a.

$$\text{Max} \quad 3x_1 \quad + \quad 4x_2 \quad + \quad 0s_1 \quad + \quad 0s_2 \quad + \quad 0s_3$$

s.t.

$$-1x_1 \quad + \quad 2x_2 \quad + \quad 1s_1 \qquad\qquad\qquad = \quad 8 \qquad (1)$$
$$1x_1 \quad + \quad 2x_2 \qquad\qquad + \quad 1s_2 \qquad\qquad = \quad 12 \qquad (2)$$
$$2x_1 \quad + \quad 1x_2 \qquad\qquad\qquad\qquad + \quad 1s_3 \quad = \quad 16 \qquad (3)$$

$$x_1, \ x_2, \ s_1, \ s_2, \ s_3 \ \geq 0$$

b.

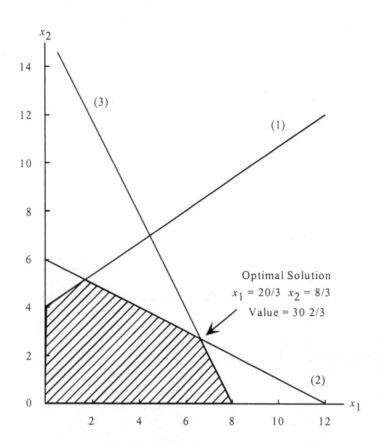

Optimal Solution
$x_1 = 20/3$ $x_2 = 8/3$
Value = 30 2/3

c. $s_1 = 8 + x_1 - 2x_2 = 8 + 20/3 - 16/3 = 28/3$

$s_2 = 12 - x_1 - 2x_2 = 12 - 20/3 - 16/3 = 0$

$s_3 = 16 - 2x_1 - x_2 = 16 - 40/3 - 8/3 = 0$

20. a.   Let E = number of units of the EZ-Rider produced
         L = number of units of the Lady-Sport produced

Max $2400E$ + $1800L$
s.t.
          $6E$ + $3L$ ≤ 2100 Engine time
                       L ≤ 280 Lady-Sport maximum
          $2E$ + $2.5L$ ≤ 1000 Assembly and testing
                 $E, L \geq 0$

b.

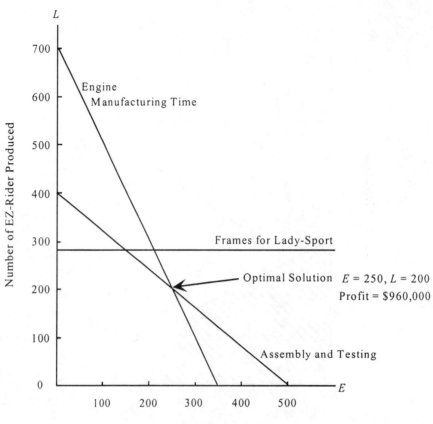

Number of Lady-Sport Produced

c. The binding constraints are the manufacturing time and the assembly and testing time.

21. a. Let F = number of tons of fuel additive

   S = number of tons of solvent base

$$\text{Max} \quad 40F \quad + \quad 30S$$

s.t.

$2/5F$	+	$\frac{1}{2}S$	$\leq$	200	Material 1
		$\frac{1}{5}S$	$\leq$	5	Material 2
$\frac{3}{5}F$	+	$\frac{3}{10}S$	$\leq$	21	Material 3

$F,\ S \geq 0$

b.

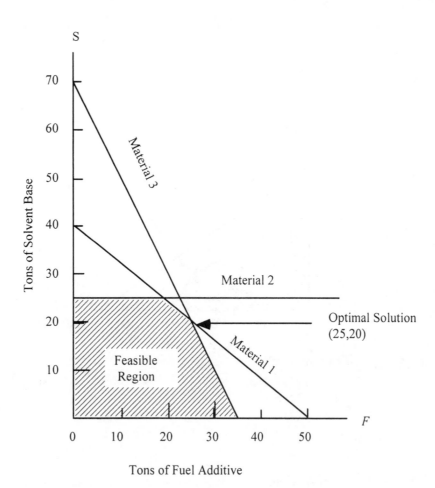

Tons of Fuel Additive

c. Material 2: 4 tons are used, 1 ton is unused.

d. No redundant constraints.

22. a. Let R = number of units of regular model.
    C = number of units of catcher's model.

Max		$5R$	+	$8C$			
s.t.							
		$1R$	+	$\frac{3}{2}C$	$\leq$	900	Cutting and sewing
		$\frac{1}{2}R$	+	$\frac{1}{3}C$	$\leq$	300	Finishing
		$\frac{1}{8}R$	+	$\frac{1}{4}C$	$\leq$	100	Packing and Shipping

$R, \ C \geq 0$

b.

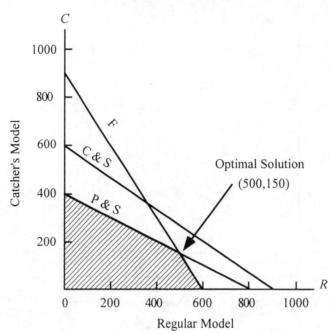

c. $5(500) + 8(150) = \$3,700$

d.   C & S $1(500) + \frac{3}{2}(150) = 725$

F $\frac{1}{2}(500) + \frac{1}{3}(150) = 300$

P & S $\frac{1}{8}(500) + \frac{1}{4}(150) = 100$

e.

Department	Capacity	Usage	Slack
C & S	900	725	175 hours
F	300	300	0 hours
P & S	100	100	0 hours

23. a.   Let B = percentage of funds invested in the bond fund
S = percentage of funds invested in the stock fund

Max	$0.06 B$	+	$0.10 S$			
s.t.						
	B			$\geq$	0.3	Bond fund minimum
	$0.06 B$	+	$0.10 S$	$\geq$	0.075	Minimum return
	B	+	S	=	1	Percentage requirement

b.   Optimal solution: $B = 0.3, S = 0.7$

Value of optimal solution is 0.088 or 8.8%

24. a.   a.   Let N = amount spent on newspaper advertising
          R = amount spent on radio advertising

Max $50N$ + $80R$
s.t.

N	+	R	=	1000	Budget
N			$\geq$	250	Newspaper min.
		R	$\geq$	250	Radio min.
N			$\geq$	$2R$	News $\geq$ 2 Radio

$N, R \geq 0$

b.

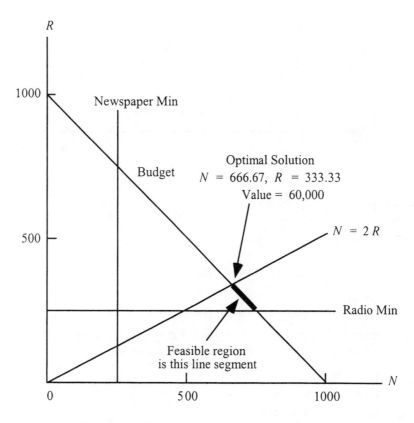

25.   Let I = Internet fund investment in thousands
      B = Blue Chip fund investment in thousands

Max $0.12I$ + $0.09B$
s.t.

$1I$	+	$1B$	$\leq$	50	Available investment funds
$1I$			$\leq$	35	Maximum investment in the internet fund
$6I$	+	$4B$	$\leq$	240	Maximum risk for a moderate investor
	$I, B \geq 0$				

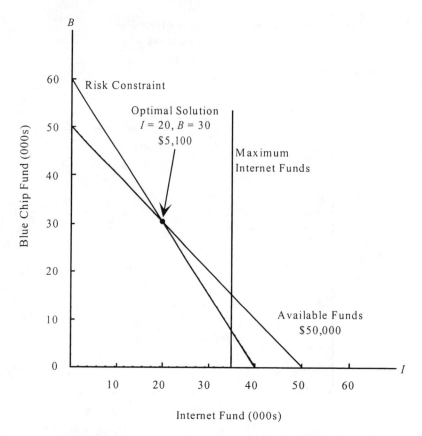

Internet fund	$20,000
Blue Chip fund	$30,000
Annual return	$ 5,100

b. The third constraint for the aggressive investor becomes

$$6I + 4B \leq 320$$

This constraint is redundant; the available funds and the maximum Internet fund investment constraints define the feasible region. The optimal solution is:

Internet fund	$35,000
Blue Chip fund	$15,000
Annual return	$ 5,550

The aggressive investor places as much funds as possible in the high return but high risk Internet fund.

c. The third constraint for the conservative investor becomes

$$6I + 4B \leq 160$$

This constraint becomes a binding constraint. The optimal solution is

Internet fund	$0
Blue Chip fund	$40,000
Annual return	$ 3,600

The slack for constraint 1 is $10,000. This indicates that investing all $50,000 in the Blue Chip fund is still too risky for the conservative investor. $40,000 can be invested in the Blue Chip fund. The remaining $10,000 could be invested in low-risk bonds or certificates of deposit.

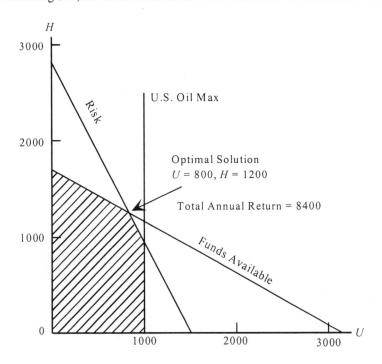

26. a. Let W = number of jars of Western Foods Salsa produced
    M = number of jars of Mexico City Salsa produced

Max	$1W$	+	$1.25M$			
s.t.						
	$5W$		$7M$	$\leq$	4480	Whole tomatoes
	$3W$	+	$1M$	$\leq$	2080	Tomato sauce
	$2W$	+	$2M$	$\leq$	1600	Tomato paste
	$W, M \geq 0$					

    Note: units for constraints are ounces

    b. Optimal solution: $W = 560$, $M = 240$

    Value of optimal solution is 860

27. a. Let B = proportion of Buffalo's time used to produce component 1
    D = proportion of Dayton's time used to produce component 1

    Maximum Daily Production

	Component 1	Component 2
Buffalo	2000	1000
Dayton	600	1400

    Number of units of component 1 produced: $2000B + 600D$

    Number of units of component 2 produced: $1000(1 - B) + 600(1 - D)$

For assembly of the ignition systems, the number of units of component 1 produced must equal the number of units of component 2 produced.

Therefore,

$$2000B + 600D = 1000(1 - B) + 1400(1 - D)$$

$$2000B + 600D = 1000 - 1000B + 1400 - 1400D$$

$$3000B + 2000D = 2400$$

Note: Because every ignition system uses 1 unit of component 1 and 1 unit of component 2, we can maximize the number of electronic ignition systems produced by maximizing the number of units of subassembly 1 produced.

Max $2000B + 600D$

In addition, $B \leq 1$ and $D \leq 1$.

The linear programming model is:

$$
\begin{array}{lrll}
\text{Max} & 2000B & + \ 600D & \\
\text{s.t.} & & & \\
& 3000B & + \ 2000D & = 2400 \\
& B & & \leq 1 \\
& & D & \leq 1 \\
& B, D & & \geq 0
\end{array}
$$

The graphical solution is shown below.

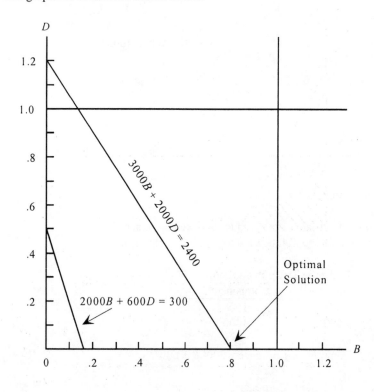

Optimal Solution: $B = .8, D = 0$

Optimal Production Plan
Buffalo - Component 1	$.8(2000) = 1600$
Buffalo - Component 2	$.2(1000) = 200$
Dayton - Component 1	$0(600) = 0$
Dayton - Component 2	$1(1400) = 1400$

Total units of electronic ignition system = 1600 per day.

28. a. Let E = number of shares of Eastern Cable
         C = number of shares of ComSwitch

$$
\begin{array}{lllll}
\text{Max} & 15E & + & 18C & \\
\text{s.t.} & & & & \\
& 40E & + & 25C & \leq 50{,}000 & \text{Maximum Investment} \\
& 40E & & & \geq 15{,}000 & \text{Eastern Cable Minimum} \\
& & & 25C & \geq 10{,}000 & \text{ComSwitch Minimum} \\
& & & 25C & \leq 25{,}000 & \text{ComSwitch Maximum} \\
& & E, C \geq 0 & & &
\end{array}
$$

b.

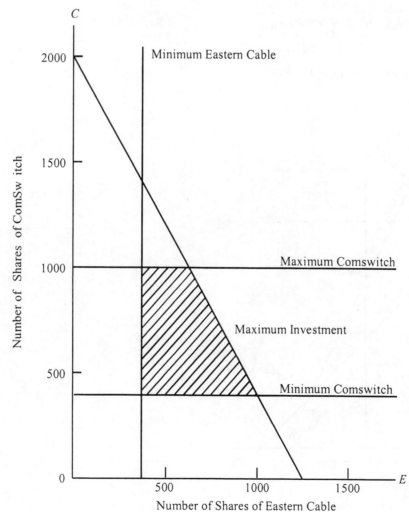

c. There are four extreme points: (375,400); (1000,400);(625,1000); (375,1000)

d. Optimal solution is $E = 625$, $C = 1000$
    Total return = $27,375

29.

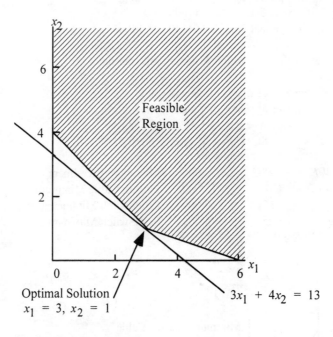

Objective Function Value = 13

30.

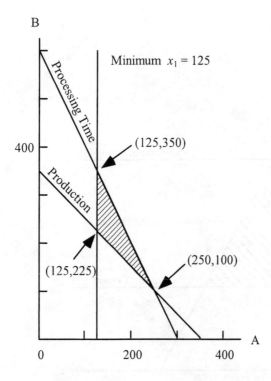

Extreme Points	Objective Function Value	Surplus Demand	Surplus Total Production	Slack Processing Time
$(A = 250, B = 100)$	800	125	—	—
$(A = 125, B = 225)$	925	—	—	125
$(A = 125, B = 350)$	1300	—	125	—

31. a.

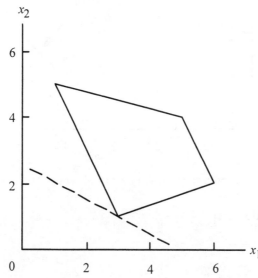

Optimal Solution: $x_1 = 3$, $x_2 = 1$, value = 5

b.

(1)	$3 + 4(1) = 7$	Slack = 21 - 7 = 14
(2)	$2(3) + 1 = 7$	Surplus = 7 - 7 = 0
(3)	$3(3) + 1.5 = 10.5$	Slack = 21 - 10.5 = 10.5
(4)	$-2(3) + 6(1) = 0$	Surplus = 0 - 0 = 0

c.

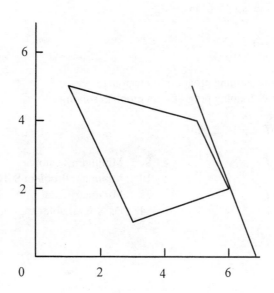

Optimal Solution: $x_1 = 6$, $x_2 = 2$, value = 34

32. a.

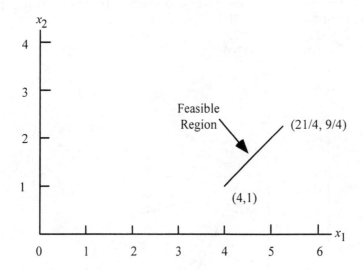

b.   There are two extreme points: $(x_1 = 4, x_2 = 1)$ and $(x_1 = 21/4, x_2 = 9/4)$

c.   The optimal solution is $x_1 = 4, x_2 = 1$

33. a.

$$
\begin{array}{llllllllll}
\text{Min} & 6x_1 & + & 4x_2 & + & 0s_1 & + & 0s_2 & + & 0s_3 \\
\text{s.t.} \\
& 2x_1 & + & 1x_2 & - & s_1 & & & & & = & 12 \\
& 1x_1 & + & 1x_2 & & & - & s_2 & & & = & 10 \\
& & & 1x_2 & & & & & + & s_3 & = & 4
\end{array}
$$

$$x_1, \ x_2, \ s_1, \ s_2, \ s_3 \geq 0$$

b.   The optimal solution is $x_1 = 6, x_2 = 4$.

c. $s_1 = 4, s_2 = 0, s_3 = 0$.

34. a.   Let T = number of training programs on teaming
            P = number of training programs on problem solving

$$
\begin{array}{llll}
\text{Max} & 10{,}000T & + & 8{,}000P \\
\text{s.t.}
\end{array}
$$

T			$\geq$	8	Minimum Teaming
		P	$\geq$	10	Minimum Problem Solving
T	+	P	$\geq$	25	Minimum Total
$3\,T$	+	$2\,P$	$\leq$	84	Days Available

$$T, P \geq 0$$

b.

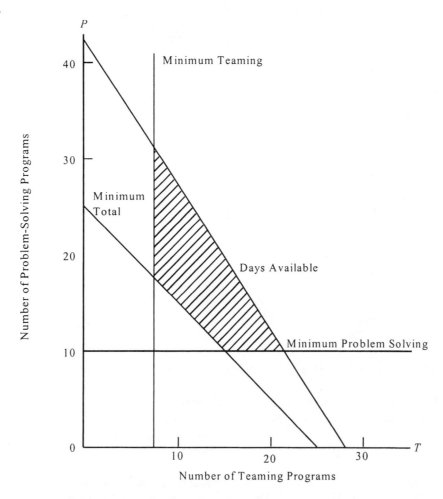

c.   There are four extreme points: (15,10); (21.33,10); (8,30); (8,17)

d.   The minimum cost solution is $T = 8$, $P = 17$
Total cost = $216,000

35.

	Regular	Zesty	
Mild	80%	60%	8100
Extra Sharp	20%	40%	3000

Let R = number of containers of Regular
    Z = number of containers of Zesty

Each container holds 12/16 or 0.75 pounds of cheese

Pounds of mild cheese used   =   0.80 (0.75) R + 0.60 (0.75) Z
                             =   0.60 R + 0.45 Z

Pounds of extra sharp cheese used =   0.20 (0.75) R + 0.40 (0.75) Z
                                   =   0.15 R + 0.30 Z

Cost of Cheese	=	Cost of mild + Cost of extra sharp
	=	$1.20 (0.60 R + 0.45 Z) + 1.40 (0.15 R + 0.30 Z)$
	=	$0.72 R + 0.54 Z + 0.21 R + 0.42 Z$
	=	$0.93 R + 0.96 Z$

Packaging Cost	=	$0.20 R + 0.20 Z$

Total Cost	=	$(0.93 R + 0.96 Z) + (0.20 R + 0.20 Z)$
	=	$1.13 R + 1.16 Z$

Revenue	=	$1.95 R + 2.20 Z$

Profit Contribution	=	Revenue - Total Cost
	=	$(1.95 R + 2.20 Z) - (1.13 R + 1.16 Z)$
	=	$0.82 R + 1.04 Z$

Max $0.82 R$ + $1.04 Z$
s.t.

$0.60 R$	+	$0.45 Z$	$\leq$	8100	Mild
$0.15 R$	+	$0.30 Z$	$\leq$	3000	Extra Sharp

$R, Z \geq 0$

Optimal Solution: $R = 9600$, $Z = 5200$, profit $= 0.82(9600) + 1.04(5200) = \$13,280$

36. a.   Let $S =$ yards of the standard grade material per frame
              $P =$ yards of the professional grade material per frame

Min $7.50S + 9.00P$
s.t.

$0.10S$	+	$0.30P$	$\geq$	6	carbon fiber (at least 20% of 30 yards)
$0.06S$	+	$0.12P$	$\leq$	3	kevlar (no more than 10% of 30 yards)
S	+	P	$=$	30	total (30 yards)

$S, P \geq 0$

b.

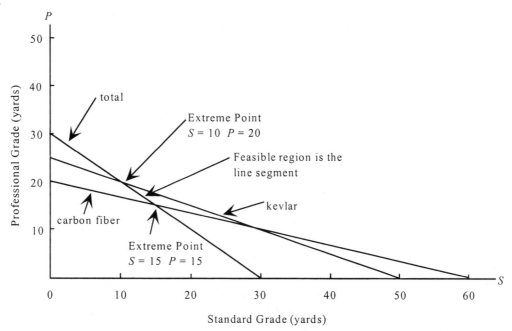

Standard Grade (yards)

c.

Extreme Point	Cost
(15, 15)	7.50(15) + 9.00(15) = 247.50
(10, 20)	7.50(10) + 9.00(20) = 255.00

The optimal solution is $S = 15$, $P = 15$

d. Optimal solution does not change: $S = 15$ and $P = 15$. However, the value of the optimal solution is reduced to 7.50(15) + 8(15) = $232.50.

e. At $7.40 per yard, the optimal solution is $S = 10$, $P = 20$. The value of the optimal solution is reduced to 7.50(10) + 7.40(20) = $223.00. A lower price for the professional grade will not change the $S = 10$, $P = 20$ solution because of the requirement for the maximum percentage of kevlar (10%).

37. a. Let S = number of units purchased in the stock fund
M = number of units purchased in the money market fund

Min		$8S$	+	$3M$			
s.t.							
		$50S$	+	$100M$	$\leq$	1,200,000	Funds available
		$5S$	+	$4M$	$\geq$	60,000	Annual income
				M	$\geq$	3,000	Minimum units in money market
		$S, M, \geq 0$					

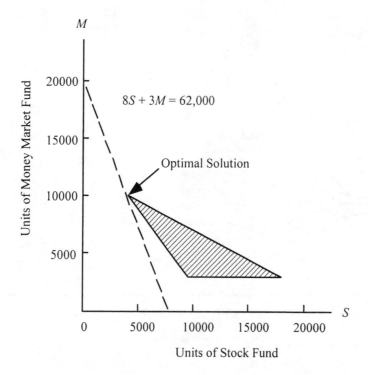

Optimal Solution: $S = 4000$, $M = 10000$, value = 62000

b. Annual income = 5(4000) + 4(10000) = 60,000

c. Invest everything in the stock fund.

38.   Let P_1 = gallons of product 1
        P_2 = gallons of product 2

Min $1P_1$ + $1P_2$
s.t.
        $1P_1$ + $\geq$ 30   Product 1 minimum
                      $1P_2$ $\geq$ 20   Product 2 minimum
        $1P_1$ + $2P_2$ $\geq$ 80   Raw material
                $P_1, P_2 \geq 0$

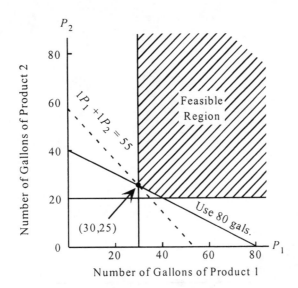

Optimal Solution: $P_1 = 30$, $P_2 = 25$ Cost = $55

39. a. Let R = number of gallons of regular gasoline produced
       P = number of gallons of premium gasoline produced

Max	$0.30R$	$+$	$0.50P$			
s.t.						
	$0.30R$	$+$	$0.60P$	$\leq$	18,000	Grade A crude oil available
	$1R$	$+$	$1P$	$\leq$	50,000	Production capacity
			$1P$	$\leq$	20,000	Demand for premium
	$R,\ P \geq 0$					

b.

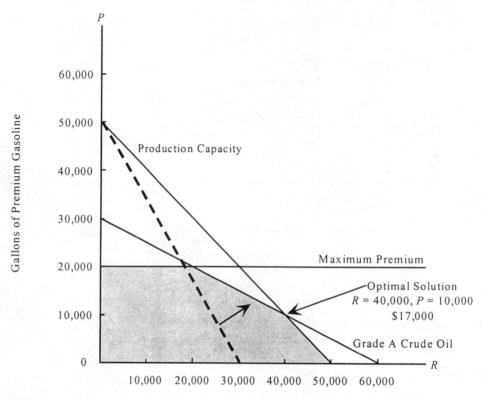

Optimal Solution:
40,000 gallons of regular gasoline
10,000 gallons of premium gasoline
Total profit contribution = $17,000

c.

Constraint	Value of Slack Variable	Interpretation
1	0	All available grade A crude oil is used
2	0	Total production capacity is used
3	10,000	Premium gasoline production is 10,000 gallons less than the maximum demand

d.   Grade A crude oil and production capacity are the binding constraints.

40.

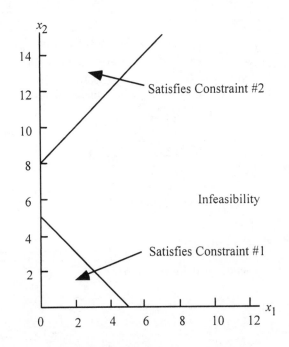

41.

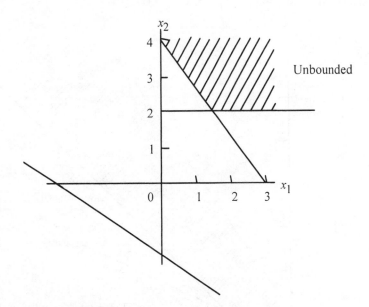

42. a.

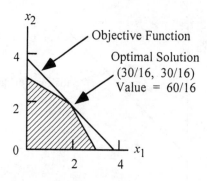

b. New optimal solution is $x_1 = 0$, $x_2 = 3$, value = 6.

c. Slope of constraint is -3/5

Slope of objective function when $c_1 = 1$ is $-1/c_2$

Set slopes equal: $-1/c_2 = -3/5$

$$-5 = -3c_2$$

$$c_2 = 5/3$$

Objective function needed: max $x_1 + \frac{5}{3}x_2$

43. a.

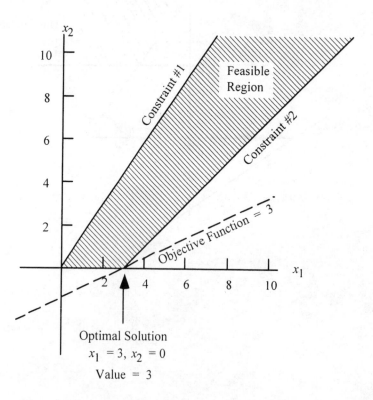

b. Feasible region is unbounded.

c. Optimal Solution: $x_1 = 3, x_2 = 0, z = 3$.

d. An unbounded feasible region does not imply the problem is unbounded. This will only be the case when it is unbounded in the direction of improvement for the objective function.

44. Let N = number of sq. ft. for national brands
         G = number of sq. ft. for generic brands

Problem Constraints:

$$N + G \leq 200 \quad \text{Space available}$$
$$N \geq 120 \quad \text{National brands}$$
$$G \geq 20 \quad \text{Generic}$$

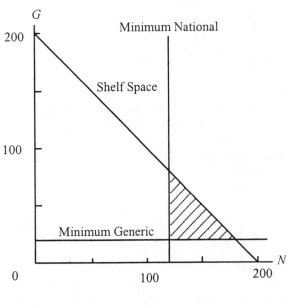

Extreme Point	N	G
1	120	20
2	180	20
3	120	80

a. Optimal solution is extreme point 2; 180 sq. ft. for the national brand and 20 sq. ft. for the generic brand.

b. Alternative optimal solutions. Any point on the line segment joining extreme point 2 and extreme point 3 is optimal.

c. Optimal solution is extreme point 3; 120 sq. ft. for the national brand and 80 sq. ft. for the generic brand.

45.

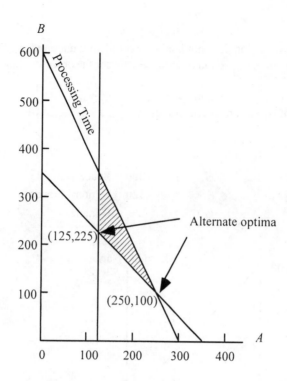

Alternative optimal solutions exist at extreme points (A = 125, B = 225) and (A = 250, B = 100).

Cost = 3(125) + 3(225) = 1050

or

Cost = 3(250) + 3(100) = 1050

The solution (A = 250, B = 100) uses all available processing time. However, the solution (A = 125, B = 225) uses only 2(125) + 1(225) = 475 hours.

Thus, (A = 125, B = 225) provides 600 - 475 = 125 hours of slack processing time which may be used for other products.

46.

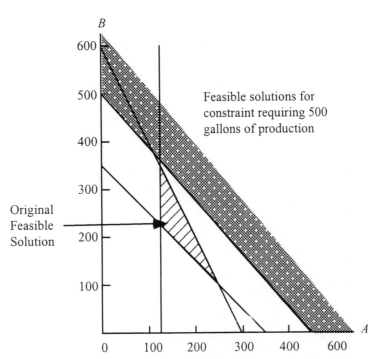

Possible Actions:

i.   Reduce total production to $A = 125$, $B = 350$ on 475 gallons.

ii. Make solution $A = 125$, $B = 375$ which would require $2(125) + 1(375) = 625$ hours of processing time. This would involve 25 hours of overtime or extra processing time.

iii. Reduce minimum A production to 100, making $A = 100$, $B = 400$ the desired solution.

47. a.

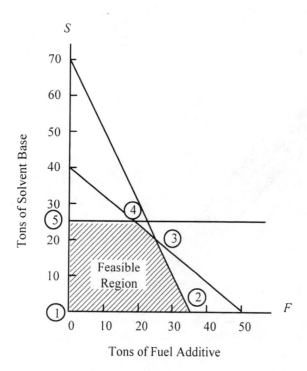

b. Yes. New optimal solution is $F = 18.75$, $S = 25$. Value of the new optimal solution is $40(18.75) + 60(25) = 2250$.

c. An optimal solution occurs at extreme point 3, extreme point 4, and any point on the line segment joining these two points. This is the special case of alternative optimal solutions. For the manager attempting to implement the solution this means that the manager can select the specific solution that is most appropriate.

48. a.

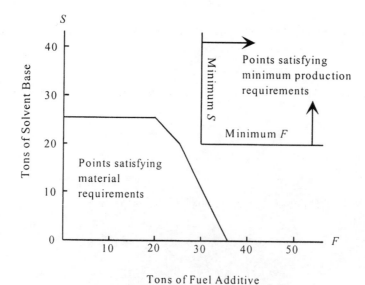

There are no points satisfying both sets of constraints; thus there will be no feasible solution.

b.

Materials	Minimum Tons Required for $F = 30$, $S = 15$	Tons Available	Additional Tons Required
Material 1	2/5(30) + 1/2(15) = 19.5	20	-
Material 2	0(30) + 1/5(15) = 3	5	-
Material 3	3/5(30) + 3/10(15) = 22.5	21	1.5

Thus RMC will need 1.5 additional tons of material 3.

49. a. Let   P = number of full-time equivalent pharmacists
         T = number of full-time equivalent physicians

The model and the optimal solution obtained using The Management Scientist is shown below:

```
MIN 40P+10T

    S.T.
     1)   1P+1T>250
     2)   2P-1T>0
     3)   1P>90
```

OPTIMAL SOLUTION

```
Objective Function Value =        5200.000

    Variable            Value          Reduced Costs
    --------        ---------------    ------------------
       P                  90.000             0.000
       T                 160.000             0.000

    Constraint      Slack/Surplus        Dual Prices
    --------        ---------------    ------------------
       1                   0.000            -10.000
       2                  20.000              0.000
       3                   0.000            -30.000
```

The optimal solution requires 90 full-time equivalent pharmacists and 160 full-time equivalent technicians. The total cost is $5200 per hour.

b.

	Current Levels	Attrition	Optimal Values	New Hires Required
Pharmacists	85	10	90	15
Technicians	175	30	160	15

The payroll cost using the current levels of 85 pharmacists and 175 technicians is 40(85) + 10(175) = $5150 per hour.

The payroll cost using the optimal solution in part (a) is $5200 per hour.

Thus, the payroll cost will go up by $50

50.   Let M = number of Mount Everest Parkas
                R = number of Rocky Mountain Parkas

$$\text{Max}\quad 100M + 150R$$
$$\text{s.t.}$$

$30M$	+	$20R$	$\leq$	7200	Cutting time
$45M$	+	$15R$	$\leq$	7200	Sewing time
$0.8M$	-	$0.2R$	$\geq$	0	% requirement

Note: Students often have difficulty formulating constraints such as the % requirement constraint. We encourage our students to proceed in a systematic step-by-step fashion when formulating these types of constraints. For example:

M must be at least 20% of total production
$M \geq 0.2$ (total production)
$M \geq 0.2 (M + R)$
$M \geq 0.2M + 0.2R$
$0.8M - 0.2R \geq 0$

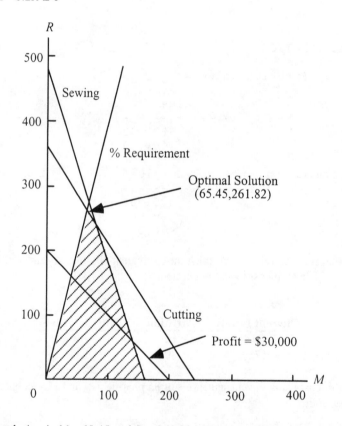

The optimal solution is $M = 65.45$ and $R = 261.82$; the value of this solution is $z = 100(65.45) + 150(261.82) = \$45,818$. If we think of this situation as an on-going continuous production process, the fractional values simply represent partially completed products. If this is not the case, we can approximate the optimal solution by rounding down; this yields the solution $M = 65$ and $R = 261$ with a corresponding profit of $\$45,650$.

51.   Let C = number sent to current customers
                 N = number sent to new customers

Note:

Number of current customers that test drive $= .25\,C$
Number of new customers that test drive $= .20\,N$
Number sold $= .12\,(.25\,C) + .20\,(.20\,N)$
                  $= .03\,C + .04\,N$

$$
\begin{array}{llllll}
\text{Max} & .03C & + & .04N & & \\
\text{s.t.} & & & & & \\
& .25\,C & & & \geq & 30{,}000 \quad \text{Current Min} \\
& & & .20\,N & \geq & 10{,}000 \quad \text{New Min} \\
& .25\,C & - & .40\,N & \geq & 0 \quad\quad\;\; \text{Current vs. New} \\
& 4\,C & + & 6\,N & \leq & 1{,}200{,}000 \quad \text{Budget} \\
\end{array}
$$

$$C,\ N,\ \geq 0$$

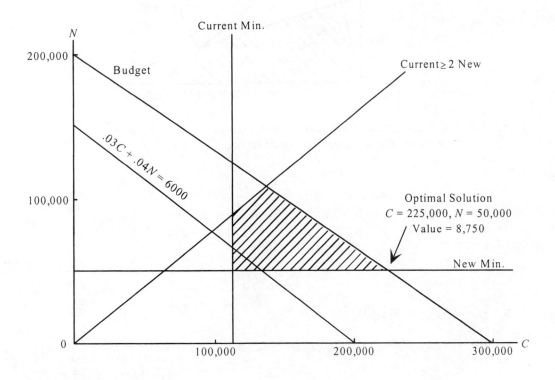

52.   Let S = number of standard size rackets
                O = number of oversize size rackets

Max	10S	+	15O			
s.t.						
	0.8S	-	0.2O	≥	0	% standard
	10S	+	12O	≤	4800	Time
	0.125S	+	0.4O	≤	80	Alloy
		$S,\ O,\ \geq 0$				

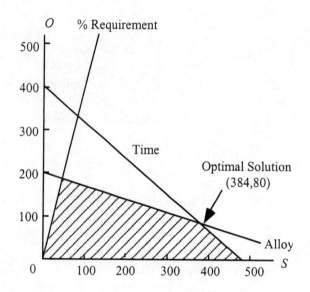

53. a. Let R = time allocated to regular customer service
                   N = time allocated to new customer service

Max	1.2R	+	N		
s.t.					
	R	+	N	≤	80
	25R	+	8N	≥	800
	-0.6R	+	N	≥	0

$$R,\ N \geq 0$$

b. OPTIMAL SOLUTION

Objective Function Value =   90.000

Variable	Value	Reduced Costs
R	50.000	0.000
N	30.000	0.000

Constraint	Slack/Surplus	Dual Prices
1	0.000	1.125
2	690.000	0.000
3	0.000	-0.125

Optimal solution: $R = 50$, $N = 30$, value $= 90$

HTS should allocate 50 hours to service for regular customers and 30 hours to calling on new customers.

54. a.   Let M_1 = number of hours spent on the M-100 machine

M_2 = number of hours spent on the M-200 machine

Total Cost

$$6(40)M_1 + 6(50)M_2 + 50M_1 + 75M_2 = 290M_1 + 375M_2$$

Total Revenue

$$25(18)M_1 + 40(18)M_2 = 450M_1 + 720M_2$$

Profit Contribution

$$(450 - 290)M_1 + (720 - 375)M_2 = 160M_1 + 345M_2$$

Max $160 M_1$ + $345M_2$

s.t.

M_1		$\leq$	15	M-100 maximum
	M_2	$\leq$	10	M-200 maximum
M_1		$\geq$	5	M-100 minimum
	M_2	$\geq$	5	M-200 minimum
$40 M_1$ +	$50 M_2$	$\leq$	1000	Raw material available

$$M_1, M_2 \geq 0$$

b.

OPTIMAL SOLUTION

Objective Function Value =   5450.000

Variable	Value	Reduced Costs
M1	12.500	0.000
M2	10.000	0.000

Constraint	Slack/Surplus	Dual Prices
1	2.500	0.000
2	0.000	145.000
3	7.500	0.000
4	5.000	0.000
5	0.000	4.000

The optimal decision is to schedule 12.5 hours on the M-100 and 10 hours on the M-200.

Chapter 3
Linear Programming: Sensitivity Analysis and Interpretation of Solution

Learning Objectives

1. Be able to conduct graphical sensitivity analysis for two variable linear programming problems.

2. Be able to compute and interpret the range of optimality for objective function coefficients.

3. Be able to compute and interpret the dual price for a constraint.

4. Learn how to formulate, solve, and interpret the solution for linear programs with more than two decision variables.

5. Understand the following terms:

    sensitivity analysis
    range of optimality
    dual price
    reduced cost
    range of feasibility
    100 percent rule
    sunk cost
    relevant cost

Chapter 3

Solutions:

1.   Note: Feasible region is shown as part of the solution to problem 21 in Chapter 2.

     Optimal Solution: $F = 25$, $S = 20$

     Binding Constraints: material 1 and material 3

     Let Line A = material 1 = $2/5\ F + 1/2\ S = 20$
           Line B = material 3 = $3/5\ F + 3/10\ S = 21$

     The slope of Line A = -4/5
     The slope of Line B = -2

     Current solution is optimal for

$$-2 \le -\frac{C_F}{30} \le -\frac{4}{5}$$
     or

$$24 \le C_F \le 60$$

     Current solution is optimal for

$$-2 \le -\frac{40}{C_S} \le -\frac{4}{5}$$
     or

$$20 \le C_S \le 50$$

2.

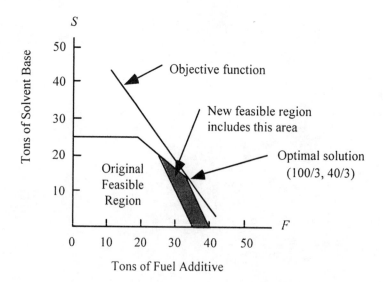

Application of the graphical solution procedure to the problem with the enlarged feasible region shows that the extreme point with $F = 100/3$ and $S = 40/3$ now provides the optimal solution. The new value for the objective function is $40(100/3) + 30(40/3) = 1733.33$, providing an increase in profit of $1733.33 - 1600 = \$133.33$. Thus the increased profit occurs at a rate of $\$133.33/3 = \$44.44$ per ton of material 3 added. Thus the dual price for the material 3 constraint is $\$44.44$.

3. a.

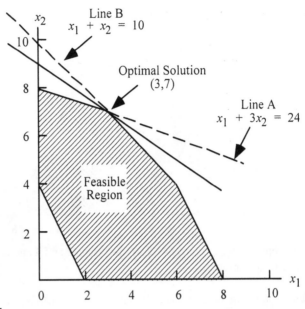

Optimal Value $= 27$

b. Slope of Line B $= -1$
    Slope of Line A $= -1/3$

    Let C_1 = objective function coefficient of x_1
        C_2 = objective function coefficient of x_2

$$-1 \le -C_1/3 \le -1/3$$

$$1 \ge C_1/3 \quad C_1/3 \ge 1/3$$

$$C_1 \le 3 \quad C_1 \ge 1$$

Range: $1 \le C_1 \le 3$

c. $-1 \le -2/C_2 \le -1/3$

$$1 \ge 2/C_2 \quad 2/C_2 \ge 1/3$$

$$C_2 \ge 2 \quad C_2 \le 6$$

Range : $2 \le C_2 \le 6$

d. Since this change leaves C_1 in its range of optimality, the same solution ($x_1 = 3$, $x_2 = 7$) is optimal.

e.   This change moves C_2 outside its range of optimality. The new optimal solution is shown below.

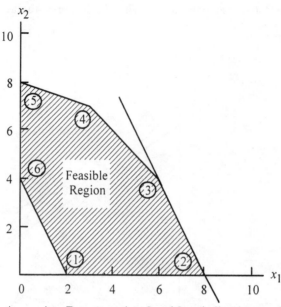

Alternative optimal solutions exist. Extreme points 2 and 3 and all points on the line segment between them are optimal.

4.   By making a small increase in the right-hand side of constraint one and resolving we find a dual price of 1.5 for the constraint. Thus the objective function will increase at the rate of 1.5 per unit increase in the right-hand side.

Since constraint two is not binding, its dual price is zero.

5.   a.

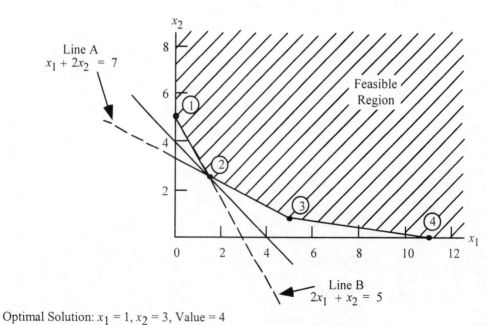

Optimal Solution: $x_1 = 1$, $x_2 = 3$, Value = 4

b. Slope of Line B = -2
   Slope of Line A = -1/2

   Let C_1 = objective function coefficient of x_1
   C_2 = objective function coefficient of x_2

$$-2 \leq -C_1/1 \leq -1/2$$

$$2 \geq C_1 \quad C_1 \geq 1/2$$

Range: $1/2 \leq C_1 \leq 2$

c. $$-2 \leq -1/C_2 \leq -1/2$$

$$2 \geq 1/C_2 \quad 1/C_2 \geq 1/2$$

$$C_2 \geq 1/2 \quad 2 \leq C_2$$

Range: $1/2 \leq C_2 \leq 2$

d. Since this change leaves C_1 in its range of optimality, the same solution is optimal.

e. This change moves C_2 outside of its range of optimality. The new optimal solution is found at extreme point 1; $x_1 = 0$, $x_2 = 5$.

6. Constraint 1:   Dual price = -0.333
    Constraint 2:   Dual price = -0.333
    Constraint 3:   Dual price = 0

Since this is a minimization problem, the negative dual prices for constraints one and two indicate that by increasing the right-hand side of these constraints by one unit, the value of the objective function will increase by 0.333. The dual price for constraint three indicates that increasing the right hand side a small amount will not affect the value of the optimal solution.

7. a.

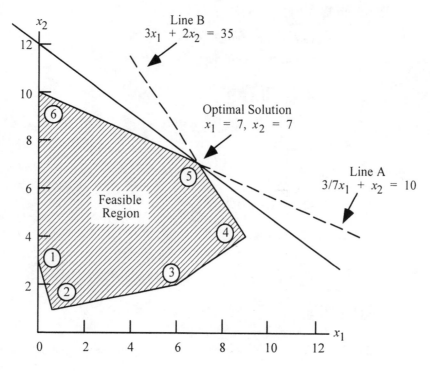

b. Slope of Line B = -3/2
    Slope of Line A = -3/7

    Let C_1 = objective function coefficient of x_1
    $\quad\ C_2$ = objective function coefficient of x_2

    $-3/2 \leq -C_1/7 \leq -3/7$

    $3/2 \geq C_1/7 \quad C_1/7 \geq 3/7$

    $C_1 \leq 21/2 \quad C_1 \geq 3$

    Range: $3 \leq C_1 \leq 10.5$

c. $-3/2 \leq -5/C_2 \leq -3/7$

    $3/2 \geq 5/C_2 \quad 5/C_2 \geq 3/7$

    $C_2 \geq 10/3 \quad C_2 \leq 35/3$

    Range: $10/3 \leq C_2 \leq 35/3$

d. This change moves C_1 outside its range of optimality. The new optimal solution is found at extreme point 6. It is $x_1 = 0$, $x_2 = 10$. The value is 70.

e. Since this change leaves C_2 in its range of optimality, the same solution, $x_1 = 7$ and $x_2 = 7$, with a value of $5(7) + 10(7) = 105$, is optimal.

8. a.

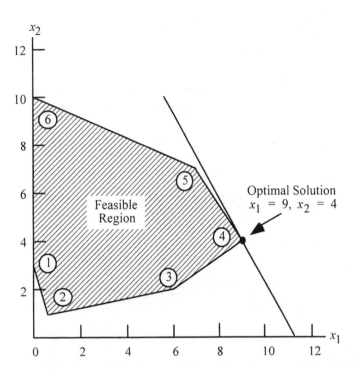

b. Constraint 2: Dual price $= 0$

Constraint 3: Dual price $= 0.0769$

9. From the solution to Problem 3, we see that the optimal solution will not change as long as the slope of the objective function stays in the following interval:

$-1 \leq -C_1/C_2 \leq -1/3$

a. The slope of the new objective function is

$-C_1/C_2 = -3/4$

Since this is in the above interval, these simultaneous changes do not cause a change in the optimal solution.

b. The slope of the new objective function is

$-C_1/C_2 = -3/2.$

This is outside the above interval; therefore, the optimal solution will change. Extreme point 3 is now optimal; the optimal solution is $x_1 = 6$, $x_2 = 4$, and value $= 26$.

10. From the Solution to problem 7, we see that the optimal solution will not change as long as the slope of the objective function stays in the following interval:

$$-3/2 \leq -C_1/C_2 \leq -3/7$$

a. The slope of the new objective function is

$$-C_1/C_2 = -4/10 = -0.40$$

Since -0.40 > -3/7, we conclude that the optimal solution will change. Extreme point 6 is now optimal. The new optimal solution is $x_1 = 0$, $x_2 = 10$. The value of the new optimal solution is 100.

b. The slope of the new objective function is

$$-C_1/C_2 = -4/8 = -0.50$$

Since

$$-3/2 \leq -0.50 \leq -3/7$$

these simultaneous changes do not cause a change in the optimal solution; it remains $x_1 = 7$, $x_2 = 7$.

11. a. Regular Glove = 500
Catcher's Mitt = 150
Value = 3700

b. The finishing and packaging and shipping constraints are binding.

c. Cutting and Sewing = 0
Finishing = 3
Packaging and Shipping = 28

Additional finishing time is worth $3 per unit and additional packaging and shipping time is worth $28 per unit.

d. In the packaging and shipping department. Each additional hour is worth $28.

12. a.

Variable	Range of Optimality
Regular Glove	4 to 12
Catcher's Mitt	3.33 to 10

b. As long as the profit contribution for the regular glove is between $4.00 and $12.00, the current solution is optimal.

As long as the profit contribution for the catcher's mitt stays between $3.33 and $10.00, the current solution is optimal.

The optimal solution is not sensitive to small changes in the profit contributions for the gloves.

c.   The dual prices for the resources are applicable over the following ranges:

Constraint	Range of Feasibility
Cutting and Sewing	725 to No Upper Limit
Finishing	133.33 to 400
Packaging	75 to 135

d.   Amount of increase = (28)(20) = $560

13. a. $U = 800$
$H = 1200$
Estimated Annual Return = $8400

b.   Constraints 1 and 2. All funds available are being utilized and the maximum permissible risk is being incurred.

c.

Constraint	Dual Prices
Funds Avail.	0.09
Risk Max	1.33
U.S. Oil Max	0

d.   No, the optimal solution does not call for investing the maximum amount in U.S. Oil.

14. a.   By more than $7.00 per share.

b.   By more than $3.50 per share.

c.   None. This is only a reduction of 100 shares and the allowable decrease is 200.
management may want to address.

15. a.   Optimal solution calls for the production of 560 jars of Western Foods Salsa and 240 jars of Mexico City Salsa; profit is $860.

b.

Variable	Range of Optimality
Western Foods Salsa	0.893 to 1.250
Mexico City Salsa	1.000 to 1.400

c.

Constraint	Dual Price	Interpretation
1	0.125	One more ounce of whole tomatoes will increase profits by $0.125
2	0.000	Additional ounces of tomato sauce will not improve profits; slack of 160 ounces.
3	0.187	One more ounce of tomato paste will increase profits by $0.187

d.

Constraint	Range of Feasibility
1	4320 to 5600
2	1920 to No Upper Limit
3	1280 to 1640

16. a. $S = 4000$

    $M = 10,000$

    Total risk = 62,000

    b.

Variable	Range of Optimality
S	3.75 to No Upper Limit
M	No Upper Limit to 6.4

    c. $5(4000) + 4(10,000) = \$60,000$

    d. $60,000/1,200,000 = 0.05$ or 5%

    e. 0.057 risk units

    f. $0.057(100) = 5.7\%$

17. a. No change in optimal solution; there is no upper limit for the range of optimality for the objective coefficient for S.

    b. No change in the optimal solution; the objective coefficient for M can increase to 6.4.

    c. There is no upper limit on the allowable increase for C_S; thus the percentage increase is 0%.

    For C_M, we obtain $0.3/3.4 = 0.088$ The accumulated percentage change is 8.8%. Thus, the 100% rule is satisfied and the optimal solution will not change.

18. a. $E = 80, S = 120, D = 0$

    Profit = \$16,440

    b. Fan motors and cooling coils

    c. Labor hours; 320 hours available.

    d. Objective function coefficient range of optimality

    No lower limit to 159.

    Since $150 is in this range, the optimal solution would not change.

19. a. Range of optimality

    E 47.5 to 75
    S 87 to 126
    D No lower limit to 159.

    b.

Model	Profit	Change	Allowable Increase/Decrease	%
E	\$63	Increase \$6	\$75 - \$63 = \$12	6/12 = 0.50
S	\$95	Decrease \$2	\$95 - \$87 = \$8	2/8 = 0.25
D	\$135	Increase \$4	\$159 - \$135 = \$24	4/24 = 0.17
				0.92

Since changes are 92% of allowable changes, the optimal solution of $E = 80$, $S = 120$, $D = 0$ will not change.

However, the change in total profit will be:

E 80 unit @ + \$6 =   \$480
S 120 unit @ - \$2 = $\underline{-240}$
                           \$240

∴ Profit = \$16,440 + 240 = 16,680.

c.   Range of feasibility

Constraint 1   160 to 180
Constraint 2   200 to 400
Constraint 3   2080 to No Upper Limit

d.   Yes, fan motors = 200 + 100 = 300 is outside the range of feasibility.

The dual price will change.

20. a.   Manufacture 100 cases of model A
Manufacture 60 cases of model B
Purchase 90 cases of model B
Total Cost = \$2170

b.   Demand for model A
Demand for model B
Assembly time

c.
Constraint	Dual Price
1	-12.25
2	-9.0
3	0
4	.375

If demand for model A increases by 1 unit, total cost will increase by \$12.25
If demand for model B increases by 1 unit, total cost will increase by \$9.00
If an additional minute of assembly time is available, total cost will decrease by \$.375

d.   The assembly time constraint. Each additional minute of assembly time will decrease costs by \$.375. Note that this will be true up to a value of 1133.33 hours.

Some students may say that the demand constraint for model A should be selected because decreasing the demand by one unit will decrease cost by \$12.25. But, carrying this argument to the extreme would argue for a demand of 0.

21. a.
Decision Variable	Ranges of Optimality
AM	No lower limit to 11.75
BM	3.667 to 9
AP	12.25 to No Upper Limit
BP	6 to 11.333

Provided a single change of an objective function coefficient is within its above range, the optimal solution AM = 100, BM = 60, AP = 0, and BP = 90 will not change.

b.   This change is within the range of optimality. The optimal solution remains AM = 100, BM = 60, AP = 0, and BP = 90. The $11.20 - $10.00 = $1.20 per unit cost increase will increase the total cost to $2170 = $1.20(100) = $2290.

c.

Variable	Cost	Change	Allowable Increase/Decrease	Percentage Change
AM	10	Increase 1.20	11.75 - 10 = 1.75	(1.20/1.75)100 = 68.57
BM	6	Decrease 1	6.0 - 3.667 = 2.333	(1/2.333)100 = 42.86
				111.43

111.43% exceeds 100%; therefore, we must resolve the problem.

Resolving the problem provides the new optimal solution: AM = 0, BM = 135, AP = 100, and BP = 15; the total cost is $22,100.

22. a.   The optimal solution calls for the production of 100 suits and 150 sport coats. Forty hours of cutting overtime should be scheduled, and no hours of sewing overtime should be scheduled. The total profit is $40,900.

b.   The objective coefficient range for suits shows and upper limit of $225. Thus, the optimal solution will not change. But, the value of the optimal solution will increase by ($210-$190)100 = $2000. Thus, the total profit becomes $42,990.

c.   The slack for the material coefficient is 0. Because this is a binding constraint, Tucker should consider ordering additional material. The dual price of $34.50 is the maximum extra cost per yard that should be paid. Because the additional handling cost is only $8 per yard, Tucker should order additional material. Note that the dual price of $34.50 is valid up to 1333.33 -1200 = 133.33 additional yards.

d.   The dual price of -$35 for the minimum suit requirement constraint tells us that lowering the minimum requirement by 25 suits will improve profit by $35(25) = $875.

23. a.   Let S1 = SuperSaver rentals allocated to room type I
          S2 = SuperSaver rentals allocated to room type II
          D1 = Deluxe rentals allocated to room type I
          D2 = Deluxe rentals allocated to room type II
          B1 = Business rentals allocated to room type II

The linear programming formulation and solution is given.

```
MAX  30S1+20S2+35D1+30D2+40B2

    S.T.

    1)   1S1+1S2<130
    2)   1D1+1D2<60
    3)   1B2<50
    4)   1S1+1D1<100
    5)   1S2+1D2+1B2<120
```

OPTIMAL SOLUTION

Objective Function Value =   7000.000

Variable	Value	Reduced Costs
S1	100.000	0.000
S2	10.000	0.000
D1	0.000	5.000
D2	60.000	0.000
B2	50.000	0.000

Constraint	Slack/Surplus	Dual Prices
1	20.000	0.000
2	0.000	10.000
3	0.000	20.000
4	0.000	30.000
5	0.000	20.000

OBJECTIVE COEFFICIENT RANGES

Variable	Lower Limit	Current Value	Upper Limit
S1	25.000	30.000	No Upper Limit
S2	0.000	20.000	25.000
D1	No Lower Limit	35.000	40.000
D2	25.000	30.000	No Upper Limit
B2	20.000	40.000	No Upper Limit

RIGHT HAND SIDE RANGES

Constraint	Lower Limit	Current Value	Upper Limit
1	110.000	130.000	No Upper Limit
2	40.000	60.000	70.000
3	30.000	50.000	60.000
4	0.000	100.000	120.000
5	110.000	120.000	140.000

20 SuperSaver rentals will have to be turned away if demands materialize as forecast.

b. RoundTree should accept 110 SuperSaver reservations, 60 Deluxe reservations and 50 Business reservations.

c. Yes, the effect of a person upgrading is an increase in demand for Deluxe accommodations from 60 to 61. From constraint 2, we see that such an increase in demand will increase profit by $10. The added cost of the breakfast is only $5.

d. Convert to a Type I room. From the dual price to constraint 4 we see that this will increase profit by $30.

e. Yes. We would need the forecast of demand for each rental class on the next night. Using the demand forecasts, we would modify the right-hand sides of the first three constraints and resolve.

24. a. Let H =   amount allocated to home loans
         P =   amount allocated to personal loans
         A =   amount allocated to automobile loans

Max $0.07H$ + $0.12P$ + $0.09A$
s.t.

H	+	P	+	A	=	1,000,000	Amount of New Funds
$0.6H$	−	$0.4P$	−	$0.4A$	≥	0	Minimum Home Loans
		P	−	$0.6A$	≤	0	Personal Loan Requirement

b. $H = \$400,000$ $P = \$225,000$ $A = \$375,000$
    Total annual return = $88,750
    Annual percentage return = 8.875%

c. The range of optimality for H is No Lower Limit to 0.101. Since 0.09 is within the range of optimality, the solution obtained in part (b) will not change.

d. The dual price for constraint 1 is 0.089. The range of feasibility for constraint 1 is 0 to No Upper Limit. Therefore, increasing the amount of new funds available by \$10,000 will increase the total annual return by 0.089 (10,000) = \$890.

e. The second constraint now becomes
        $-0.61H - 0.39P - 0.39A \geq 0$

    The new optimal solution is
        $H = \$390,000$ $P = \$228,750$ $A = \$381,250$

    Total annual return = $89,062.50, an increase of \$312.50

    Annual percentage return = 8.906%, an increase of approximately 0.031%.

25. a. Let P_1 = units of product 1
         P_2 = units of product 2
         P_3 = units of product 3

Max $30P_1$ + $50P_2$ + $20P_3$
s.t. $0.5P_1$ + $2P_2$ + $0.75P_3$ ≤   40   Machine 1
        P_1 + P_2 + $0.5P_3$ ≤   40   Machine 2
       $2P_1$ + $5P_2$ + $2P_3$ ≤   100   Labor
       $0.5P_1$ − $0.5P_2$ − $0.5P_3$ ≤   0   Max P_1
       $-0.2P_1$ − $0.2P_2$ + $0.8P_3$ ≥   0   Min P_3
                $P_1, P_2, P_3 \geq 0$

A portion of the optimal solution obtained using *The Management Scientist* is shown.

```
Objective Function Value =          1250.000

        Variable          Value              Reduced Costs
    --------------    ---------------     -------------------
          P1             25.000                   0.000
          P2              0.000                   7.500
          P3             25.000                   0.000
```

Constraint	Slack/Surplus	Dual Prices
1	8.750	0.000
2	2.500	0.000
3	0.000	12.500
4	0.000	10.000
5	15.000	0.000

RIGHT HAND SIDE RANGES

Constraint	Lower Limit	Current Value	Upper Limit
1	31.250	40.000	No Upper Limit
2	37.500	40.000	No Upper Limit
3	0.000	100.000	106.667
4	-25.000	0.000	5.000
5	No Lower Limit	0.000	15.000

b. Machine Hours Schedule:
Machine 1   31.25 Hours
Machine 2   37.50 Hours

c. $12.50

d. Increase labor hours to 120; the new optimal product mix is

$$P_1 = 24$$
$$P_2 = 8$$
$$P_3 = 16$$
$$\text{Profit} = \$1440$$

26. a. Let L = number of hours assigned to Lisa
D = number of hours assigned to David
S = amount allocated to Sarah

Max $30L$ + $25D$ + $18S$
s.t.

L +	D +	S =	100	Total Time
$0.6L$ -	$0.4D$	$\geq$	0	Lisa 40% requirement
$-0.15L$ -	$0.15D$ +	$0.85S$ $\geq$	0	Minimum Sarah
$-0.25L$ -	$0.25D$ +	S $\leq$	0	Maximum Sarah
L		$\leq$	50	Maximum Lisa

b. $L = 48$ hours $D = 72$ Hours $S = 30$ Hours
Total Cost = $3780

c. The dual price for constraint 5 is 0. Therefore, additional hours for Lisa will not change the solution.

d. The dual price for constraint 3 is 0. Because there is No Lower Limit on the range of feasibility, the optimal solution will not change. Resolving the problem without this constraint will also show that the solution obtained in (b) does not change. Constraint 3, therefore, is really a redundant constraint.

27 a.   Let C_1 = units of component 1 manufactured
             C_2 = units of component 2 manufactured
             C_3 = units of component 3 manufactured

$$
\begin{array}{llrcrcrcr}
\text{Max} & & 8C_1 & + & 6C_2 & + & 9C_3 & & \\
\text{s.t.} & & 6C_1 & + & 4C_2 & + & 4C_3 & \leq & 7200 \\
 & & 4C_1 & + & 5C_2 & + & 2C_3 & \leq & 6600 \\
 & & & & & & C_3 & \leq & 200 \\
 & & C_1 & & & & & \leq & 1000 \\
 & & & & C_2 & & & \leq & 1000 \\
 & & C_1 & & & & & \geq & 600 \\
 & & & & & & C_1,\ C_2,\ C_3 & \geq & 0
\end{array}
$$

The optimal solution is

$C_1 = 600$
$C_2 = 700$
$C_3 = 200$

b.

Variable	Range of Optimality
C_1	No Lower Limit to 9.0
C_2	5.33 to 9.0
C_3	6.00 to No Lower Limit

Individual changes in the profit coefficients within these ranges will not cause a change in the optimal number of components to produce.

Constraint	Range of Feasibility
1	4400 to 7440
2	6300 to No Upper Limit
3	100 to 900
4	600 to No Upper Limit
5	700 to No Upper Limit
6	514.29 to 1000

These are the ranges over which the dual prices for the associated constraints are applicable.

d.   Nothing, since there are 300 minutes of slack time on the grinder at the optimal solution.

e.   No, since at that price it would not be profitable to produce any of component 3.

28.   Let A = number of shares of stock A
             B = number of shares of stock B
             C = number of shares of stock C
             D = number of shares of stock D

a. To get data on a per share basis multiply price by rate of return or risk measure value.

$$\text{Min} \quad 10A \; + \; 3.5B \; + \; 4C \; + \; 3.2D$$

s.t.

$100A$	$+$	$50B$	$+$	$80C$	$+ \; 40D \; =$	$200,000$
$12A$	$+$	$4B$	$+$	$4.8C$	$+ \; 4D \; \geq$	$18,000 \quad (9\% \text{ of } 200,00)$
$100A$					$\leq$	$100,000$
		$50B$			$\leq$	$100,000$
				$80C$	$\leq$	$100,000$
					$40D \; \leq$	$100,000$

$$A, \; B, \; C, \; D \; \geq 0$$

Solution: $A = 333.3$, $B = 0$, $C = 833.3$, $D = 2500$
Risk: 14,666.7
Return: 18,000 (9%) from constraint 2

b.

$$\text{Max} \quad 12A \; + \; 4B \; + \; 4.8C \; + \; 4D$$

s.t.

$100A$	$+$	$50B$	$+$	$80C$	$+ \; 40D \; =$	$200,000$
$100A$					$\leq$	$100,000$
		$50B$			$\leq$	$100,000$
				$80C$	$\leq$	$100,000$
					$40D \; \leq$	$100,000$

$$A, \; B, \; C, \; D \geq 0$$

Solution: $A = 1000$, $B = 0$, $C = 0$, $D = 2500$
Risk: $10A + 3.5B + 4C + 3.2D = 18,000$
Return: 22,000 (11%)

c. The return in part (b) is $4,000 or 2% greater, but the risk index has increased by 3,333.

Obtaining a reasonable return with a lower risk is a preferred strategy in many financial firms. The more speculative, higher return investments are not always preferred because of their associated higher risk.

29. a. Let $O1$ = percentage of Oak cabinets assigned to cabinetmaker 1
$O2$ = percentage of Oak cabinets assigned to cabinetmaker 2
$O3$ = percentage of Oak cabinets assigned to cabinetmaker 3
$C1$ = percentage of Cherry cabinets assigned to cabinetmaker 1
$C2$ = percentage of Cherry cabinets assigned to cabinetmaker 2
$C3$ = percentage of Cherry cabinets assigned to cabinetmaker 3

$$\text{Min} \quad 1800\,O1 \; + \; 1764\,O2 \; + \; 1650\,O3 \; + \; 2160\,C1 \; + 2016\,C2 \; + 1925\,C3$$

s.t.

$50\,O1$			$+$	$60\,C1$		≤ 40	Hours avail. 1
	$42\,O2$				$+ \; 48\,C2$	≤ 30	Hours avail. 2
		$30\,O3$			$+ \; 35\,C3$	≤ 35	Hours avail. 3
$O1 \; +$	$O2 \; +$	$O3$				$= 1$	Oak
			$C1 \; +$	$C2 \; +$	$C3 = 1$		Cherry

$$O1, O2, O3, C1, C2, C3 \geq 0$$

Note: objective function coefficients are obtained by multiplying the hours required to complete all the oak or cherry cabinets times the corresponding cost per hour. For example, 1800 for $O1$ is the product of 50 and 36, 1764 for $O2$ is the product of 42 and 42 and so on.

b.

	Cabinetmaker 1	Cabinetmaker 2	Cabinetmaker 3
Oak	$O1 = 0.271$	$O2 = 0.000$	$O3 = 0.729$
Cherry	$C1 = 0.000$	$C2 = 0.625$	$C3 = 0.375$

Total Cost = $3672.50

c. No, since cabinetmaker 1 has a slack of 26.458 hours. Alternatively, since the dual price for constraint 1 is 0, increasing the right hand side of constraint 1 will not change the value of the optimal solution.

d. The dual price for constraint 2 is 1.750. The upper limit on the range of feasibility is 41.143. Therefore, each additional hour of time for cabinetmaker 2 will reduce total cost by $1.75 per hour, up to a maximum of 41.143 hours.

e. The new objective function coefficients for $O2$ and $C2$ are 42(38) = 1596 and 48(38) = 1824, respectively. The optimal solution does not change but the total cost decreases to $3552.50.

30. a. Let M_1 = units of component 1 manufactured

M_2 = units of component 2 manufactured

M_3 = units of component 3 manufactured

P_1 = units of component 1 purchased

P_2 = units of component 2 purchased

P_3 = units of component 3 purchased

Min $4.50 M_1 + 5.00 M_2 + 2.75 M_3 + 6.50 P_1 + 8.80 P_2 + 7.00 P_3$

s.t.

$$2M_1 + 3M_2 + 4M_3 \leq 21{,}600 \text{ Production}$$
$$1M_1 + 1.5M_2 + 3M_3 \leq 15{,}000 \text{ Assembly}$$
$$1.5M_1 + 2M_2 + 5M_3 \leq 18{,}000 \text{ Testing/Packaging}$$
$$M_1 \quad\quad\quad + 1P_1 \quad\quad\quad = 6{,}000 \text{ Component 1}$$
$$1M_2 \quad\quad\quad + 1P_2 \quad = 4{,}000 \text{ Component 2}$$
$$1M_3 \quad\quad\quad + 1P_3 = 3{,}500 \text{ Component 3}$$

$M_1, M_2, M_3, P_1, P_2, P_3 \geq 0$

b.

Source	Component 1	Component 2	Component 3
Manufacture	2000	4000	1400
Purchase	4000	0	2100

Total Cost: $73,550

c. Since the slack is 0 in the production and the testing & packaging departments, these department are limiting Benson's manufacturing quantities.

Dual prices information:

Production	$0.906/minute x 60 minutes = $54.36 per hour
Testing/Packaging	$0.125/minute x 60 minutes = $ 7.50 per hour

d. The dual price is -$7.969. this tells us that the value of the optimal solution will worsen (the cost will increase) by $7.969 for an additional unit of component 2. Note that although component 2 has a purchase cost per unit of $8.80, it would only cost Benson $7.969 to obtain an additional unit of component 2.

31. Let RS = number of regular flex shafts made in San Diego
RT = number of regular flex shafts made in Tampa
SS = number of stiff flex shafts made in San Diego
ST = number of shift flex shafts made in Tampa

$$\text{Min} \quad 5.25\,RS \ + \ 4.95\,RT \ + \ 5.40\,SS \ + \ 5.70\,ST$$

s.t.

$$
\begin{aligned}
RS \quad\quad\quad + \quad SS \quad\quad\quad &\leq 120{,}000 \\
RT \quad + \quad\quad\quad ST &\leq 180{,}000 \\
RS \quad + \quad RT \quad\quad\quad\quad &= 200{,}000 \\
SS \ + \quad ST &= 75{,}000
\end{aligned}
$$

$$RS, RT, SS, ST \geq 0$$

OPTIMAL SOLUTION

Objective Function Value =   1401000.000

Variable	Value	Reduced Costs
RS	20000.000	0.000
ST	180000.000	0.000
SS	75000.000	0.000
ST	0.000	0.600

Constraint	Slack/Surplus	Dual Prices
1	25000.000	0.000
2	0.000	0.300
3	0.000	-5.250
4	0.000	-5.40

OBJECTIVE COEFFICIENT RANGES

Variable	Lower Limit	Current Value	Upper Limit
RS	4.950	5.250	No Upper Limit
ST	No Lower Limit	4.950	5.250
SS	No Lower Limit	5.400	6.000
ST	5.100	5.700	No Upper Limit

RIGHT HAND SIDE RANGES

Constraint	Lower Limit	Current Value	Upper Limit
1	95000.000	120000.000	No Upper Limit
2	155000.000	180000.000	200000.000
3	180000.000	200000.000	225000.000
4	0.000	75000.000	100000.000

Chapter 3

32. a. Let G = amount invested in growth stock fund
            S = amount invested in income stock fund
            M = amount invested in money market fund

Max	$0.20G$	+	$0.10S$	+	$0.06M$			
s.t.								
	$0.10G$	+	$0.05S$	+	$0.01M$	$\leq$	(0.05)(300,000)	Hartmann's max risk
	G					$\geq$	(0.10)(300,000)	Growth fund min.
			S			$\geq$	(0.10)(300,000)	Income fund min.
					M	$\geq$	(0.20)(300,000)	Money market min,
	G	+	S	+	M	$\leq$	300,000	Funds available

$G, S, M \geq 0$

b. The solution to Hartmann's portfolio mix problem is given.

Objective Function Value =   36000.000

Variable	Value	Reduced Costs
G	120000.000	0.000
S	30000.000	0.000
M	150000.000	0.000

Constraint	Slack/Surplus	Dual Prices
1	0.000	1.556
2	90000.000	0.000
3	0.000	-0.022
4	90000.000	0.000
5	0.000	0.044

OBJECTIVE COEFFICIENT RANGES

Variable	Lower Limit	Current Value	Upper Limit
G	0.150	0.200	0.600
S	No Lower Limit	0.100	0.122
M	0.020	0.060	0.200

RIGHT HAND SIDE RANGES

Constraint	Lower Limit	Current Value	Upper Limit
1	6900.000	15000.000	23100.000
2	No Lower Limit	30000.000	120000.000
3	0.000	30000.000	192000.016
4	No Lower Limit	60000.000	150000.000
5	219000.000	300000.000	1110000.500

c. These are given by the ranges of optimality on the objective function coefficients. The portfolio above will be optimal as long as the yields remain in the following intervals:

Growth stock	$0.15 \leq c_1 \leq 0.60$
Income stock	No Lower Limit $< c_2 \leq 0.122$
Money Market	$0.02 \leq c_3 \leq 0.20$

d. The dual price for the first constraint provides this information. A change in the risk index from 0.05 to 0.06 would increase the constraint RHS by 3000 (from 15,000 to 18,000). This is within the range of feasibility, so the dual price of 1.556 is applicable. The value of the optimal solution would increase by (3000)(1.556) = 4668.

Hartmann's yield with a risk index of 0.05 is

36,000 / 300,000 = 0.12
His yield with a risk index of 0.06 would be

40,668 / 300,000 = 0.1356

e. This change is outside the range of optimality so we must resolve the problem. The solution is shown below.

LINEAR PROGRAMMING PROBLEM

MAX .1G + .1S + .06M

    S.T.

    1)   .1G + .05S + .01M < 15000
    2)   G > 30000
    3)   S > 30000
    4)   M > 60000
    5)   G + S + M < 300000

OPTIMAL SOLUTION

Objective Function Value =   27600.000

Variable	Value	Reduced Costs
G	48000.000	0.000
S	192000.000	0.000
M	60000.000	0.000

Constraint	Slack/Surplus	Dual Prices
1	0.000	0.000
2	18000.000	0.000
3	162000.000	0.000
4	0.000	-0.040
5	0.000	0.100

OBJECTIVE COEFFICIENT RANGES

Variable	Lower Limit	Current Value	Upper Limit
G	0.100	0.100	0.150
S	0.078	0.100	0.100
M	No Lower Limit	0.060	0.100

RIGHT HAND SIDE RANGES

Constraint	Lower Limit	Current Value	Upper Limit
1	14100.000	15000.000	23100.000
2	No Lower Limit	30000.000	48000.000
3	No Lower Limit	30000.000	192000.000
4	37500.000	60000.000	150000.000
5	219000.000	300000.000	318000.000

    f.   The client's risk index and the amount of funds available.

    g. With the new yield estimates, Pfeiffer would solve a new linear program to find the optimal portfolio mix for each client. Then by summing across all 50 clients he would determine the total amount that should be placed in a growth fund, an income fund, and a money market fund. Pfeiffer then would make the necessary switches to have the correct total amount in each account. There would be no actual switching of funds for individual clients.

33. a. Relevant cost since LaJolla Beverage Products can purchase wine and fruit juice on an as - needed basis.

    b. Let W = gallons of white wine
                R = gallons of rose wine
                F = gallons of fruit juice

$$
\begin{array}{llllllll}
\text{Max} & 1.5\,W & + & 1R & + & 2F \\
\text{s.t.} \\
& 0.5W & - & 0.5R & - & 0.5F & \geq & 0 & \text{\% white} \\
& -0.2W & + & 0.8R & - & 0.2F & \geq & 0 & \text{\% rose minimum} \\
& -0.3W & + & 0.7R & - & 0.3F & \leq & 0 & \text{\% rose maximum} \\
& -0.2W & - & 0.2R & + & 0.8F & = & 0 & \text{\% fruit juice} \\
& W & & & & & \leq & 10000 & \text{Available white} \\
& & & R & & & \leq & 8000 & \text{Available rose} \\
& W, & R, & F \geq 0
\end{array}
$$

Optimal Solution: $W = 10{,}000$, $R = 6000$, $F = 4000$
profit contribution = \$29,000.

    c. Since the cost of the wine is a relevant cost, the dual price of \$2.90 is the maximum premium (over the normal price of \$1.00) that LaJolla Beverage Products should be willing to pay to obtain one additional gallon of white wine. In other words, at a price of \$3.90 = \$2.90 + \$1.00, the additional cost is exactly equal to the additional revenue.

    d. No; only 6000 gallons of the rose are currently being used.

    e. Requiring 50% plus one gallon of white wine would reduce profit by \$2.40. Note to instructor: Although this explanation is technically correct, it does not provide an explanation that is especially useful in the context of the problem. Alternatively, we find it useful to explore the question of what would happen if the white wine requirement were changed to at least 51%. Note that in this case, the first constraint would change to $0.49W - 0.51R - 0.51F \geq 0$. This shows the student that the coefficients on the left-hand side are changing; note that this is beyond the scope of sensitivity analysis discussed in this chapter. Resolving the problem with this revised constraint will show the effect on profit of a 1% change.

    f. Allowing the amount of fruit juice to exceed 20% by one gallon will increase profit by \$1.00.

34. a. Let L = minutes devoted to local news
N = minutes devoted to national news
W = minutes devoted to weather
S = minutes devoted to sports

Min	$300L$	+	$200N$	+	$100W$	+	$100S$			
s.t.										
	L	+	N	+	W	+	S	=	20	Time available
	L							$\geq$	3	15% local
	L	+	N					$\geq$	10	50% requirement
					W	-	S	$\leq$	0	Weather - sports
	$-L$	-	N			+	S	$\leq$	0	Sports requirement
					W			$\geq$	4	20% weather

$$L, N, W, S \geq 0$$

Optimal Solution: $L = 3$, $N = 7$, $W = 5$, $S = 5$
Total cost = $3,300

b. Each additional minute of broadcast time increases cost by $100; conversely, each minute reduced will decrease cost by $100. These interpretations are valid for increase up to 10 minutes and decreases up to 2 minutes from the current level of 20 minutes.

c. If local coverage is increased by 1 minute, total cost will increase by $100.

d. If the time devoted to local and national news is increased by 1 minute, total cost will increase by $100.

e. Increasing the sports by one minute will have no effect for this constraint since the dual price is 0.

35. a. Let B = number of copies done by Benson Printing
J = number of copies done by Johnson Printing
L = number of copies done by Lakeside Litho

min	$2.45B$	+	$2.5J$	+	$2.75L$			
s.t.								
	B					$\leq$	30,000	Benson
			J			$\leq$	50,000	Johnson
					L	$\leq$	50,000	Lakeside
	$0.9B$	+	$0.99J$	+	$0.995L$	=	75,000	# useful reports
	B	-	$0.1J$			$\geq$	0	Benson - Johnson %
					L	$\geq$	30,000	Minimum Lakeside

$$B, J, L \geq 0$$

Optimal Solution: $B = 4,181$, $J = 41,806$, $L = 30,000$

b. Suppose that Benson printing has a defective rate of 2% instead of 10%. The new optimal solution would increase the copies assigned to Benson printing to 30,000. In this case, the additional copies assigned to Benson Printing would reduce on a one-for-one basis the number assigned to Johnson Printing.

c. If the Lakeside Litho requirement is reduced by 1 unit, total cost will decrease by $0.2210.

Chapter 4
Linear Programming Applications

Learning Objectives

1. Learn about applications of linear programming that have been encountered in practice.

2. Develop an appreciation for the diversity of problems that can be modeled as linear programs.

3. Obtain practice and experience in formulating realistic linear programming models.

4. Understand linear programming applications such as:

media selection	production scheduling
portfolio selection	work force assignments
financial mix strategy	blending problems
data envelopment analysis	revenue management

Note to Instructor

The application problems of Chapter 9 have been designed to give the student an understanding and appreciation of the broad range of problems that can be approached by linear programming. While the problems are indicative of the many linear programming applications, they have been kept relatively small in order to ease the student's formulation and solution effort. Each problem will give the student an opportunity to practice formulating an approximate linear programming model. However, the solution and the interpretation of the solution will require the use of a software package such as *The Management Scientist*, *Microsoft Excel*'s Solver or LINDO.

Solutions:

1. a. Let T = number of television spot advertisements
        R = number of radio advertisements
        N = number of newspaper advertisements

Max	$100,000T$	+	$18,000R$	+	$40,000N$			
s.t.								
	$2,000T$	+	$300R$	+	$600N$	$\leq$	18,200	Budget
	T					$\leq$	10	Max TV
			R			$\leq$	20	Max Radio
					N	$\leq$	10	Max News
	$-0.5T$	+	$0.5R$	-	$0.5N$	$\leq$	0	Max 50% Radio
	$0.9T$	-	$0.1R$	-	$0.1N$	$\geq$	0	Min 10% TV

$$T,\ R,\ N,\ \geq 0$$

		Budget $
Solution:	$T = 4$	$8,000
	$R = 14$	4,200
	$N = 10$	6,000
		$18,200

Audience = 1,052,000.

This information can be obtained from *The Management Scientist* as follows.

```
OPTIMAL SOLUTION

Objective Function Value =        1052000.000

        Variable            Value          Reduced Costs
      -------------      ---------------    ------------------
            T                 4.000              0.000
            R                14.000              0.000
            N                10.000              0.000

      Constraint         Slack/Surplus         Dual Prices
      -------------      ---------------    ------------------
            1                 0.000             51.304
            2                 6.000              0.000
            3                 6.000              0.000
            4                 0.000          11826.087
            5                 0.000           5217.391
            6                 1.200              0.000
```

OBJECTIVE COEFFICIENT RANGES

Variable	Lower Limit	Current Value	Upper Limit
T	-18000.000	100000.000	120000.000
R	15000.000	18000.000	No Upper Limit
N	28173.913	40000.000	No Upper Limit

RIGHT HAND SIDE RANGES

Constraint	Lower Limit	Current Value	Upper Limit
1	14750.000	18200.000	31999.996
2	4.000	10.000	No Upper Limit
3	14.000	20.000	No Upper Limit
4	0.000	10.000	12.339
5	-8.050	0.000	2.936
6	No Lower Limit	0.000	1.200

b. The dual price for the budget constraint is 51.30. Thus, a $100 increase in budget should provide an increase in audience coverage of approximately 5,130. The right-hand-side range for the budget constraint will show this interpretation is correct.

2. a. Let x_1 = units of product 1 produced
x_2 = units of product 2 produced

$$\text{Max} \quad 30x_1 \quad + \quad 15x_2$$

s.t.

x_1	+	$0.35x_2$	$\leq$	100	Dept. A
$0.30x_1$	+	$0.20x_2$	$\leq$	36	Dept. B
$0.20x_1$	+	$0.50x_2$	$\leq$	50	Dept. C

$$x_1,\ x_2 \geq 0$$

Solution: x_1 = 77.89, x_2 = 63.16 Profit = 3284.21

b. The dual price for Dept. A is $15.79, for Dept. B it is $47.37, and for Dept. C it is $0.00. Therefore we would attempt to schedule overtime in Departments A and B. Assuming the current labor available is a sunk cost, we should be willing to pay up to $15.79 per hour in Department A and up to $47.37 in Department B.

c. Let x_A = hours of overtime in Dept. A
x_B = hours of overtime in Dept. B
x_C = hours of overtime in Dept. C

$$\text{Max} \quad 30x_1 + 15x_2 - 18x_A - 22.5x_B - 12x_C$$

s.t.

$$
\begin{array}{rcr}
x_1 + 0.35x_2 - x_A & \leq & 100 \\
0.30x_1 + 0.20x_2 - x_B & \leq & 36 \\
0.20x_1 + 0.50x_2 - x_C & \leq & 50 \\
x_A & \leq & 10 \\
x_B & \leq & 6 \\
x_C & \leq & 8
\end{array}
$$

$$x_1, x_2, x_A, x_B, x_C \geq 0$$

$x_1 = 87.21$

$x_2 = 65.12$

Profit = $3341.34

Overtime	
Dept. A	10 hrs.
Dept. B	3.186 hrs
Dept. C	0 hours

Increase in Profit from overtime = $3341.34 - 3284.21 = $57.13

3. $x_1 = \$$ automobile loans

   $x_2 = \$$ furniture loans

   $x_3 = \$$ other secured loans

   $x_4 = \$$ signature loans

   $x_5 = \$$ "risk free" securities

$$\text{Max} \quad 0.08x_1 + 0.10x_2 + 0.11x_3 + 0.12x_4 + 0.09x_5$$

s.t.

$$
\begin{array}{rclr}
x_5 & \leq & 600,000 & [1] \\
x_4 & \leq & 0.10(x_1 + x_2 + x_3 + x_4) & \\
\text{or} \quad -0.10x_1 - 0.10x_2 - 0.10x_3 + 0.90x_4 & \leq & 0 & [2] \\
x_2 + x_3 & \leq & x_1 & \\
\text{or} \quad -x_1 + x_2 + x_3 & \leq & 0 & [3] \\
x_3 + x_4 & \leq & x_5 & \\
\text{or} \quad x_3 + x_4 - x_5 & \leq & 0 & [4] \\
x_1 + x_2 + x_3 + x_4 + x_5 & = & 2,000,000 & [5]
\end{array}
$$

$$x_1, x_2, x_3, x_4, x_5 \geq 0$$

Solution:

Automobile Loans	(x_1)	=	$630,000
Furniture Loans	(x_2)	=	$170,000
Other Secured Loans	(x_3)	=	$460,000
Signature Loans	(x_4)	=	$140,000
Risk Free Loans	(x_5)	=	$600,000

Annual Return $188,800 (9.44%)

4. a. x_1 = pounds of bean 1
           x_2 = pounds of bean 2
           x_3 = pounds of bean 3

Max $0.50x_1$ + $0.70x_2$ + $0.45x_3$
s.t.

$$\frac{75x_1 + 85x_2 + 60x_3}{x_1 + x_2 + x_3} \geq 75$$

or $10x_2 - 15x_3 \geq 0$ Aroma

$$\frac{86x_1 + 88x_2 + 75x_3}{x_1 + x_2 + x_3} \geq 80$$

or	$6x_1$ +	$8x_2$		-	$5x_3$	$\geq$	0	Taste
	x_1					$\leq$	500	Bean 1
		x_2				$\leq$	600	Bean 2
					x_3	$\leq$	400	Bean 3
	x_1 +	x_2		+	x_3	$=$	1000	1000 pounds

$$x_1, \ x_2, \ x_3 \geq 0$$

Optimal Solution: $x_1 = 500$, $x_2 = 300$, $x_3 = 200$ Cost: $550

b. Cost per pound = $550/1000 = $0.55

c. Surplus for aroma: $s_1 = 0$; thus aroma rating = 75
    Surplus for taste: $s_2 = 4400$; thus taste rating = 80 + 4400/1000 lbs. = 84.4

d. Dual price = -$0.60. Extra coffee can be produced at a cost of $0.60 per pound.

5.   Let x_1 = amount of ingredient A
               x_2 = amount of ingredient B
               x_3 = amount of ingredient C

Min $0.10x_1$ + $0.03x_2$ + $0.09x_3$
s.t.

	$1x_1$ +	$1x_2$ +	$1x_3$	$\geq$ 10	[1]
	$1x_1$ +	$1x_2$ +	$1x_3$	$\leq$ 15	[2]
	$1x_1$			$\geq 1x_2$	
or	$1x_1$ -	$1x_2$		≥ 0	[3]
			$1x_3$	$\geq 1/2x_1$	
or	$-1/2x_1$		+ $1x_3$	≥ 0	[4]

$$x_1, \ x_2, \ x_3 \geq 0$$

Solution: $x_1 = 4$, $x_2 = 4$, $x_3 = 2$ Cost = $0.70 per gallon.

6. Let x_1 = units of product 1
x_2 = units of product 2
b_1 = labor-hours Dept. A
b_2 = labor-hours Dept. B

$$\text{Max} \quad 25x_1 + 20x_2 + 0b_1 + 0b_2$$
s.t.
$$6x_1 + 8x_2 - 1b_1 = 0$$
$$12x_1 + 10x_2 - 1b_2 = 0$$
$$1b_1 + 1b_2 \le 900$$

$$x_1, x_2, b_1, b_2 \ge 0$$

Solution: $x_1 = 50$, $x_2 = 0$, $b_1 = 300$, $b_2 = 600$ Profit: $1,250

7. a. Let F = total funds required to meet the six years of payments
G_1 = units of government security 1
G_2 = units of government security 2
S_i = investment in savings at the beginning of year i

Note: All decision variables are expressed in thousands of dollars

MIN F
S.T.

1) F - 1.055G1 - 1.000G2 - S1 = 190
2) .0675G1 + .05125G2 +1.04S1 - S2 = 215
3) .0675G1 + .05125G2 + 1.04S2 - S3 = 240
4) 1.0675G1 + .05125G2 + 1.04S3 - S4 = 285
5) 1.05125G2 + 1.04S4 - S5 = 315
6) 1.04S5 - S6 = 460

OPTIMAL SOLUTION

Objective Function Value =   1484.96655

Variable	Value	Reduced Costs
F	1484.96655	0.00000
G1	232.39356	0.00000
G2	720.38782	0.00000
S1	329.40353	0.00000
S2	180.18611	0.00000
S3	0.00000	0.02077
S4	0.00000	0.01942
S5	442.30769	0.00000
S6	0.00000	0.78551

Constraint	Slack/Surplus	Dual Prices
1	0.00000	-1.00000
2	0.00000	-0.96154
3	0.00000	-0.92456
4	0.00000	-0.86903
5	0.00000	-0.81693
6	0.00000	-0.78551

The current investment required is $1,484,967. This calls for investing $232,394 in government security 1 and $720,388 in government security 2. The amounts, placed in savings are $329,404, $180,186 and $442,308 for years 1,2 and 5 respectively. No funds are placed in savings for years 3, 4 and 6.

b. The dual price for constraint 6 indicates that each $1 reduction in the payment required at the beginning of year 6 will reduce the amount of money Hoxworth must pay the trustee by $0.78551. The lower limit on the right-hand-side range is zero so a $60,000 reduction in the payment at the beginning of year 6 will save Hoxworth $60,000 (0.78551) = $47,131.

c. The dual price for constraint 1 shows that every dollar of reduction in the initial payment is worth $1.00 to Hoxworth. So Hoxworth should be willing to pay anything less than $40,000.

d. To reformulate this problem, one additional variable needs to be added, the right-hand sides for the original constraints need to be shifted ahead by one, and the right-hand side of the first constraint needs to be set equal to zero. The value of the optimal solution with this formulation is $1,417,739. Hoxworth will save $67,228 by having the payments moved to the end of each year.

The revised formulation is shown below:

MIN F

S.T.

```
1)  F - 1.055G1 - 1.000G2 - S1 = 0
2)  .0675G1 + .05125G2 + 1.04S1 - S2 = 190
3)  .0675G1 + .05125G2 + 1.04S2 - S3 = 215
4)  1.0675G1 + .05125G2 + 1.04S3 - S4 = 240
5)  1.05125G2 +1.04S4 - S5 = 285
6)  1.04S5 - S6 = 315
7)  1.04S6 - S7 = 460
```

8.   Let x_1 = the number of officers scheduled to begin at 8:00 a.m.

              x_2 = the number of officers scheduled to begin at noon

              x_3 = the number of officers scheduled to begin at 4:00 p.m.

              x_4 = the number of officers scheduled to begin at 8:00 p.m.

              x_5 = the number of officers scheduled to begin at midnight

              x_6 = the number of officers scheduled to begin at 4:00 a.m.

The objective function to minimize the number of officers required is as follows:

Min $x_1 + x_2 + x_3 + x_4 + x_5 + x_6$

The constraints require the total number of officers of duty each of the six four-hour periods to be at least equal to the minimum officer requirements. The constraints for the six four-hour periods are as follows:

Time of Day

8:00 a.m. - noon	x_1					$+ x_6$	$\geq$	5
noon to 4:00 p.m.	x_1	$+ x_2$					$\geq$	6
4:00 p.m. - 8:00 p.m.		x_2	$+ x_3$				$\geq$	10
8:00 p.m. - midnight			x_3	$+ x_4$			$\geq$	7
midnight - 4:00 a.m.				x_4	$+ x_5$		$\geq$	4
4:00 a.m. - 8:00 a.m.					x_5	$+ x_6$	$\geq$	6

$$x_1, x_2, x_3, x_4, x_5, x_6 \geq 0$$

Schedule 19 officers as follows:

$x_1 = 3$ begin at 8:00 a.m.

$x_2 = 3$ begin at noon

$x_3 = 7$ begin at 4:00 p.m.

$x_4 = 0$ begin at 8:00 p.m.

$x_5 = 4$ begin at midnight

$x_6 = 2$ begin at 4:00 a.m.

9.   a.   Let each decision variable, A, P, M, H and G, represent the fraction or proportion of the total investment placed in each investment alternative.

Max $.073A + .103P + .064M + .075H + .045G$
s.t.

A	+	P	+	M	+	H	+	G	=	1
.5A	+	.5P	-	.5M	-	.5H			$\leq$	0
-.5A	-	.5P	+	.5M	+	.5H			$\leq$	0
			-	.25M	-	.25H	+	G	$\geq$	0
-.6A	+	.4P							$\leq$	0

$$A, P, M, H, G \geq 0$$

Solution: Objective function = 0.079 with

Atlantic Oil	=	0.178
Pacific Oil	=	0.267
Midwest Oil	=	0.000
Huber Steel	=	0.444
Government Bonds	=	0.111

b. For a total investment of $100,000, we show

Atlantic Oil	=	$17,800
Pacific Oil	=	26,700
Midwest Oil	=	0.000
Huber Steel	=	44,400
Government Bonds	=	11,100
Total		$100,000

c. Total earnings = $100,000 (.079) = $7,900

d. Marginal rate of return is .079

10. a. Let S = the proportion of funds invested in stocks
B = the proportion of funds invested in bonds
M = the proportion of funds invested in mutual funds
C = the proportion of funds invested in cash

The linear program and optimal solution obtained using The Management Scientist is as follows:

```
MAX  0.1S+0.03B+0.04M+0.01C

     S.T.

     1)   1S+1B+1M+1C=1
     2)   0.8S+0.2B+0.3M<0.4
     3)   1S<0.75
     4)   -1B+1M>0
     5)   1C>0.1
     6)   1C<0.3
```

OPTIMAL SOLUTION

Objective Function Value =   0.054

Variable	Value	Reduced Costs
S	0.409	0.000
B	0.145	0.000
M	0.145	0.000
C	0.300	0.000

Constraint	Slack/Surplus	Dual Prices
1	0.000	0.005
2	0.000	0.118
3	0.341	0.000
4	0.000	-0.001
5	0.200	0.000
6	0.000	0.005

OBJECTIVE COEFFICIENT RANGES

Variable	Lower Limit	Current Value	Upper Limit
S	0.090	0.100	No Upper Limit
B	0.028	0.030	0.036
M	No Lower Limit	0.040	0.042
C	0.005	0.010	No Upper Limit

RIGHT HAND SIDE RANGES

Constraint	Lower Limit	Current Value	Upper Limit
1	0.800	1.000	1.900
2	0.175	0.400	0.560
3	0.409	0.750	No Upper Limit
4	-0.267	0.000	0.320
5	No Lower Limit	0.100	0.300
6	0.100	0.300	0.500

The optimal allocation among the four investment alternatives is

Stocks	40.9%
Bonds	14.5%
Mutual Funds	14.5%
Cash	30.0%

The annual return associated with the optimal portfolio is 5.4%

The total risk = 0.409(0.8) + 0.145(0.2) + 0.145(0.3) + 0.300(0.0) = 0.4

b. Changing the right-hand-side value for constraint 2 to 0.18 and resolving using *The Management Scientist* we obtain the following optimal solution:

Stocks	0.0%
Bonds	36.0%
Mutual Funds	36.0%
Cash	28.0%

The annual return associated with the optimal portfolio is 2.52%

The total risk = 0.0(0.8) + 0.36(0.2) + 0.36(0.3) + 0.28(0.0) = 0.18

c. Changing the right-hand-side value for constraint 2 to 0.7 and resolving using *The Management Scientist* we obtain the following optimal solution:

The optimal allocation among the four investment alternatives is

Stocks	75.0%
Bonds	0.0%
Mutual Funds	15.0%
Cash	10.0%

The annual return associated with the optimal portfolio is 8.2%

The total risk = 0.75(0.8) + 0.0(0.2) + 0.15(0.3) + 0.10(0.0) = 0.65

d. Note that a maximum risk of 0.7 was specified for this aggressive investor, but that the risk index for the portfolio is only 0.65. Thus, this investor is willing to take more risk than the solution shown above provides. There are only two ways the investor can become even more aggressive: increase the proportion invested in stocks to more than 75% or reduce the cash requirement of at least 10% so that additional cash could be put into stocks. For the data given here, the investor should ask the investment advisor to relax either or both of these constraints.

e. Defining the decision variables as proportions means the investment advisor can use the linear programming model for any investor, regardless of the amount of the investment. All the investor advisor needs to do is to establish the maximum total risk for the investor and resolve the problem using the new value for maximum total risk.

11. Let x_{ij} = units of component i purchased from supplier j

$$\text{Min} \quad 12x_{11} + 13x_{12} + 14x_{13} + 10x_{21} + 11x_{22} + 10x_{23}$$

s.t.

$$
\begin{array}{rcl}
x_{11} + x_{12} + x_{13} & = & 1000 \\
x_{21} + x_{22} + x_{23} & = & 800 \\
x_{11} + x_{21} & \leq & 600 \\
x_{12} + x_{22} & \leq & 1000 \\
x_{13} + x_{23} & \leq & 800
\end{array}
$$

$$x_{11}, x_{12}, x_{13}, x_{21}, x_{22}, x_{23} \geq 0$$

Solution:

	Supplier		
	1	2	3
Component 1	600	400	0
Component 2	0	0	800

Purchase Cost = $20,400

12. Let B_i = pounds of shrimp bought in week i, $i = 1,2,3,4$
S_i = pounds of shrimp sold in week i, $i = 1,2,3,4$
I_i = pounds of shrimp held in storage (inventory) in week i

Total purchase cost = $6.00B_1 + 6.20B_2 + 6.65B_3 + 5.55B_4$
Total sales revenue = $6.00S_1 + 6.20S_2 + 6.65S_3 + 5.55S_4$
Total storage cost = $0.15I_1 + 0.15I_2 + 0.15I_3 + 0.15I_4$

Total profit contribution = (total sales revenue) - (total purchase cost) - (total storage cost)

Objective: maximize total profit contribution subject to balance equations for each week, storage capacity for each week, and ending inventory requirement for week 4.

$$\text{Max} \quad 6.00S_1 + 6.20S_2 + 6.65S_3 + 5.55S_4 - 6.00B_1 - 6.20B_2 - 6.65B_3 - 5.55B_4 - 0.15I_1 - 0.15I_2 - 0.15I_3 - 0.15I_4$$

s.t.

$20,000 + B_1 - S_1$	$=$	I_1	Balance eq. - week 1
$I_1 + B_2 - S_2$	$=$	I_2	Balance eq. - week 2
$I_2 + B_3 - S_3$	$=$	I_3	Balance eq. - week 3
$I_3 + B_4 - S_4$	$=$	I_4	Balance eq. - week 4
I_1	$\leq$	$100,000$	Storage cap. - week 1
I_2	$\leq$	$100,000$	Storage cap. - week 2
I_3	$\leq$	$100,000$	Storage cap. - week 3
I_4	$\leq$	$100,000$	Storage cap. - week 4
I_4	$\geq$	$25,000$	Req'd inv. - week 4

all variables ≥ 0

Note that the first four constraints can be written as follows:

$$I_1 - B_1 + S_1 = 20,000$$
$$I_1 - I_2 + B_2 - S_2 = 0$$
$$I_2 - I_3 + B_3 - S_3 = 0$$
$$I_3 - I_4 + B_4 - S_4 = 0$$

The optimal solution obtained using *The Management Scientist* follows:

Week (i)	B_i	S_i	I_i
1	80,000	0	100,000
2	0	0	100,000
3	0	100,000	0
4	25,000	0	25,000

Total profit contribution = $12,500

Note however, ASC started week 1 with 20,000 pounds of shrimp and ended week 4 with 25,000 pounds of shrimp. During the 4-week period, ASC has taken profits to reinvest and build inventory by 5000 pounds in anticipation of future higher prices. The amount of profit reinvested in inventory is ($5.55 + $0.15)(5000) = $28,500. Thus, total profit for the 4-week period including reinvested profit is $12,500 + $28,500 = $41,000.

13. Let BR = pounds of Brazilian beans purchased to produce Regular
     BD = pounds of Brazilian beans purchased to produce DeCaf
     CR = pounds of Colombian beans purchased to produce Regular
     CD = pounds of Colombian beans purchased to produce DeCaf

Type of Bean	Cost per pound ($)
Brazilian	1.10(0.47) = 0.517
Colombian	1.10(0.62) = 0.682

Total revenue = 3.60(BR + CR) + 4.40(BD + CD)

Total cost of beans = 0.517(BR + BD) + 0.682(CR + CD)

Total production cost = 0.80(BR + CR) + 1.05(BD + CD)

Total packaging cost = 0.25(BR + CR) + 0.25(BD + CD)

Total contribution to profit = (total revenue) - (total cost of beans) - (total production cost)

∴ Total contribution to profit = 2.033BR + 2.583BD + 1.868CR + 2.418CD

Regular % constraint

    BR = 0.75(BR + CR)
    0.25BR - 0.75CR = 0

DeCaf % constraint

    BD = 0.40(BD + CD)
    0.60BD - 0.40CD = 0

Pounds of Regular: BR + CR = 1000

Pounds of DeCaf: BD + CD = 500

The complete linear program is

Max   2.033BR + 2.583BD + 1.868CR + 2.418CD
s.t.

$$
\begin{array}{rcrcrcrclr}
0.25BR & & & - & 0.75CR & & & = & 0 \\
& 0.60BD & & & & - & 0.40CD & = & 0 \\
BR & & & + & CR & & & = & 1000 \\
& BD & & & & + & CD & = & 500 \\
\end{array}
$$

BR, BD, CR, CD $\geq$ 0

Using *The Management Scientist*, the optimal solution is BR = 750, BD = 200, CR = 250, and CD = 300.

The value of the optimal solution is $3233.75

14. a.   Let x_i = number of Classic 21 boats produced in Quarter i; i = 1,2,3,4

   s_i = ending inventory of Classic 21 boats in Quarter i; i = 1,2,3,4

Min $10,000x_1 + 11,000x_2 + 12,100x_3 + 13,310x_4 + 250s_1 + 250s_2 + 300s_3 + 300s_4$
s.t.

$x_1 - s_1 = 1900$	Quarter 1 demand
$s_1 + x_2 - s_2 = 4000$	Quarter 2 demand
$s_2 + x_3 - s_3 = 3000$	Quarter 3 demand
$s_3 + x_4 - s_4 = 1500$	Quarter 4 demand
$s_4 \geq 500$	Ending Inventory
$x_1 \leq 4000$	Quarter 1 capacity
$x_2 \leq 3000$	Quarter 2 capacity
$x_3 \leq 2000$	Quarter 3 capacity
$x_4 \leq 4000$	Quarter 4 capacity

b.

Quarter	Production	Ending Inventory	Cost
1	4000	2100	40,525,000
2	3000	1100	33,275,000
3	2000	100	24,230,000
4	1900	500	25,439,000
			$123,469,000

c.   The dual prices tell us how much it would cost if demand were to increase by one additional unit. For example, in Quarter 2 the dual price is -12,760; thus, demand for one more boat in Quarter 2 will increase costs by $12,760.

d.   The dual price of 0 for Quarter 4 tells us we have excess capacity in Quarter 4. The positive dual prices in Quarters 1-3 tell us how much increasing the production capacity will improve the objective function. For example, the dual price of $2510 for Quarter 1 tells us that if capacity is increased by 1 unit for this quarter, costs will go down $2510.

15. Let x_{11} = gallons of crude 1 used to produce regular

   x_{12} = gallons of crude 1 used to produce high-octane

   x_{21} = gallons of crude 2 used to produce regular

   x_{22} = gallons of crude 2 used to produce high-octane

Min $0.10x_{11} + 0.10x_{12} + 0.15x_{21} + 0.15x_{22}$
s.t.

Each gallon of regular must have at least 40% A.

$$x_{11} + x_{21} \quad = \text{amount of regular produced}$$
$$0.4(x_{11} + x_{21}) = \text{amount of A required for regular}$$
$$0.2x_{11} + 0.50x_{21} = \text{amount of A in } (x_{11} + x_{21}) \text{ gallons of regular gas}$$

$\therefore 0.2x_{11} + 0.50x_{21} \geq 0.4x_{11} + 0.40x_{21}$ [1]

$\therefore -0.2x_{11} + 0.10x_{21} \geq 0$

Each gallon of high octane can have at most 50% B.

$$x_{12} + x_{22} \quad = \text{amount high-octane}$$
$$0.5(x_{12} + x_{22}) = \text{amount of B required for high octane}$$
$$0.60x_{12} + 0.30x_{22} = \text{amount of B in } (x_{12} + x_{22}) \text{ gallons of high octane.}$$

$\therefore 0.60x_{12} + 0.30x_{22} \qquad \leq 0.5x_{12} + 0.5x_{22}$

$\therefore 0.1x_{12} - 0.2x_{22} \qquad \leq 0$ [2]

$\qquad\qquad x_{11} + x_{21} \qquad \geq 800,000$ [3]

$\qquad\qquad x_{12} + x_{22} \qquad \geq 500,000$ [4]

$\qquad x_{11}, x_{12}, x_{21}, x_{22} \geq 0$

Optimal Solution: $x_{11} = 266,667$, $x_{12} = 333,333$, $x_{21} = 533,333$, $x_{22} = 166,667$
Cost = $165,000

16. Let x_i = number of 10-inch rolls of paper processed by cutting alternative i; $i = 1,2...,7$

Min $x_1 + x_2 + x_3 + x_4 + x_5 + x_6 + x_7$
s.t.

$6x_1 \qquad + 2x_3 \qquad + x_5 + x_6 + 4x_7 \geq 1000$ 1 1/2" production

$\qquad 4x_2 \qquad\quad + x_4 + 3x_5 + 2x_6 \qquad \geq 2000$ 2 1/2" production

$\qquad\qquad 2x_3 + 2x_4 \qquad\quad + x_6 + x_7 \geq 4000$ 3 1/2" production

$x_1, x_2, x_3, x_4, x_5, x_6, x_7 \geq 0$

$x_1 = 0$

$x_2 = 125$

$x_3 = 500$ 2125 Rolls

$x_4 = 1500$

$x_5 = 0$ Production:

$x_6 = 0$ 1 1/2"   1000

$x_7 = 0$ 2 1/2"   2000

                   3 1/2"   4000

Waste: Cut alternative #4 (1/2" per roll)

$\therefore$ 750 inches.

b. Only the objective function needs to be changed. An objective function minimizing waste production and the new optimal solution are given.

Min $x_1 + 0x_2 + 0x_3 + 0.5x_4 + x_5 + 0x_6 + 0.5x_7$

     $x_1 = 0$

     $x_2 = 500$

     $x_3 = 2000$ 2500 Rolls

     $x_4 = 0$

     $x_5 = 0$ Production:

     $x_6 = 0$ 1 1/2"   4000

     $x_7 = 0$ 2 2/1"   2000

                   3 1/2"   4000

Waste is 0; however, we have over-produced the 1 1/2" size by 3000 units. Perhaps these can be inventoried for future use.

c. Minimizing waste may cause you to over-produce. In this case, we used 375 more rolls to generate a 3000 surplus of the 1 1/2" product. Alternative b might be preferred on the basis that the 3000 surplus could be held in inventory for later demand. However, in some trim problems, excess production cannot be used and must be scrapped. If this were the case, the 3000 unit 1 1/2" size would result in 4500 inches of waste, and thus alternative a would be the preferred solution.

17. a. Let   FM   = number of frames manufactured

           FP   = number of frames purchased

           SM   = number of supports manufactured

           SP   = number of supports purchased

           TM   = number of straps manufactured

           TP   = number of straps purchased

$$\text{Min} \quad 38FM + 51FP + 11.5SM + 15SP + 6.5TM + 7.5TP$$

s.t.

3.5FM		+ 1.3SM		+ 0.8TM		≤	21,000
2.2FM		+ 1.7SM				≤	25,200
3.1FM		+ 2.6SM		+ 1.7TM		≤	40,800
FM +	FP					≥	5,000
		SM +	SP			≥	10,000
				TM +	TP	≥	5,000

$$FM, FP, SM, SP, TM, TP \geq 0.$$

Solution:

	Manufacture	Purchase
Frames	5000	0
Supports	2692	7308
Straps	0	5000

b. Total Cost = $368,076.91

c. Subtract values of slack variables from minutes available to determine minutes used. Divide by 60 to determine hours of production time used.

Constraint			
1	Cutting:	Slack = 0	350 hours used
2	Milling:	(25200 - 9623) / 60 = 259.62 hours	
3	Shaping:	(40800 - 18300) / 60 = 375 hours	

d. Nothing, there are already more hours available than are being used.

e. Yes. The current purchase price is $51.00 and the reduced cost of 3.577 indicates that for a purchase price below $47.423 the solution may improve. Resolving with the coefficient of FP = 45 shows that 2714 frames should be purchased.

The optimal solution is as follows:

OPTIMAL SOLUTION

Objective Function Value =   361500.000

Variable	Value	Reduced Costs
FM	2285.714	0.000
FP	2714.286	0.000
SM	10000.000	0.000
SP	0.000	0.900
TM	0.000	0.600
TP	5000.000	0.000

Constraint	Slack/Surplus	Dual Prices
1	0.000	2.000
2	3171.429	0.000
3	7714.286	0.000
4	0.000	-45.000
5	0.000	-14.100
6	0.000	-7.500

18. a. Let x_1 = number of Super Tankers purchased

x_2 = number of Regular Line Tankers purchased

x_3 = number of Econo-Tankers purchased

$$\text{Min} \quad 550x_1 + 425x_2 + 350x_3$$

s.t.

$6700x_1$ +	$55000x_2$ +	$4600x_3$	$\leq$	600,000	Budget
$15(5000)x_1$ +	$20(2500)x_2$ +	$25(1000)x_3$	$\geq$	550,000	

or

$75000x_1$ +	$50000x_2$ +	$25000x_3$	$\geq$	550,000	Meet Demand
x_1 +	x_2 +	x_3	$\leq$	15	Max. Total Vehicles
		x_3	$\geq$	3	Min. Econo-Tankers

$x_1 \leq 1/2(x_1 + x_2 + x_3)$

or

$1/2x_1 - 1/2x_2 - 1/2x_3 \leq 0$ No more than 50% Super Tankers

$x_1, x_2, x_3 \geq 0$

Solution: 5 Super Tankers, 2 Regular Tankers, 3 Econo-Tankers
Total Cost: $583,000
Monthly Operating Cost: $4,650

b. The last two constraints in the formulation above must be deleted and the problem resolved.

The optimal solution calls for 7 1/3 Super Tankers at an annual operating cost of $4033. However, since a partial Super Tanker can't be purchased we must round up to find a feasible solution of 8 Super Tankers with a monthly operating cost of $4,400.

Actually this is an integer programming problem, since partial tankers can't be purchased. We were fortunate in part (a) that the optimal solution turned out integer.

The true optimal integer solution to part (b) is $x_1 = 6$ and $x_2 = 2$ with a monthly operating cost of $4150. This is 6 Super Tankers and 2 Regular Line Tankers.

19. a. Let x_{11} = amount of men's model in month 1

x_{21} = amount of women's model in month 1

x_{12} = amount of men's model in month 2

x_{22} = amount of women's model in month 2

s_{11} = inventory of men's model at end of month 1

s_{21} = inventory of women's model at end of month 1

s_{12} = inventory of men's model at end of month 2

s_{22} = inventory of women's model at end of month

The model formulation for part (a) is given.

Min $120x_{11} + 90x_{21} + 120x_{12} + 90x_{22} + 2.4s_{11} + 1.8s_{21} + 2.4s_{12} + 1.8s_{22}$

s.t.

$20 + x_{11} - s_{11} = 150$

or

$x_{11} - s_{11} = 130$	Satisfy Demand	[1]

$30 + x_{21} - s_{21} = 125$

or

$x_{21} - s_{21} = 95$	Satisfy Demand	[2]
$s_{11} + x_{12} - s_{12} = 200$	Satisfy Demand	[3]
$s_{21} + x_{22} - s_{22} = 150$	Satisfy Demand	[4]
$s_{12} \geq 25$	Ending Inventory	[5]
$s_{22} \geq 25$	Ending Inventory	[6]

Labor Hours: Men's $= 2.0 + 1.5 = 3.5$

Women's $= 1.6 + 1.0 = 2.6$

$3.5\,x_{11} + 2.6\,x_{21} \geq 900$	Labor Smoothing for	[7]
$3.5\,x_{11} + 2.6\,x_{21} \leq 1100$	Month 1	[8]

$3.5\,x_{11} + 2.6\,x_{21} - 3.5\,x_{12} - 2.6\,x_{22} \leq 100$	Labor Smoothing for	[9]
$-3.5\,x_{11} - 2.6\,x_{21} + 3.5\,x_{12} + 2.6\,x_{22} \leq 100$	Month 2	[10]

$$x_{11},\ x_{12},\ x_{21},\ x_{22},\ s_{11},\ s_{12},\ s_{21}, s_{22} \geq 0$$

The optimal solution is to produce 193 of the men's model in month 1, 162 of the men's model in month 2, 95 units of the women's model in month 1, and 175 of the women's model in month 2. Total Cost = $67,156

Inventory Schedule		
Month 1	63 Men's	0 Women's
Month 2	25 Men's	25 Women's

Labor Levels

Previous month	1000.00 hours
Month 1	922.25 hours
Month 2	1022.25 hours

b. To accommodate this new policy the right-hand sides of constraints [7] to [10] must be changed to 950, 1050, 50, and 50 respectively. The revised optimal solution is given.

$$x_{11} = 201$$
$$x_{21} = 95$$
$$x_{12} = 154$$
$$x_{22} = 175 \qquad \text{Total Cost} = \$67,175$$

We produce more men's models in the first month and carry a larger men's model inventory; the added cost however is only $19. This seems to be a small expense to have less drastic labor force fluctuations. The new labor levels are 1000, 950, and 994.5 hours each month. Since the added cost is only $19, management might want to experiment with the labor force smoothing restrictions to enforce even less fluctuations. You may want to experiment yourself to see what happens.

20.   Let x_m = number of units produced in month m

I_m = increase in the total production level in month m

D_m = decrease in the total production level in month m

s_m = inventory level at the end of month m

where

m = 1 refers to March

m = 2 refers to April

m = 3 refers to May

Min $1.25\,I_1 + 1.25\,I_2 + 1.25\,I_3 + 1.00\,D_1 + 1.00\,D_2 + 1.00\,D_3$
s.t.

Change in production level in March

$$x_1 - 10,000 = I_1 - D_1$$

or

$$x_1 - I_1 + D_1 = 10,000$$

Change in production level in April

$$x_2 - x_1 = I_2 - D_2$$

or

$$x_2 - x_1 - I_2 + D_2 = 0$$

Change in production level in May

$$x_3 - x_2 = I_3 - D_3$$

or

$$x_3 - x_2 - I_3 + D_3 = 0$$

Demand in March

$$2500 + x_1 - s_1 = 12,000$$

or

$$x_1 - s_1 = 9,500$$

Demand in April

$$s_1 + x_2 - s_2 = 8,000$$

Demand in May

$$s_2 + x_3 = 15,000$$

Inventory capacity in March

$$s_1 \leq 3,000$$

Inventory capacity in April

$$s_2 \leq 3,000$$

Optimal Solution:

Total cost of monthly production increases and decreases $= \$2,500$

$x_1 = 10,250$ $\quad I_1 = 250$ $\quad D_1 = 0$

$x_2 = 10,250$ $\quad I_2 = 0$ $\quad D_2 = 0$

$x_3 = 12,000$ $\quad I_3 = 1750$ $\quad D_3 = 0$

$s_1 = 750$

$s_2 = 3000$

21.   Decision variables : Regular

Model	Month 1	Month 2
Bookshelf	B1R	B2R
Floor	F1R	F2R

Decision variables : Overtime

Model	Month 1	Month 2
Bookshelf	B1O	B2O
Floor	F1O	F2O

Labor costs per unit

Model	Regular	Overtime
Bookshelf	.7 (22) = 15.40	.7 (33) = 23.10
Floor	1 (22) = 22	1 (33) = 33

IB = Month 1 ending inventory for bookshelf units
IF = Month 1 ending inventory for floor model

Objective function

Min   15.40 B1R + 15.40 B2R + 22 F1R + 22 F2R
   +   23.10 B1O + 23.10 B2O + 33 F1O + 33 F2O
   +   10 B1R + 10 B2R + 12 F1R + 12 F2R
   +   10 B1O + 10 B2O + 12 F1O + 12 F2O
   +   5 IB + 5 IF

or

Min   25.40 B1R + 25.40 B2R + 34 F1R + 34 F2R
   +   33.10 B1O + 33.10 B2O + 45 F1O + 45 F2O
   +   5 IB + 5 IF

s.t.

.7 B1R + 1 F1R	≤	2400	Regular time: month 1
.7 B2R + 1 F2R	≤	2400	Regular time: month 2
.7B1O + 1 F1O	≤	1000	Overtime: month 1
.7B2O + 1 F2O	≤	1000	Overtime: month 2
B1R + B1O - IB	=	2100	Bookshelf: month 1
IB + B2R + B2O	=	1200	Bookshelf: month 2
F1R + F1O - IF	=	1500	Floor: month 1
IF + F2R + F2O	=	2600	Floor: month 2

OPTIMAL SOLUTION

Objective Function Value =   241130.000

Variable	Value	Reduced Costs
B1R	2100.000	0.000
B2R	1200.000	0.000
F1R	930.000	0.000
F2R	1560.000	0.000
B1O	0.000	0.000
B2O	0.000	0.000
F1O	610.000	0.000
F2O	1000.000	0.000
IB	0.000	1.500
IF	40.000	0.000

Constraint	Slack/Surplus	Dual Prices
1	0.000	11.000
2	0.000	16.000
3	390.000	0.000
4	0.000	5.000
5	0.000	-33.100
6	0.000	-36.600
7	0.000	-45.000
8	0.000	-50.000

OBJECTIVE COEFFICIENT RANGES

Variable	Lower Limit	Current Value	Upper Limit
B1R	23.900	25.400	25.400
B2R	No Lower Limit	25.400	25.400
F1R	34.000	34.000	36.143
F2R	34.000	34.000	50.000
B1O	33.100	33.100	No Upper Limit
B2O	33.100	33.100	No Upper Limit
F1O	40.000	45.000	45.000
F2O	No Lower Limit	45.000	45.000
IB	3.500	5.000	No Upper Limit
IF	0.000	5.000	7.143

RIGHT HAND SIDE RANGES

Constraint	Lower Limit	Current Value	Upper Limit
1	2010.000	2400.000	3010.000
2	2010.000	2400.000	2440.000
3	610.000	1000.000	No Upper Limit
4	610.000	1000.000	1040.000
5	1228.571	2100.000	2657.143
6	1142.857	1200.000	1757.143
7	890.000	1500.000	1890.000
8	2560.000	2600.000	2990.000

22. Let $SM1$ = No. of small on machine M1
$SM2$ = No. of small on machine M2
$SM3$ = No. of small on machine M3
$LM1$ = No. of large on machine M1
$LM2$ = No. of large on machine M2
$LM3$ = No. of large on machine M3
$MM2$ = No. of meal on machine M2
$MM3$ = No. of meal on machine M3

Output from *The Management Scientist* showing the formulation and solution follows. Note that constraints 1-3 guarantee that next week's schedule will be met and constraints 4-6 enforce machine capacities.

LINEAR PROGRAMMING PROBLEM

MIN 20SM1+24SM2+32SM3+15LM1+28LM2+35LM3+18MM2+36MM3

S.T.

    1)   1SM1+1SM2+1SM3>80000
    2)   +1LM1+1LM2+1LM3>80000
    3)   +1MM2+1MM3>65000
    4)   0.03333SM1+0.04LM1<2100
    5)   +0.02222SM2+0.025LM2+0.03333MM2<2100
    6)   +0.01667SM3+0.01923LM3+0.02273MM3<2400

OPTIMAL SOLUTION

Objective Function Value =   5515886.58866

Variable	Value	Reduced Costs
SM1	0.00000	4.66500
SM2	0.00000	4.00000
SM3	80000.00000	0.00000
LM1	52500.00000	0.00000
LM2	0.00000	6.50135
LM3	27500.00000	0.00000
MM2	63006.30063	0.00000
MM3	1993.69937	0.00000

Constraint	Slack/Surplus	Dual Prices
1	0.00000	-32.00000
2	0.00000	-35.00000
3	0.00000	-36.00000
4	0.00000	500.00000
5	0.00000	540.05401
6	492.25821	0.00000

OBJECTIVE COEFFICIENT RANGES

Variable	Lower Limit	Current Value	Upper Limit
SM1	15.33500	20.00000	No Upper Limit
SM2	20.00000	24.00000	No Upper Limit
SM3	0.00000	32.00000	36.00000
LM1	No Lower Limit	15.00000	20.59856
LM2	21.49865	28.00000	No Upper Limit
LM3	29.40144	35.00000	41.50135
MM2	No Lower Limit	18.00000	24.00000
MM3	30.00000	36.00000	No Upper Limit

RIGHT HAND SIDE RANGES

Constraint	Lower Limit	Current Value	Upper Limit
1	0.00000	80000.00000	109529.58688
2	52500.00000	80000.00000	105598.45103
3	63006.30063	65000.00000	86656.76257
4	1076.06196	2100.00000	3200.00000
5	1378.18010	2100.00000	2166.45000
6	1907.74179	2400.00000	No Upper Limit

Note that 5,515,887 square inches of waste are generated. Machine 3 has 492 minutes of idle capacity.

23. Let F = number of windows manufactured in February
         M = number of windows manufactured in March
         A = number of windows manufactured in April
         I_m = increase in production level necessary during month m
         D_m = decrease in production level necessary during month m
         s_m = ending inventory in month m

Min $\quad 1I_1 + 1I_2 + 1I_3 + 0.65D_1 + 0.65D_2 + 0.65D_3$

s.t.

$\quad\quad 9000 + F - s_1 = 15,000 \quad$ February Demand

or

(1) $\quad F_1 - s_1 = 6000$

(2) $\quad s_1 + M - s_2 = 16,500 \quad$ March Demand

(3) $\quad s_2 + A - s_3 = 20,000 \quad$ April Demand

$\quad\quad F - 15,000 = I_1 - D_1 \quad$ Change in February Production

or

(4) $\quad F - I_1 + D_1 = 15,000$

$\quad\quad M - F = I_2 - D_2 \quad$ Change in March Production

or

(5) $\quad M - F - I_2 + D_2 = 0$

$\quad\quad A - M = I_3 - D_3 \quad$ Change in April Production

or

(6) $\quad A - M - I_3 + D_3 = 0$

(7) $\quad F \le 14,000 \quad$ February Production Capacity

(8) $\quad M \le 14,000 \quad$ March Production Capacity

(9) $\quad A \le 18,000 \quad$ April Production Capacity

(10) $\quad s_1 \le 6,000 \quad$ February Storage Capacity

(11) $\quad s_2 \le 6,000 \quad$ March Storage Capacity

(12) $\quad s_3 \le 6,000 \quad$ April Storage Capacity

Optimal Solution: Cost = $6,450

	February	March	April
Production Level	12,000	14,000	16,500
Increase in Production	0	2,000	2,500
Decrease in Production	3,000	0	0
Ending Inventory	6,000	3,500	0

24.   Let x_1 = proportion of investment A undertaken
x_2 = proportion of investment B undertaken
s_1 = funds placed in savings for period 1
s_2 = funds placed in savings for period 2
s_3 = funds placed in savings for period 3
s_4 = funds placed in savings for period 4
L_1 = funds received from loan in period 1
L_2 = funds received from loan in period 2
L_3 = funds received from loan in period 3
L_4 = funds received from loan in period 4

Objective Function:

In order to maximize the cash value at the end of the four periods, we must consider the value of investment A, the value of investment B, savings income from period 4, and loan expenses for period 4.

Max $3200x_1 + 2500x_2 + 1.1s_4 - 1.18L_4$

Constraints require the *use* of funds to equal the *source* of funds for each period.

Period 1:
$$1000x_1 + 800x_2 + s_1 = 1500 + L_1$$
or
$$1000x_1 + 800x_2 + s_1 - L_1 = 1500$$

Period 2:
$$800x_1 + 500x_2 + s_2 + 1.18L_1 = 400 + 1.1s_1 + L_2$$
or
$$800x_1 + 500x_2 - 1.1s_1 + s_2 + 1.18L_1 - L_2 = 400$$

Period 3
$$200x_1 + 300x_2 + s_3 + 1.18L_2 = 500 + 1.1s_2 + L_3$$
or
$$200x_1 + 300x_2 - 1.1s_2 + s_3 + 1.18L_2 - L_3 = 500$$
Period 4
$$s_4 + 1.18L_3 = 100 + 200x_1 + 300x_2 + 1.1s_3 + L_4$$
or
$$-200x_1 - 300x_2 - 1.1s_3 + s_4 + 1.18L_3 - L_4 = 100$$

Limits on Loan Funds Available

$$L_1 \le 200$$
$$L_2 \le 200$$
$$L_3 \le 200$$
$$L_4 \le 200$$

Proportion of Investment Undertaken

$$x_1 \leq 1$$
$$x_2 \leq 1$$

Optimal Solution: $4340.40

Investment A	$x_1 = 0.458$	or	45.8%
Investment B	$x_2 = 1.0$	or	100.0%

Savings/Loan Schedule:

	Period 1	Period 2	Period 3	Period 4
Savings	242.11	—	—	341.04
Loan	—	200.00	127.58	—

25. Let

x_1 = number of part-time employees beginning at 11:00 a.m.
x_2 = number of part-time employees beginning at 12:00 p.m.
x_3 = number of part-time employees beginning at 1:00 p.m.
x_4 = number of part-time employees beginning at 2:00 p.m.
x_5 = number of part-time employees beginning at 3:00 p.m.
x_6 = number of part-time employees beginning at 4:00 p.m.
x_7 = number of part-time employees beginning at 5:00 p.m.
x_8 = number of part-time employees beginning at 6:00 p.m.

Each part-time employee assigned to a four-hour shift will be paid $7.60 (4 hours) = $30.40.

$$\text{Min } 30.4x_1 + 30.4x_2 + 30.4x_3 + 30.4x_4 + 30.4x_5 + 30.4x_6 + 30.4x_7 + 30.4x_8$$

Part-Time Employees Needed

s.t.

							Part-Time Needed	Time
x_1							≥ 8	11:00 a.m.
$x_1 + x_2$							≥ 8	12:00 p.m.
$x_1 + x_2 + x_3$							≥ 7	1:00 p.m.
$x_1 + x_2 + x_3 + x_4$							≥ 1	2:00 p.m.
$x_2 + x_3 + x_4 + x_5$							≥ 2	3:00 p.m.
$x_3 + x_4 + x_5 + x_6$							≥ 1	4:00 p.m.
$x_4 + x_5 + x_6 + x_7$							≥ 5	5:00 p.m.
$x_5 + x_6 + x_7 + x_8$							≥ 10	6:00 p.m.
$x_6 + x_7 + x_8$							≥ 10	7:00 p.m.
$x_7 + x_8$							≥ 6	8:00 p.m.
x_8							≥ 6	9:00 p.m.

$$x_j \geq 0 \quad j = 1,2,...8$$

Full-time employees reduce the number of part-time employees needed.

A portion of *The Management Scientist* solution to the model follows.

```
OPTIMAL SOLUTION

Objective Function Value =            608.000
```

Variable	Value	Reduced Costs
X1	8.000	0.000
X2	0.000	0.000
X3	0.000	0.000
X4	0.000	0.000
X5	2.000	0.000
X6	0.000	0.000
X7	4.000	0.000
X8	6.000	0.000

Constraint	Slack/Surplus	Dual Prices
1	0.000	-18.400
2	0.000	0.000
3	1.000	0.000
4	7.000	0.000
5	0.000	-18.400
6	1.000	0.000
7	1.000	0.000
8	2.000	0.000
9	0.000	-18.400
10	4.000	0.000
11	0.000	0.000

The optimal schedule calls for
8 starting at 11:00 a.m.
2 starting at 3:00 p.m.
4 starting at 5:00 p.m.
6 starting at 6:00 p.m.

b.   Total daily salary cost = $608

There are 7 surplus employees scheduled from 2:00 - 3:00 p.m. and 4 from 8:00 - 9:00 p.m. suggesting the desirability of rotating employees off sooner.

c.   Considering 3-hour shifts

Let x denote 4-hour shifts and y denote 3-hour shifts where

y_1 = number of part-time employees beginning at 11:00 a.m.
y_2 = number of part-time employees beginning at 12:00 p.m.
y_3 = number of part-time employees beginning at 1:00 p.m.
y_4 = number of part-time employees beginning at 2:00 p.m.
y_5 = number of part-time employees beginning at 3:00 p.m.
y_6 = number of part-time employees beginning at 4:00 p.m.

y_7 = number of part-time employees beginning at 5:00 p.m.

y_8 = number of part-time employees beginning at 6:00 p.m.

y_9 = number of part-time employees beginning at 7:00 p.m.

Each part-time employee assigned to a three-hour shift will be paid $7.60 (3 hours) = $22.80

New objective function:

$$\min \sum_{j=1}^{8} 30.40x_j + \sum_{i=1}^{9} 22.80y_i$$

Each constraint must be modified with the addition of the y_i variables. For instance, the first constraint becomes

$$x_1 + y_1 \geq 8$$

and so on. Each y_i appears in three constraints because each refers to a three hour shift. The optimal solution is shown below.

$x_8 = 6$ $y_1 = 8$

$y_3 = 1$

$y_5 = 1$

$y_7 = 4$

Optimal schedule for part-time employees:

4-Hour Shifts	3-Hour Shifts
$x_8 = 6$	$y_1 = 8$
	$y_3 = 1$
	$y_5 = 1$
	$y_7 = 4$

Total cost reduced to $501.60. Still have 20 part-time shifts, but 14 are 3-hour shifts. The surplus has been reduced by a total of 14 hours.

26. a.

Min E

s.t.

	wg	+	wu	+	wc	+	ws	=	1
	$48.14wg$	+	$34.62wu$	+	$36.72wc$	+	$33.16ws$	$\geq$	48.14
	$43.10wg$	+	$27.11wu$	+	$45.98wc$	+	$56.46ws$	$\geq$	43.10
	$253wg$	+	$148wu$	+	$175wc$	+	$160ws$	$\geq$	253
	$41wg$	+	$27wu$	+	$23wc$	+	$84ws$	$\geq$	41
$-285.2E +$	$285.2wg$	+	$162.3wu$	+	$275.7wc$	+	$210.4ws$	$\leq$	0
$-123.80E +$	$1123.80wg$	+	$128.70wu$	+	$348.50wc$	+	$154.10ws$	$\leq$	0
$-106.72E +$	$106.72wg$	+	$64.21wu$	+	$104.10wc$	+	$104.04ws$	$\leq$	0

$$wg, wu, wc, ws \geq 0$$

b. Since $wg = 1.0$, the solution does not indicate General Hospital is relatively inefficient.

c. The composite hospital is General Hospital. For any hospital that is not relatively inefficient, the composite hospital will be that hospital because the model is unable to find a weighted average of the other hospitals that is better.

27. a.

Min E

s.t.

$wa +$	$wb +$	$wc +$	$wd +$	$we +$	$wf +$	wg	$=$	1
$55.31wa +$	$37.64wb +$	$32.91wc +$	$33.53wd +$	$32.48we +$	$48.78wf +$	$58.41wg$	$\geq$	33.53
$49.52wa +$	$55.63wb +$	$25.77wc +$	$41.99wd +$	$55.30we +$	$81.92wf +$	$119.70wg$	$\geq$	41.99
$281wa +$	$156wb +$	$141wc +$	$160wd +$	$157we +$	$285wf +$	$111wg$	$\geq$	160
$47wa +$	$3wb +$	$26wc +$	$21wd +$	$82we +$	$92wf +$	$89wg$	$\geq$	21
$-250E+310wa +$	$278.5wb +$	$165.6wc +$	$250wd +$	$206.4we +$	$384wf +$	$530.1wg$	$\leq$	0
$-316E+134.6wa +$	$114.3wb +$	$131.3wc +$	$316wd +$	$151.2we +$	$217wf +$	$770.8wg$	$\leq$	0
$-94.4E+116wa +$	$106.8wb +$	$65.52wc +$	$94.4wd +$	$102.1we +$	$153.7wf +$	$215wg$	$\leq$	0

$$wa, \ wb, \ wc, \ wd, \ we, \ wf, \ wg \geq 0$$

b. $E = 0.924$
$wa = 0.074$
$wc = 0.436$
$we = 0.489$
All other weights are zero.

c. D is relatively inefficient
Composite requires 92.4 of D's resources.

d. 34.37 patient days (65 or older)
41.99 patient days (under 65)

e. Hospitals A, C, and E.

28. a. Make the following changes to the model in problem 27.

New Right-Hand Side Values for
Constraint 2	32.48
Constraint 3	55.30
Constraint 4	157
Constraint 5	82

New Coefficients for E in
Constraint 6	-206.4
Constraint 7	-151.2
Constraint 8	-102.1

b. $E = 1$; $we = 1$; all other weights $= 0$

c. No; $E = 1$ indicates that all the resources used by Hospital E are required to produce the outputs of Hospital E.

d. Hospital E is the only hospital in the composite. If a hospital is not relatively inefficient, the hospital will make up the composite hospital with weight equal to 1.

29. a.

Min E

s.t.

		wb +	wc +	wj +	wn +	ws =	1
		$3800wb$ +	$4600wc$ +	$4400wj$ +	$6500wn$ +	$6000ws$ ≥	4600
		$25wb$ +	$32wc$ +	$35wj$ +	$30wn$ +	$28ws$ ≥	32
		$8wb$ +	$8.5wc$ +	$8wj$ +	$10wn$ +	$9ws$ ≥	8.5
- 110E +		$96wb$ +	$110wc$ +	$100wj$ +	$125wn$ +	$120ws$ ≤	0
- 22E +		$16wb$ +	$22wc$ +	$18wj$ +	$25wn$ +	$24ws$ ≤	0
-1400E +		$850wb$ +	$1400wc$ +	$1200wj$ +	$1500wn$ +	$1600ws$ ≤	0

$$wb,\ wc,\ wj,\ wn,\ ws \geq 0$$

b.

OPTIMAL SOLUTION

Objective Function Value =   0.960

Variable	Value	Reduced Costs
E	0.960	0.000
WB	0.175	0.000
WC	0.000	0.040
WJ	0.575	0.000
WN	0.250	0.000
WS	0.000	0.085

Constraint	Slack/Surplus	Dual Prices
1	0.000	0.200
2	220.000	0.000
3	0.000	-0.004
4	0.000	-0.123
5	0.000	0.009
6	1.710	0.000
7	129.614	0.000

c. Yes; $E = 0.960$ indicates a composite restaurant can produce Clarksville's output with 96% of Clarksville's available resources.

d. More Output (Constraint 2 Surplus) $220 more profit per week.
    Less Input

> Hours of Operation 110E = 105.6 hours
> FTE Staff 22E - 1.71 (Constraint 6 Slack) = 19.41
> Supply Expense 1400E - 129.614 (Constraint 7 Slack) = $1214.39

The composite restaurant uses 4.4 hours less operation time, 2.6 less employees and $185.61 less supplies expense when compared to the Clarksville restaurant.

e. $wb = 0.175$, $wj = 0.575$, and $wn = 0.250$. Consider the Bardstown, Jeffersonville, and New Albany restaurants.

30. a. If the larger plane is based in Pittsburgh, the total revenue increases to $107,849. If the larger plane is based in Newark, the total revenue increases to $108,542. Thus, it would be better to locate the larger plane in Newark.

    Note: The optimal solution to the original Leisure Air problem resulted in a total revenue of $103,103. The difference between the total revenue for the original problem and the problem that has a larger plane based in Newark is $108,542 - $103,103 = $5,439. In order to make the decision to change to a larger plane based in Newark, management must determine if the $5,439 increase in revenue is sufficient to cover the cost associated with changing to the larger plane.

b. Using a larger plane based in Newark, the optimal allocations are:

PCQ = 33	**PMQ** = 23	**POQ** = 43
PCY = 16	PMY= 6	POY = 11
NCQ = 26	**NMQ** = 56	NOQ = 39
NCY = 15	NMY = 7	NOY = 9
CMQ = 32	CMY = 8	
COQ = 46	COY = 10	

    The differences between the new allocations above and the allocations for the original Leisure Air problem involve the five ODIFs that are boldfaced in the solution shown above.

c. Using a larger plane based in Pittsburgh and a larger plane based in Newark, the optimal allocations are:

PCQ = 33	PMQ = 44	**POQ** = 45
PCY = 16	PMY= 6	POY = 11
NCQ = 26	**NMQ** = 56	NOQ = 39
NCY = 15	NMY = 7	NOY = 9
CMQ = 37	CMY = 8	
COQ = 44	COY = 10	

    The differences between the new allocations above and the allocations for the original Leisure Air problem involve the four ODIFs that are boldfaced in the solution shown above. The total revenue associated with the new optimal solution is $115,073, which is a difference of $115,073 - $103,103 = $11,970.

d. In part (b), the ODIF that has the largest bid price is COY, with a bid price of $443. The bid price tells us that if one more Y class seat were available from Charlotte to Myrtle Beach that revenue would increase by $443. In other words, if all 10 seats allocated to this ODIF had been sold, accepting another reservation will provide additional revenue of $443.

31. a. The calculation of the number of seats still available on each flight leg is shown below:

ODIF	ODIF Code	Original Allocation	Seats Sold	Seats Available
1	PCQ	33	25	8
2	PMQ	44	44	0
3	POQ	22	18	4
4	PCY	16	12	4
5	PMY	6	5	1
6	POY	11	9	2
7	NCQ	26	20	6
8	NMQ	36	33	3
9	NOQ	39	37	2
10	NCY	15	11	4
11	NMY	7	5	2
12	NOY	9	8	1
13	CMQ	31	27	4
14	CMY	8	6	2
15	COQ	41	35	6
16	COY	10	7	3

Flight Leg 1: 8 + 0 + 4 + 4 + 1 + 2 = 19
Flight Leg 2: 6 + 3 + 2 + 4 + 2 + 1 = 18
Flight Leg 3: 0 + 1 + 3 + 2 + 4 + 2 = 12
Flight Leg 4: 4 + 2 + 2 + 1 + 6 + 3 = 18

Note: See the demand constraints for the ODIFs that make up each flight leg.

b. The calculation of the remaining demand for each ODIF is shown below:

ODIF	ODIF Code	Original Allocation	Seats Sold	Seats Available
1	PCQ	33	25	8
2	PMQ	44	44	0
3	POQ	45	18	27
4	PCY	16	12	4
5	PMY	6	5	1
6	POY	11	9	2
7	NCQ	26	20	6
8	NMQ	56	33	23
9	NOQ	39	37	2
10	NCY	15	11	4
11	NMY	7	5	2
12	NOY	9	8	1
13	CMQ	64	27	37
14	CMY	8	6	2
15	COQ	46	35	11
16	COY	10	7	3

c. The LP model and solution are shown below:

MAX
178PCQ+268PMQ+228POQ+380PCY+456PMY+560POY+199NCQ+249NMQ+349NOQ+385NCY+444NMY
+580NOY+179CMQ+380CMY+224COQ+582COY

S.T.

```
 1)   1PCQ+1PMQ+1POQ+1PCY+1PMY+1POY<19
 2)   1NCQ+1NMQ+1NOQ+1NCY+1NMY+1NOY<18
 3)   1PMQ+1PMY+1NMQ+1NMY+1CMQ+1CMY<12
 4)   1POQ+1POY+1NOQ+1NOY+1COQ+1COY<18
 5)   1PCQ<8
 6)   1PMQ<1
 7)   1POQ<27
 8)   1PCY<4
 9)   1PMY<1
10)   1POY<2
11)   1NCQ<6
12)   1NMQ<23
13)   1NOQ<2
14)   1NCY<4
15)   1NMY<2
16)   1NOY<1
17)   1CMQ<37
18)   1CMY<2
19)   1COQ<11
20)   1COY<3
```

OPTIMAL SOLUTION

Objective Function Value =   15730.000

Variable	Value	Reduced Costs
PCQ	8.000	0.000
PMQ	1.000	0.000
POQ	3.000	0.000
PCY	4.000	0.000
PMY	1.000	0.000
POY	2.000	0.000
NCQ	6.000	0.000
NMQ	3.000	0.000
NOQ	2.000	0.000
NCY	4.000	0.000
NMY	2.000	0.000
NOY	1.000	0.000
CMQ	3.000	0.000
CMY	2.000	0.000
COQ	7.000	0.000
COY	3.000	0.000

Note: The values shown above provide the allocations for the remaining seats available. The bid prices for each ODIF are provide by the deal prices in the following output.

Constraint	Slack/Surplus	Dual Prices
1	0.000	4.000
2	0.000	70.000
3	0.000	179.000
4	0.000	224.000
5	0.000	174.000
6	0.000	85.000
7	24.000	0.000
8	0.000	376.000
9	0.000	273.000
10	0.000	332.000
11	0.000	129.000
12	20.000	0.000
13	0.000	55.000
14	0.000	315.000
15	0.000	195.000
16	0.000	286.000
17	34.000	0.000
18	0.000	201.000
19	4.000	0.000
20	0.000	358.000

32. a.   Let CT = number of convention two-night rooms
          CF = number of convention Friday only rooms
          CS = number of convention Saturday only rooms
          RT = number of regular two-night rooms
          RF = number of regular Friday only rooms
          RS = number of regular Saturday only room

b./c. The formulation and output obtained using *The Management Scientist* is shown below.

LINEAR PROGRAMMING PROBLEM

MAX 225CT+123CF+130CS+295RT+146RF+152RS

    S.T.

    1)   1CT<40
    2)   1CF<20
    3)   1CS<15
    4)   1RT<20
    5)   1RF<30
    6)   1RS<25
    7)   1CT+1CF>48
    8)   1CT+1CS>48
    9)   1CT+1CF+1RT+1RF<96
    10) 1CT+1CS+1RT+1RS<96

OPTIMAL SOLUTION

Objective Function Value =   25314.000

Variable	Value	Reduced Costs
CT	36.000	0.000
CF	12.000	0.000
CS	15.000	0.000
RT	20.000	0.000
RF	28.000	0.000
RS	25.000	0.000

Constraint	Slack/Surplus	Dual Prices
1	4.000	0.000
2	8.000	0.000
3	0.000	28.000
4	0.000	47.000
5	2.000	0.000
6	0.000	50.000
7	0.000	-23.000
8	3.000	0.000
9	0.000	146.000
10	0.000	102.000

OBJECTIVE COEFFICIENT RANGES

Variable	Lower Limit	Current Value	Upper Limit
CT	123.000	225.000	253.000
CF	95.000	123.000	146.000
CS	102.000	130.000	No Upper Limit
RT	248.000	295.000	No Upper Limit
RF	123.000	146.000	193.000
RS	102.000	152.000	No Upper Limit

RIGHT HAND SIDE RANGES

Constraint	Lower Limit	Current Value	Upper Limit
1	36.000	40.000	No Upper Limit
2	12.000	20.000	No Upper Limit
3	11.000	15.000	23.000
4	18.000	20.000	23.000
5	28.000	30.000	No Upper Limit
6	21.000	25.000	28.000
7	46.000	48.000	56.000
8	No Lower Limit	48.000	51.000
9	68.000	96.000	98.000
10	93.000	96.000	100.000

d. The dual price for constraint 10 shows an added profit of $50 if this additional reservation is accepted.

Chapter 5
Linear Programming: The Simplex Method

Learning Objectives

1. Learn how to find basic and basic feasible solutions to systems of linear equations when the number of variables is greater than the number of equations.

2. Learn how to use the simplex method for solving linear programming problems.

3. Obtain an understanding of why and how the simplex calculations are made.

4. Understand how to use slack, surplus, and artificial variables to set up tableau form to get started with the simplex method for all types of constraints.

5. Understand the following terms:

   simplex method   net evaluation row
   basic solution   basis
   basic feasible solution   iteration
   tableau form   pivot element
   simplex tableau   artificial variable

6. Know how to recognize the following special situations when using the simplex method to solve linear programs.

   infeasibility
   unboundedness
   alternative optimal solutions
   degeneracy

Solutions:

1. a. With $x_1 = 0$, we have

$$
\begin{aligned}
x_2 \qquad\qquad &= 6 \quad (1) \\
4x_2 \quad + x_3 &= 12 \quad (2)
\end{aligned}
$$

From (1), we have $x_2 = 6$. Substituting for x_2 in (2) yields

$$
\begin{aligned}
4(6) \quad + x_3 &= 12 \\
x_3 &= 12 - 24 = -12
\end{aligned}
$$

Basic Solution: $x_1 = 0, x_2 = 6, x_3 = -12$

   b. With $x_2 = 0$, we have

$$
\begin{aligned}
3x_1 \qquad\qquad &= 6 \quad (3) \\
2x_1 \quad + x_3 &= 12 \quad (4)
\end{aligned}
$$

From (3), we find $x_1 = 2$. Substituting for x_1 in (4) yields

$$
\begin{aligned}
2(2) \quad + x_3 &= 12 \\
x_3 &= 12 - 4 = 8
\end{aligned}
$$

Basic Solution: $x_1 = 2, x_2 = 0, x_3 = 8$

   c. With $x_3 = 0$, we have

$$
\begin{aligned}
3x_1 \quad + x_2 &= 6 \quad (5) \\
2x_1 \quad + 4x_2 &= 12 \quad (6)
\end{aligned}
$$

Multiplying (6) by 3/2 and Subtracting form (5) yields

$$
\begin{aligned}
3x_1 \quad + \qquad x_2 &= 6 \\
-(3x_1 \quad + \qquad 6x_2) &= -18 \\
\hline
-5x_2 &= -12 \\
x_2 &= 12/5
\end{aligned}
$$

Substituting $x_2 = 12/5$ into (5) yields

$$
\begin{aligned}
3x_1 \quad + 12/5 &= 6 \\
3x_1 &= 18/5 \\
x_1 &= 6/5
\end{aligned}
$$

Basic Solution: $x_1 = 6/5, x_2 = 12/5, x_3 = 0$

   d. The basic solutions found in (b) and (c) are basic feasible solutions. The one in (a) is not because $x_3 = -12$.

2. a. Standard Form:

$$\text{Max} \quad x_1 + 2x_2$$
$$\text{s.t.}$$
$$x_1 + 5x_2 + s_1 \qquad = 10$$
$$2x_1 + 6x_2 \qquad + s_2 = 16$$
$$x_1, x_2, s_1, s_2 \geq 0$$

b. We have $n = 4$ and $m = 2$ in standard form. So $n - m = 4 - 2 = 2$ variables must be set equal to zero in each basic solution.

c. There are 6 combinations of the two variables that may be set equal to zero and hence 6 possible basic solutions.

$x_1 = 0, x_2 = 0$

$$s_1 = 10$$
$$s_2 = 16$$

This is a basic feasible solution.

$x_1 = 0, s_1 = 0$

$$5x_2 \qquad\qquad = 10 \quad (1)$$
$$6x_2 + s_2 = 16 \quad (2)$$

From (1) we have $x_2 = 2$. And substituting for x_2 in (2) yields

$$6(2) + s_2 = 16$$
$$s_2 = 16 - 12 = 4$$

This is a basic feasible solution.

$x_1 = 0, s_2 = 0$

$$5x_2 + s_1 = 10 \quad (3)$$
$$6x_2 \qquad = 16 \quad (4)$$

From (4), we have $x_2 = 8/3$. Substituting for x_2 in (3) yields

$$5(8/3) + s_1 = 10$$
$$s_1 = 10 - 40/3 = -10/3$$

This is not a basic feasible solution.

$x_2 = 0, s_1 = 0$

$$x_1 \qquad\qquad = 10 \quad (5)$$
$$2x_1 + s_2 = 16 \quad (6)$$

From (5) we have $x_1 = 10$. And substituting for x_1 in (6) yields

$$2(10) + s_2 = 16$$
$$s_2 = 16 - 20 = -4$$

This is not a basic feasible solution.

$x_2 = 0, s_2 = 0$

$$
\begin{array}{llll}
x_1 & + & s_1 & = 10 \quad (7) \\
2x_1 & & & = 16 \quad (8)
\end{array}
$$

From (8) we find $x_1 = 8$. And substituting for x_1 in (7) yields

$$
\begin{array}{lll}
8 & + & s_1 & = 10 \\
& & s_1 & = 2
\end{array}
$$

This is a basic feasible solution

$s_1 = 0, s_2 = 0$

$$
\begin{array}{llll}
x_1 & + & 5x_2 & = 10 \quad (9) \\
2x_1 & + & 6x_2 & = 16 \quad (10)
\end{array}
$$

From (9) we have $x_1 = 10 - 5x_2$. Substituting for x_1 in (10) yields

$$
\begin{array}{lll}
2(10 - 5x_2) & + & 6x_2 & = 16 \\
20 - 10x_2 & + & 6x_2 & = 16 \\
& - & 4x_2 & = 16 - 20 \\
& - & 4x_2 & = -4 \\
& & x_2 & = 1
\end{array}
$$

Then, $x_1 = 10 - 5(1) = 5$

This is a basic feasible solution.

d. The optimal solution is the basic feasible solution with the largest value of the objective function. There are 4 basic feasible solutions from part (c) to evaluate in the objective function.

$x_1 = 0, x_2 = 0, s_1 = 10, s_2 = 16$

$$\text{Value} = 1(0) + 2(0) = 0$$

$x_1 = 0, x_2 = 2, s_1 = 0, s_2 = 4$

$$\text{Value} = 1(0) + 2(2) = 4$$

$x_1 = 8, x_2 = 0, s_1 = 2, s_2 = 0$

$$\text{Value} = 1(8) + 2(0) = 8$$

$x_1 = 5, x_2 = 1, s_1 = 0, s_2 = 0$

$$\text{Value} = 1(5) + 2(1) = 7$$

The optimal solution is $x_1 = 8, x_2 = 0$ with value $= 8$.

3. a.

$$\text{Max} \quad 5x_1 \quad + \quad 9x_2 \quad + \quad 0s_1 \quad + \quad 0s_2 \quad + \quad 0s_3$$

s.t.

$$\tfrac{1}{2}x_1 \quad + \quad 1x_2 \quad + \quad 1s_1 \qquad\qquad\qquad = \quad 8$$
$$1x_1 \quad + \quad 1x_2 \quad - \quad 1s_2 \qquad\qquad = \quad 10$$
$$\tfrac{1}{4}x_1 \quad + \quad \tfrac{3}{2}x_2 \qquad\qquad - \quad 1s_3 \quad = \quad 6$$
$$x_1,\ x_2,\ s_1,\ s_2,\ s_3, \ \geq 0$$

b. 2

c. $x_1 = 4$, $x_2 = 6$, and $s_3 = 4$.

d. $x_2 = 4$, $s_1 = 4$, and $s_2 = -6$.

e. The answer to part c is a basic feasible solution and an extreme point solution. The answer to part d is not a basic feasible solution because s_2 is negative.

f. The graph below shows that the basic solution for part c is an extreme point and the one for part d is

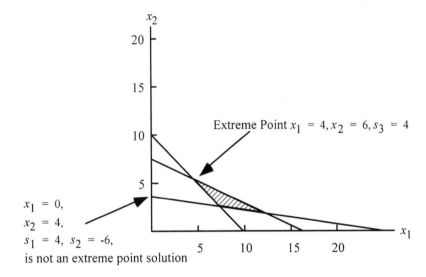

4. a. Standard Form:

$$\text{Max} \quad 60x_1 \quad + \quad 90x_2$$

s.t.

$$15x_1 \quad + \quad 45x_2 \quad + \quad s_1 \qquad\qquad = \quad 90$$
$$5x_1 \qquad\quad 5x_2 \qquad\qquad + \quad s_2 \quad = \quad 20$$
$$x_1, x_2, s_1, s_2 \geq 0$$

b.   Partial initial simplex tableau:

	x_1	x_2	s_1	s_2	
	60	90	0	0	
	15	45	1	0	90
	5	5	0	1	20

5.   a.   Initial Tableau

		x_1	x_2	s_1	s_2	
Basis	c_B	5	9	0	0	
s_1	0	10	9	1	0	90
s_2	0	-5	3	0	1	15
	z_j	0	0	0	0	0
	$c_j - z_j$	5	9	0	0	

b.   We would introduce x_2 at the first iteration.

c.   Max $5x_1 + 9x_2$
     s.t.

$$10x_1 + 9x_2 \leq 90$$
$$-5x_1 + 3x_2 \leq 15$$
$$x_1, x_2 \geq 0$$

6.   a.

		x_1	x_2	x_3	s_1	s_2	s_3	
Basis	c_B	5	20	25	0	0	0	
s_1	0	2	1	0	1	0	0	40
s_2	0	0	2	1	0	1	0	30
s_3	0	3	0	-1/2	0	0	1	15
	z_j	0	0	0	0	0	0	0
	$c_j - z_j$	5	20	25	0	0	0	

b.

$$
\begin{array}{llllllll}
\text{Max} & 5x_1 & + 20x_2 & + 25x_3 & + 0s_1 & + 0s_2 & + 0s_3 \\
\text{s.t.} \\
& 2x_1 & + 1x_2 & & + 1s_1 & & & = 40 \\
& & 2x_2 & + 1x_3 & & + 1s_2 & & = 30 \\
& 3x_1 & & - 1/2x_3 & & & + 1s_3 & = 15
\end{array}
$$

$$x_1,\ x_2,\ x_3,\ s_1,\ s_2,\ s_3,\ \geq 0.$$

c. The original basis consists of s_1, s_2, and s_3. It is the origin since the nonbasic variables are x_1, x_2, and x_3 and are all zero.

d. 0.

e. x_3 enters because it has the largest $c_j - z_j$ and s_2 will leave because row 2 has the only positive coefficient.

f. 30; objective function value is 30 times 25 or 750.

g. Optimal Solution:

$x_1 = 10 \qquad s_1 = 20$

$x_2 = 0 \qquad s_2 = 0$

$x_3 = 30 \qquad s_3 = 0$

$z = 800.$

7.

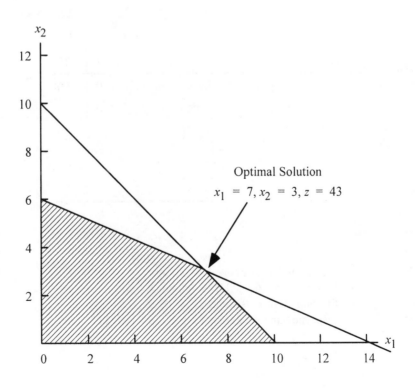

Optimal Solution
$x_1 = 7, x_2 = 3, z = 43$

Sequence of extreme points generated by the simplex method:

$(x_1 = 0, x_2 = 0)$

$(x_1 = 0, x_2 = 6)$

$(x_1 = 7, x_2 = 3)$

8. a. Initial simplex tableau

Basis	c_B	x_1 10	x_2 9	s_1 0	s_2 0	s_3 0	s_4 0	
s_1	0	7/10	1	1	0	0	0	630
s_2	0	1/2	5/6	0	1	0	0	600
s_3	0	1	2/3	0	0	1	0	708
s_4	0	1/10	1/4	0	0	0	1	135
	z_j	0	0	0	0	0	0	0
	$c_j - z_j$	10	9	0	0	0	0	

Final simplex tableau

Basis	c_B	x_1 10	x_2 9	s_1 0	s_2 0	s_3 0	s_4 0	
x_2	9	0	1	30/16	0	-21/16	0	252
s_2	0	0	0	-15/16	1	5/32	0	120
x_1	10	1	0	-20/16	0	30/16	0	540
s_4	0	0	0	-11/32	0	9/64	1	18
	z_j	10	9	70/16	0	111/16	0	7668
	$c_j - z_j$	0	0	-70/16	0	-111/16	0	

$x_1 = 540$ standard bags
$x_2 = 252$ deluxe bags

b. $7668

c. & d.

Slack	Production Time
$s_1 = 0$	Cutting and dyeing time = 630 hours
$s_2 = 120$	Sewing time = 600 - 120 = 480 hours
$s_3 = 0$	Finishing time = 708 hours
$s_4 = 18$	Inspection and Packaging time = 135 - 18 = 117 hours

9. Note: Refer to Chapter 2, problem 21 for a graph showing the location of the extreme points.

Initial simplex tableau (corresponds to the origin)

		x_1	x_2	s_1	s_2	s_3		
Basis	c_B	40	30	0	0	0		$b_i \,/\, a_{i1}$
s_1	0	2/5	1/2	1	0	0	20	20/(2/5) = 50
s_2	0	0	1/5	0	1	0	5	—
s_3	0	3/5	3/10	0	0	1	21	21/(3/5) = 35
z_j		0	0	0	0	0	0	
$c_j - z_j$		40	30	0	0	0		

First iteration: x_1 enters the basis and s_3 leaves (new basic feasible solution)

		x_1	x_2	s_1	s_2	s_3		
Basis	c_B	40	30	0	0	0		$\overline{b}_i \,/\, \overline{a}_{i2}$
s_1	0	0	3/10	1	0	-2/3	6	6/(3/10) = 20
s_2	0	0	1/5	0	1	0	5	5/(1/5) = 25
x_1	40	1	1/2	0	0	5/3	35	35/(1/2) = 70
z_j		40	20	0	0	200/3	1400	
$c_j - z_j$		0	10	0	0	-200/3		

Next iteration: x_2 enters the basis and s_1 leaves (new basic feasible solution)

		x_1	x_2	s_1	s_2	s_3	
Basis	c_B	40	30	0	0	0	
x_2	30	0	1	10/3	0	-20/9	20
s_2	0	0	0	-2/3	1	4/9	1
x_1	40	1	0	-5/3	0	25/9	25
z_j		40	30	100/3	0	400/9	1600
$c_j - z_j$		0	0	-100/3	0	-400/9	

Optimal Solution:

$x_1 = 25 \quad x_2 = 20$
$s_1 = 0 \quad s_2 = 1 \quad s_3 = 0.$

10.   Initial simplex tableau:

Basis	c_B	x_1 5	x_2 5	x_3 24	s_1 0	s_2 0	s_3 0		$\overline{b}_i / \overline{a}_{i\,3}$
s_1	0	15	4	12	1	0	0	2800	$2800/12 = 233.33$
s_2	0	15	8	0	0	1	0	6000	—
s_3	0	1	0	8	0	0	1	1200	$1200/8 = 150$
z_j		0	0	0	0	0	0	0	
$c_j - z_j$		5	5	24	0	0	0		

First iteration: x_3 enters, s_3 leaves

Basis	c_B	x_1 5	x_2 5	x_3 24	s_1 0	s_2 0	s_3 0		$\overline{b}_i / \overline{a}_{i\,2}$
s_1	0	27/2	4	0	1	0	-3/2	1000	$1000/4 = 250$
s_2	0	15	8	0	0	1	0	6000	$6000/8 = 750$
x_3	24	1/8	0	1	0	0	1/8	150	—
z_j		3	0	24	0	0	3	3600	
$c_j - z_j$		2	5	0	0	0	-3		

Second iteration: x_2 enters, s_1 leaves

Basis	c_B	x_1 5	x_2 5	x_3 0	s_1 0	s_2 0	s_3 0	
x_2	5	27/8	1	0	1/4	0	-3/8	250
s_2	0	-12	0	0	-2	1	3	4000
x_3	24	1/8	0	1	0	0	1/8	150
z_j		159/8	5	24	5/4	0	9/8	4850
$c_j - z_j$		-119/8	0	0	-5/4	0	-9/8	

Optimal Solution:

$x_2 = 250, \quad x_3 = 150, \quad s_2 = 4000, \quad \text{Value} = 4850$

11.

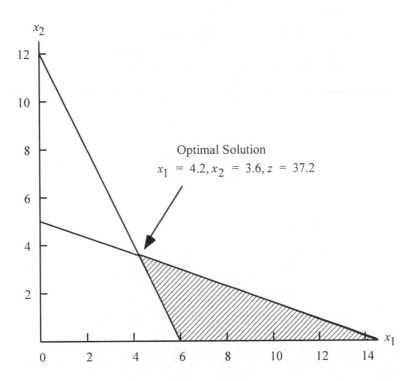

Extreme Points:

$(x_1 = 6, x_2 = 0)$, $(x_1 = 4.2, x_2 = 3.6)$,

$(x_1 = 15, x_2 = 0)$

Simplex Solution Sequence:

$(x_1 = 0, x_2 = 0)$

$(x_1 = 6, x_2 = 0)$

$(x_1 = 4.2, x_2 = 3.6)$

12.

Let x_1 = units of product A.

         x_2 = units of product B.

         x_3 = units of product C.

$$\text{Max} \quad 20x_1 + 20x_2 + 15x_3$$

s.t.

$$7x_1 + 6x_2 + 3x_3 \leq 100$$
$$5x_1 + 4x_2 + 2x_3 \leq 200$$
$$x_1,\ x_2,\ x_3 \geq 0$$

Optimal Solution: $x_1 = 0, x_2 = 0, x_3 = 33\ 1/3$

Profit = 500.

13.

Let x_1 = number of units of Grade A Plywood produced
x_2 = number of units of Grade B Plywood produced
x_3 = number of units of Grade X Plywood produced

Max $40x_1 + 30x_2 + 20x_3$
s.t.

$$2x_1 + 5x_2 + 10x_3 \leq 900$$
$$2x_1 + 5x_2 + 3x_3 \leq 400$$
$$4x_1 + 2x_2 - 2x_3 \leq 600$$

$$x_1, x_2, x_3 \geq 0$$

Optimal Solution:

$x_1 = 137.5, x_2 = 25, x_3 = 0$

Profit = 6250.

14.

Let x_1 = gallons of Heidelberg Sweet produced
x_2 = gallons of Heidelberg Regular produced
x_3 = gallons of Deutschland Extra Dry produced

Max $1.00x_1 + 1.20x_2 + 2.00x_3$
s.t.

$1x_1 + 2x_2$		$\leq$	150	Grapes Grade A
$1x_1 +$	$+ 2x_3$	$\leq$	150	Grapes Grade B
$2x_1 + 1x_2$		$\leq$	80	Sugar
$2x_1 + 3x_2$	$+ 1x_3$	$\leq$	225	Labor-hours

$$x_1, x_2, x_3, x_4, \geq 0$$

a.
$x_1 = 0$	$s_1 = 50$
$x_2 = 50$	$s_2 = 0$
$x_3 = 75$	$s_3 = 30$
	$s_4 = 0$

Profit = $210

b. s_1 = unused bushels of grapes (Grade A)

s_2 = unused bushels of grapes (Grade B)

s_3 = unused pounds of sugar

s_4 = unused labor-hours

c. $s_2 = 0$ and $s_4 = 0$. Therefore the Grade B grapes and the labor-hours are the binding resources. Increasing the amounts of these resources will improve profit.

15.

$$\text{Max} \quad 4x_1 + 2x_2 - 3x_3 + 5x_4 + 0s_1 - Ma_1 + 0s_2 - Ma_3$$

s.t.

$$
\begin{aligned}
2x_1 - 1x_2 + 1x_3 + 2x_4 - 1s_1 + 1a_1 &= 50 \\
3x_1 \qquad\quad - 1x_3 + 2x_4 \qquad\qquad\quad + 1s_2 &= 80 \\
1x_1 + 1x_2 \qquad\quad + 1x_4 \qquad\qquad\qquad\qquad + 1a_3 &= 60
\end{aligned}
$$

$$x_1, \ x_2, \ x_3, \ x_4, \ s_1, \ s_2, \ a_1, \ a_3 \geq 0$$

16.

$$\text{Max} \quad -4x_1 - 5x_2 - 3x_3 + 0s_1 + 0s_2 + 0s_4 - Ma_1 - Ma_2 - Ma_3$$

s.t.

$$
\begin{aligned}
4x_1 \qquad\quad + 2x_3 - 1s_1 \qquad\qquad\qquad + 1a_1 &= 20 \\
- 1x_2 + 1x_3 \qquad\quad - 1s_2 \qquad\qquad\quad + 1a_2 &= 8 \\
-1x_1 + 2x_2 \qquad\qquad\qquad\qquad\qquad\qquad\quad + 1a_3 &= 5 \\
2x_1 + 1x_2 + 1x_3 \qquad\qquad\qquad + 1s_4 &= 12
\end{aligned}
$$

$$x_1, \ x_2, \ x_3, \ s_1, \ s_2, \ s_4, \ a_1, \ a_2, \ a_3 \geq 0$$

17. $x_1 = 1, \ x_2 = 4, \ z = 19$

Converting to a max problem and solving using the simplex method, the final simplex tableau is:

Basis	c_B	x_1	x_2	x_3	s_1	s_2	
		-3	-4	-8	0	0	
x_1	-3	1	0	-1	-1/4	1/8	1
x_2	-4	0	1	2	0	-1/4	4
z_j		-3	-4	-5	3/4	5/8	-19
$c_j - z_j$		0	0	-3	-3/4	-5/8	

18. Initial tableau (Note: Min objective converted to Max.)

Basis	c_B	x_1	x_2	x_3	s_1	s_2	s_3	a_2	a_3		b_i / a_{il}
		-84	-4	-30	0	0	0	-M	-M		
s_1	0	8	1	3	1	0	0	0	0	240	240/8 = 30
a_2	-M	16	1	7	0	-1	0	1	0	480	480/16 = 30
a_3	-M	8	-1	4	0	0	-1	0	1	160	160/8 = 20
z_j		-24M	0	-11M	0	M	M	-M	-M	-640M	
$c_j - z_j$		-84+24M	-4	-30+11M	0	-M	-M	0	0		

Chapter 5

Iteration 1: x_1 enters, a_3 leaves (Drop a_3 column)

Basis	c_B	x_1 -84	x_2 -4	x_3 -30	s_1 0	s_2 0	s_3 0	a_2 $-M$	
s_1	0	0	2	-1	1	0	1	0	80
a_2	$-M$	0	3	-1	0	-1	2	1	160
x_1	-84	1	$-1/8$	$1/2$	0	0	$-1/8$	0	20
	z_j	-84	$\frac{21}{2}-3M$	$42+M$	0	M	$\frac{21}{2}-2M$	$-M$	$-1680-160M$
	c_j-z_j	0	$\frac{-29}{2}+3M$	$-72-M$	0	$-M$	$\frac{-21}{2}+2M$	0	

Iteration 2: x_2 enters, s_1 leaves

Basis	c_B	x_1 -84	x_2 -4	x_3 -30	s_1 0	s_2 0	s_3 0	a_2 $-M$	
x_2	-4	0	1	$-1/2$	$1/2$	0	$1/2$	0	40
a_2	$-M$	0	0	$1/2$	$-3/2$	-1	$1/2$	1	40
x_1	-84	1	0	$7/16$	$1/16$	0	$-1/16$	0	25
	z_j	-84	-4	$\frac{-139}{4}-\frac{M}{2}$	$\frac{-29}{4}+\frac{3M}{2}$	M	$\frac{13}{4}-\frac{M}{2}$	$-M$	$-2260-100M$
	c_j-z_j	0	0	$\frac{19}{4}+\frac{M}{2}$	$\frac{29}{4}-\frac{3M}{2}$	$-M$	$\frac{-13}{4}+\frac{M}{2}$	0	

Iteration 3: x_3 enters, x_1 leaves

Basis	c_B	x_1 -84	x_2 -4	x_3 -30	s_1 0	s_2 0	s_3 0	a_2 $-M$	
x_2	-4	$8/7$	1	0	$4/7$	0	$3/7$	0	$480/7$
a_2	$-M$	$-8/7$	0	0	$-11/7$	-1	$4/7$	1	$80/7$
x_3	-30	$16/7$	0	1	$1/7$	0	$-1/7$	0	$400/7$
	z_j	$\frac{-512+8M}{7}$	-4	-30	$\frac{-46+11M}{7}$	M	$\frac{-42-4M}{7}$	$-M$	$\frac{-13920-80M}{7}$
	c_j-z_j	$\frac{-76-8M}{7}$	0	0	$\frac{46-11M}{7}$	$-M$	$\frac{42+4M}{7}$	0	

Iteration 4: s_3 enters, a_2 leaves (Drop a_2 column)

Basis	c_B	x_1	x_2	x_3	s_1	s_2	s_3	
		-84	-4	-30	0	0	0	
x_2	-4	2	1	0	7/4	3/4	0	60
s_3	0	-2	0	0	-11/4	-7/4	1	20
x_3	-30	2	0	1	-1/4	-1/4	0	60
	z_j	-68	-4	-30	1/2	9/2	0	-2040
	$c_j - z_j$	-16	0	0	-1/2	-9/2	0	

Optimal Solution: $x_2 = 60, x_3 = 60, s_3 = 20$ Value $= 2040$

19. Let x_1 = no. of sailboats rented
       x_2 = no. of cabin cruisers rented
       x_3 = no. of luxury yachts rented

The mathematical formulation of this problem is:

Max $50x_1 + 70x_2 + 100x_3$
s.t.

$$
\begin{aligned}
x_1 & & & & & \le 4 \\
& & x_2 & & & \le 8 \\
& & & & x_3 & \le 3 \\
x_1 & + & x_2 & + & x_3 & \le 10 \\
x_1 & + & 2x_2 & + & 3x_3 & \le 18
\end{aligned}
$$

$$x_1, \; x_2, \; x_3, \; \ge 0$$

Optimal Solution:

$x_1 = 4, x_2 = 4, x_3 = 2$

Profit $= \$680$.

20.

Let x_1 = number of 20-gallon boxes produced
     x_2 = number of 30-gallon boxes produced
     x_3 = number of 33-gallon boxes produced

Max $0.10x_1 + 0.15x_2 + 0.20x_3$
s.t.

$$
\begin{aligned}
2x_1 & + & 3x_2 & + & 3x_3 & \le 7200 & \text{Cutting} \\
2x_1 & + & 2x_2 & + & 3x_3 & \le 10800 & \text{Sealing} \\
3x_1 & + & 4x_2 & + & 5x_3 & \le 14400 & \text{Packaging}
\end{aligned}
$$

$$x_1, \; x_2, \; x_3, \; \ge 0$$

Optimal Solution
$x_1 = 0, x_2 = 0, x_3 = 2400$

Profit $= \$480$.

21.

Let x_1 = no. of gallons of Chocolate produced
x_2 = no. of gallons of Vanilla produced
x_3 = no. of gallons of Banana produced

Max $1.00x_1 + .90x_2 + .95x_3$
s.t.

$$.45x_1 + .50x_2 + .40x_3 \leq 200 \quad \text{Milk}$$
$$.50x_1 + .40x_2 + .40x_3 \leq 150 \quad \text{Sugar}$$
$$.10x_1 + .15x_2 + .20x_3 \leq 60 \quad \text{Cream}$$
$$x_1, x_2, x_3, \geq 0$$

Optimal Solution

$x_1 = 0, x_2 = 300, x_3 = 75$

Profit = \$341.25. Additional resources: Sugar and Cream.

22.

Let x_1 = number of cases of Incentive sold by John
x_2 = number of cases of Temptation sold by John
x_3 = number of cases of Incentive sold by Brenda
x_4 = number of cases of Temptation sold by Brenda
x_5 = number of cases of Incentive sold by Red
x_6 = number of cases of Temptation sold by Red

Max $30x_1 + 25x_2 + 30x_3 + 25x_4 + 30x_5 + 25x_6$
s.t.

$$10x_1 + 15x_2 \qquad\qquad\qquad\qquad\qquad \leq 4800$$
$$15x_3 + 10x_4 \qquad\qquad\qquad \leq 4800$$
$$12x_5 + 6x_6 \leq 4800$$
$$x_1, x_2, x_3, x_4, x_5, x_6, \geq 0$$

Optimal Solution:

$x_1 = 480 \qquad x_4 = 480$

$x_2 = 0 \qquad x_5 = 0$

$x_3 = 0 \qquad x_6 = 800$

Objective Function maximized at 46400.

Time Allocation:

	Incentive	Temptation
John	4800 min.	no time
Brenda	no time	4800 min.
Red	no time	4800 min.

23.   Final simplex tableau

Basis	c_B	x_1	x_2	s_1	s_2	a_2	
		4	8	0	0	-M	
x_2	8	1	1	1/2	0	0	5
a_2	-M	-2	0	-1/2	-1	1	3
z_j		$8+2M$	8	$4+M/2$	$+M$	$-M$	$40-3M$
$c_j - z_j$		$-4-2M$	0	$-4-M/2$	$-M$	0	

Infeasible; optimal solution condition is reached with the artificial variable a_2 still in the solution.

24.   Alternative Optimal Solutions

Basis	c_B	x_1	x_2	s_1	s_2	s_3	
		-3	-3	0	0	0	
s_2	0	0	0	-4/3	1	1/6	4
x_1	-3	1	0	-2/3	0	1/12	4
x_2	-3	0	1	2/3	0	-1/3	4
z_j		-3	-3	0	0	3/4	-24
$c_j - z_j$		0	0	0	0	-3/4	

indicates alternative optimal solutions exist

$x_1 = 4, x_2 = 4, z = 24$

$x_1 = 8, x_2 = 0, z = 24$

25.   Unbounded Solution

Basis	c_B	x_1	x_2	s_1	s_2	s_3	
		1	1	0	0	0	
s_3	0	8/3	0	-1/3	0	1	4
s_2	0	4	0	-1	1	0	36
x_2	1	4/3	1	-1/6	0	0	4
z_j		4/3	1	-1/6	0	0	4
$c_j - z_j$		-1/3	0	1/6	0	0	

Incoming Column

26.   Alternative Optimal Solutions

Basis	c_B	x_1 2	x_2 1	x_3 1	s_1 0	s_2 0	s_3 0	
x_1	2	1	2	1/2	0	0	1/4	4
s_2	0	0	0	-1	0	1	-1/2	12
s_1	0	0	6	0	1	0	1	12
z_j		2	4	1	0	0	1/4	8
$c_j - z_j$		0	-3	0	0	0	-1/4	

Two possible solutions:
$x_1 = 4, x_2 = 0, x_3 = 0$ or $x_1 = 0, x_2 = 0, x_3 = 8$

27.   The final simplex tableau is given by:

Basis	c_B	x_1 2	x_2 4	s_1 0	s_2 0	
s_1	0	1/2	0	1	0	4
x_2	4	1	1	0	0	12
s_3	0	-1/2	0	0	1	0
z_j		4	4	0	0	48
$c_j - z_j$		-2	0	0	0	

This solution is degenerate since the basic variable s_3 is in solution at a zero value.

28.   The final simplex tableau is:

Basis	c_B	x_1 +4	x_2 -5	x_3 -5	s_1 0	s_2 0	s_3 0	a_1 -M	a_3 -M	
a_1	-M	1	-2	0	-1	1	0	1	0	1
x_3	-5	-1	1	1	0	-1	0	0	0	1
a_3	-M	-1	1	0	0	-1	-1	0	1	2
z_j		+5	-5+M	-5	+M	+5	+M	-M	-M	-5-3M
$c_j - z_j$		-1	-M	0	-M	-5	-M	0	0	

Since both artificial variables a_1 and a_3 are contained in this solution, we can conclude that we have an infeasible problem.

29. We must add an artificial variable to the equality constraint to obtain tableau form.

Tableau form:

$$\text{Max} \quad 120x_1 + 80x_2 + 14x_3 + 0s_1 + 0s_2 - Ma_3$$

s.t.

$$4x_1 + 8x_2 + x_3 + 1s_1 \qquad\qquad = 200$$
$$2x_2 + x_3 \qquad + s_2 \qquad = 300$$
$$32x_1 + 4x_2 + 2x_3 \qquad\qquad + a_3 = 400$$
$$x_1, x_2, x_3, s_1, s_2, a_3 \geq 0$$

Initial Tableau:

Basis	c_B	x_1 120	x_2 80	x_3 14	s_1 0	s_2 0	a_3 -M		b_i / a_{il}
s_1	0	4	8	1	1	0	0	200	200/4 = 50
s_2	0	0	2	1	0	1	0	300	—
a_3	-M	32	4	2	0	0	1	400	400/32 = 12.5
z_j		-32M	-4M	-2M	0	0	-M	-400M	
$c_j - z_j$		120+32M	80+4M	14+2M	0	0	0		

Iteration 1: x_1 enters, a_3 leaves (drop a_3 column)

Basis	c_B	x_1 120	x_2 80	x_3 14	s_1 0	s_2 0		$\bar{b}_i / \bar{a}_{i2}$
s_1	0	0	15/2	3/4	1	0	150	$150/ {}^{15}/_2 = 20$
s_2	0	0	2	1	0	1	300	300/2 = 150
x_1	120	1	1/8	1/16	0	0	12.5	$12.5/{}^1/_8 = 100$
z_j		120	15	15/2	0	0	1500	
$c_j - z_j$		0	65	13/2	0	0		

Iteration 2: x_2 enters, s_1 leaves

Basis	c_B	x_1 120	x_2 80	x_3 14	s_1 0	s_2 0	
x_2	80	0	1	1/10	2/15	0	20
s_2	0	0	0	8/10	-4/15	1	260
x_1	120	1	0	1/20	-1/60	0	10
z_j		120	80	14	26/3	0	2800
$c_j - z_j$		0	0	0	-26/3	0	

Optimal solution: $x_1 = 10$, $x_2 = 20$, and $s_2 = 260$, Value = 2800

Note: This problem has alternative optimal solutions; x_3 may be brought in at a value of 200.

30. a. The mathematical formulation of this problem is:

$$
\begin{array}{llllll}
\text{Max} & 3x_1 & + 5x_2 & + 4x_3 & & \\
\text{s.t.} & & & & & \\
& 12x_1 & + 10x_2 & + 8x_3 & \leq 18{,}000 & \text{C \& D} \\
& 15x_1 & + 15x_2 & + 12x_3 & \leq 12{,}000 & \text{S} \\
& 3x_1 & + 4x_2 & + 2x_3 & \leq 6{,}000 & \text{I and P} \\
& x_1 & & & \geq 1{,}000 & \\
\end{array}
$$

$$x_1,\ x_2,\ x_3,\ \geq 0$$

There is no feasible solution. Not enough sewing time is available to make 1000 All-Pro footballs.

b. The mathematical formulation of this problem is now

$$
\begin{array}{llllll}
\text{Max} & 3x_1 & + 5x_2 & + 4x_3 & & \\
\text{s.t.} & & & & & \\
& 12x_1 & + 10x_2 & + 8x_3 & \leq 18{,}000 & \text{C \& D} \\
& 15x_1 & + 15x_2 & + 12x_3 & \leq 18{,}000 & \text{S} \\
& 3x_1 & + 4x_2 & + 2x_3 & \leq 9{,}000 & \text{I \& P} \\
& x_1 & & & \geq 1{,}000 & \\
\end{array}
$$

$$x_1,\ x_2,\ x_3,\ \geq 0$$

Optimal Solution

$x_1 = 1000,\ x_2 = 0,\ x_3 = 250$

Profit = $4000

There is an alternative optimal solution with $x_1 = 1000$, $x_2 = 200$, and $x_3 = 0$.

Note that the additional Inspection and Packaging time is not needed.

Chapter 6
Simplex-Based Sensitivity Analysis and Duality

Learning Objectives

1. Be able to use the final simplex tableau to compute ranges for the coefficients of the objective function.

2. Understand how to use the optimal simplex tableau to identify dual prices.

3. Be able to use the final simplex tableau to compute ranges on the constraint right-hand sides.

4. Understand the concepts of duality and the relationship between the primal and dual linear programming problems.

5. Know the economic interpretation of the dual variables.

6. Be able to convert any maximization or minimization problem into its associated canonical form.

7. Be able to obtain the primal solution from the final simplex tableau of the dual problem.

Solutions:

1. a. Recomputing the $c_j - z_j$ values for the nonbasic variables with c_1 as the coefficient of x_1 leads to the following inequalities that must be satisfied.

    For x_2, we get no inequality since there is a zero in the x_2 column for the row x_1 is a basic variable in.

    For s_1, we get

    $$0 \ + \ 4 \ - \ c_1 \ \leq \ 0$$
    $$c_1 \ \geq \ 4$$

    For s_2, we get

    $$0 \ - \ 12 \ + \ 2c_1 \leq \ 0$$
    $$2c_1 \leq \ 12$$
    $$c_1 \leq \ 6$$
    $$\textbf{Range} \ \ \textbf{4} \ \leq \ c_1 \ \leq \ \textbf{6}$$

    b. Since x_2 is nonbasic we have

    $$c_2 \ \leq \ 8$$

    c. Since s_1 is nonbasic we have

    $$c_{s_1} \ \leq \ 1$$

2. a. For s_1 we get

    $$0 - c_2 (8/25) - 50 (-5/25) \leq 0$$

    $$c_2 (8/25) \geq 10$$

    $$c_2 \geq 31.25$$

    For s_3 we get

    $$0 - c_2 (-3/25) - 50 (5/25) \leq 0$$

    $$c_2 (3/25) \leq 10$$

    $$c_2 \leq 83.33$$

    Range: $31.25 \leq c_2 \leq 83.33$

    b. For s_1 we get

    $$0 - 40 (8/25) - c_{S2} (-8/25) - 50 (-5/25) \leq 0$$

    $$-64/5 + \ c_{S2} (8/25) + 10 \leq 0$$

    $$c_{S2} \leq 25/8 (14/5) = 70/8 = 8.75$$

For s_3 we get

$$0 - 40 \,(-3/25) - c_{S2} \,(3/25) - 50 \,(5/25) \le 0$$

$$24/5 - c_{S2} \,(3/25) - 10 \le 0$$

$$c_{S2} \ge (25/3) \,(-26/5) = -130/3 = -43.33$$

Range: $-43.33 \le c_{S2} \le 8.75$

c. $c_{S3} - 26/5 \le 0$

$$c_{S3} \le 26/5$$

d. No change in optimal solution since $c_2 = 35$ is within range of optimality. Value of solution decreases to $35 (12) + $50 (30) = $1920.

3. a. It is the z_j value for s_1. Dual Price $= 1$.

   b. It is the z_j value for s_2. Dual Price $= 2$.

   c. It is the z_j value for s_3. Dual Price $= 0$.

   d. $s_3 = 80 + 5(-2) = 70$

   $x_3 = 30 + 5(-1) = 25$

   $x_1 = 20 + 5(1) = 25$

   Value $= 220 + 5(1) = 225$

   e. $s_3 = 80 - 10(-2) = 100$

   $x_3 = 30 - 10(-1) = 40$

   $x_1 = 20 - 10(1) = 10$

   Value $= 220 - 10(1) = 210$

4. a.

$80 +$	$\Delta b_1 \,(-2)$	$\ge 0 \rightarrow$	$\Delta b_1 \le$	40
$30 +$	$\Delta b_1 \,(-1)$	$\ge 0 \rightarrow$	$\Delta b_1 \le$	30
$20 +$	$\Delta b_1 \,(1)$	$\ge 0 \rightarrow$	$\Delta b_1 \ge$	-20

   $-20 \le \Delta b_1 \le 30$

   $100 \le b_1 \le 150$

   b.

$80 +$	$\Delta b_2 \,(7)$	$\ge 0 \rightarrow$	$\Delta b_2 \ge$	$-80/7$
$30 +$	$\Delta b_2 \,(3)$	$\ge 0 \rightarrow$	$\Delta b_2 \ge$	-10
$20 +$	$\Delta b_2 \,(-2)$	$\ge 0 \rightarrow$	$\Delta b_2 \ge$	10

$$-10 \leq \Delta b_2 \leq 10$$

$$40 \leq b_2 \leq 60$$

c.

$$80 - \Delta b_3 (1) \geq 0 \rightarrow \Delta b_3 \leq 80$$
$$30 - \Delta b_3 (0) \geq 0$$
$$20 - \Delta b_3 (0) \geq 0$$

$$\Delta b_3 \leq 80$$

$$b_3 \leq 110$$

5 a.

$$12 + \Delta b_2 (0) \geq 0$$
$$8 + \Delta b_2 (1) \geq 0$$
$$30 + \Delta b_2 (0) \geq 0$$

Therefore $\Delta b_2 \geq -8$

Range: $b_2 \geq 12$

b.

$$12 + \Delta b_3 (-3/25) \geq 0 \rightarrow \Delta b_3 \leq 100$$
$$8 + \Delta b_3 (3/25) \geq 0 \rightarrow \Delta b_3 \geq -66\,^2/_3$$
$$30 + \Delta b_3 (5/25) \geq 0 \rightarrow \Delta b_3 \geq -150$$

therefore $-66\,^2/_3 \leq \Delta b_3 \leq 100$

Range: $233\,^1/_3 \leq b_3 \leq 400$

c. The dual price for the warehouse constraint is 26/5 and the 20 unit increase is within the range of feasibility, so the dual price is applicable for the entire increase.

Profit increase = 20 (26/5) = 104

6. a. The final simplex tableau with c_1 shown as the coefficient of x_1 is

Basis	c_B	x_1 c_1	x_2 9	s_1 0	s_2 0	s_3 0	s_4 0	
x_2	0	0	1	30/16	0	-21/16	0	252
s_2	0	0	0	-15/16	1	5/32	0	120
x_1	c_1	1	0	-20/16	0	30/16	0	540
s_4	0	0	0	-11/32	0	9/64	1	18
z_j		c_1	9	$(270-20c_1)/16$	0	$(30c_1-189)/16$	0	$2268+540c_1$
$c_j - z_j$		0	0	$(20c_1-270)/16$	0	$(189-30c_1)/16$	0	

$(20c_1 - 270) / 16 \leq 0 \quad \rightarrow \quad c_1 \leq 13.5$

$(189 - 30c_1) / 16 \leq 0 \quad \rightarrow \quad c_1 \geq 6.3$

Range: $6.3 \leq c_1 \leq 13.5$

b. Following a similar procedure for c_2 leads to

$(200 - 30c_2) / 16 \leq 0 \quad \rightarrow \quad c_2 \geq 6\,{}^2/_3$

$(21c_2 - 300) / 16 \leq 0 \quad \rightarrow \quad c_2 \leq 14\,{}^2/_7$

Range : $6\,{}^2/_3 \leq c_2 \leq 14\,{}^2/_7$

c. There would be no change in product mix, but profit will drop to 540 (10) + 252 (7) = 7164.

d. It would have to drop below \$6 ${}^2/_3$ or increase above \$14 ${}^2/_7$.

e. We should expect more production of deluxe bags since its profit contribution has increased. The new optimal solution is given by

$x_1 = 300, x_2 = 420$

Optimal Value: \$9300

7. a.

252	+	$\Delta b_1 (30/16)$	$\geq$	0	$\rightarrow$	$\Delta b_1 \geq$	-134.4
120	+	$\Delta b_1 (-15/16)$	$\geq$	0	$\rightarrow$	$\Delta b_1 \leq$	128
540	+	$\Delta b_1 (-20/16)$	$\geq$	0	$\rightarrow$	$\Delta b_1 \leq$	432
18	+	$\Delta b_1 (-11/32)$	$\geq$	0	$\rightarrow$	$\Delta b_1 \leq$	52.36

therefore $-134.4 \leq \Delta b_1 \leq 52.36$

Range: $495.6 \leq b_1 \leq 682.36$

b. $480 \leq b_2$

c. $580 \leq b_3 \leq 900$

d. $117 \leq b_4$

e. The cutting and dyeing and finishing since the dual prices and the allowable increases are positive for both.

8. a.

Basis	c_B	x_1 10	x_2 9	s_1 0	s_2 0	s_3 0	s_4 0	
x_2	9	0	1	30/16	0	-21/16	0	3852/11
s_2	0	0	0	-15/16	1	5/32	0	780/11
x_1	10	1	0	-20/16	0	(30/16)	0	5220/11
s_4	0	0	0	-11/32	0	9/64	1	0
z_j		10	9	70/16	0	111/16	0	86,868/11 = 7897 $^1/_{11}$
$c_j - z_j$		0	0	-70/16	0	-111/16	0	

b. No, s_4 would become nonbasic and s_1 would become a basic variable.

9. a. Since this is within the range of feasibility for b_1, the increase in profit is given by

$$\left(\frac{70}{16}\right)30 = \frac{2100}{16}$$

b. It would not decrease since there is already idle time in this department and $600 - 40 = 560$ is still within the range of feasibility for b_2.

c. Since 570 is within the range of feasibility for b_1, the lost profit would be equal to

$$\left(\frac{70}{16}\right)60 = \frac{4200}{16}$$

10. a. The value of the objective function would go up since the first constraint is binding. When there is no idle time, increased efficiency results in increased profits.

b. No. This would just increase the number of idle hours in the sewing department.

11. a.

Basis	c_B	x_1 c_1	x_2 30	s_1 0	s_2 0	s_3 0	
x_2	30	0	1	10/3	0	-20/9	20
s_2	0	0	0	-2/3	1	4/9	1
x_1	c_1	1	0	-5/3	0	25/9	25
z_j		c_1	30	$100-(5/3c_1)$	0	$\frac{-200}{3}+\frac{25}{9}c_1$	$600 + 25c_1$
$c_j - z_j$		0	0	$^5/_3c_1-100$	0	$\frac{200}{3}-\frac{25}{9}c_1$	

Hence

$^5/_3c_1 - 100 \le 0$

and

$200/3 - \, ^{25}/_9c_1 \le 0.$

Using the first inequality we obtain

$$^5/_3 c_1 \leq 100 \quad \text{or} \quad c_1 \leq 60.$$

Using the second inequality we obtain

$$^{25}/_9 c_1 \geq 200/3$$

$$c_1 \geq (9/25) \, (200/3)$$

$$c_1 \geq 24.$$

Thus the range of optimality for c_1 is given by

$24 \leq c_1 \leq 60.$

A similar approach for c_2 leads to

$$(200 - 10c_2) \, / \, 3 \leq 0 \quad \rightarrow \quad c_2 \geq 20$$

$$(20c_2 - 1000) \, / \, 9 \leq 0 \quad \rightarrow \quad c_2 \leq 50$$

Range: $20 \leq c_2 \leq 50$

b. Current solution is still optimal. However, the total profit has been reduced to \$30 (25) + \$30 (20) = \$1350.

c. From the z_j entry in the s_1 column we see that the dual price for the material 1 constraint is \$33.33. It is the increase in profit that would result from having one additional ton of material one.

d. Material 3 is the most valuable and RMC should be willing to pay up to \$44.44 per ton for it.

12. a.

$$
\begin{array}{llllll}
20 & + & \Delta b_1 \, (10/3) & \geq & 0 & \rightarrow & \Delta b_1 & \geq & -6 \\
1 & + & \Delta b_1 \, (-2/3) & \geq & 0 & \rightarrow & \Delta b_1 & \leq & 3/2 \\
25 & + & \Delta b_1 \, (-5/3) & \geq & 0 & \rightarrow & \Delta b_1 & \leq & 15
\end{array}
$$

therefore $-6 \leq \Delta b_1 \leq 1 \; ^1/_2$

Range: $14 \leq b_1 \leq 21 \, ^1/_2$

b.

$$
\begin{array}{llllll}
20 & + & \Delta b_2 \, (0) & \geq & 0 & \rightarrow & \text{no restriction} \\
1 & + & \Delta b_2 \, (1) & \geq & 0 & \rightarrow & \Delta b_2 \geq -1 \\
25 & + & \Delta b_2 \, (0) & \geq & 0 & \rightarrow & \text{no restriction}
\end{array}
$$

Range: $b_2 \geq 4$

c.

$$
\begin{array}{llllll}
20 & + & \Delta b_3 \, (-20/9) & \geq & 0 & \rightarrow & \Delta b_3 & \leq & 9 \\
1 & + & \Delta b_3 \, (4/9) & \geq & 0 & \rightarrow & \Delta b_3 & \geq & -9/4 \\
25 & + & \Delta b_3 \, (25/9) & \geq & 0 & \rightarrow & \Delta b_3 & \geq & -9
\end{array}
$$

therefore $-2\,^{1}/_{4} \le \Delta b_3 \le 9$

Range: $18\,^{3}/_{4} \le b_3 \le 30$

d. Dual price: 400/9

Valid for $18\,^{3}/_{4} \le b_3 \le 30$

13. a. The final simplex tableau is given by

		x_1	x_2	x_3	x_4	s_2	s_3	
Basis	c_B	3	1	5	3	0	0	
s_2	0	5/2	7/6	0	0	1	1/3	115/3
x_3	5	3/2	1/2	1	0	0	0	15
x_4	3	0	2/3	0	1	0	1/3	25/3
	z_j	15/2	9/2	5	3	0	1	100
	$c_j - z_j$	-9/2	-7/2	0	0	0	-1	

b. Range: $2 \le c_3$

c. Since 1 is not contained in the range of optimality, a new basis will become optimal.

The new optimal solution and its value is

$x_1 = 10$

$x_4 = 25/3$

$s_2 = 40/3$ (Surplus associated with constraint 2)

d. Since x_2 is a nonbasic variable we simply require

$c_2 - 9/2 \le 0.$

Range: $c_2 \le 4\,^{1}/_{2}$

e. Since 4 is contained in the range, a three unit increase in c_2 would have no effect on the optimal solution or on the value of that solution.

14. a. $400/3 \le b_1 \le 800$

b. $275 \le b_2$

c. $275/2 \le b_3 \le 625$

15.   The final simplex tableau is given:

Basis	c_B	x_1 15	x_2 30	x_3 20	s_1 0	s_2 0	s_3 0	
x_1	15	1	0	1	1	0	0	4
x_2	30	0	1	1/4	-1/4	1/2	0	1/2
s_3	0	0	0	3/4	-3/4	-1/2	1	3/2
z_j		15	30	45/2	15/2	15	0	75
$c_j - z_j$		0	0	-5/2	-15/2	-15	0	

a. $x_1 = 4$, $x_2 = 1/2$ Optimal value: 75

b.   75

c.   Constraints one and two.

d.   There are $1\frac{1}{2}$ units of slack in constraint three.

e.   Dual prices: 15/2, 15, 0

   Increasing the right-hand side of constraint two would have the greatest positive effect on the
   objective function.

f.

$$12.5 \leq c_1$$
$$20 \leq c_2 \leq 60$$
$$c_3 \leq 22.5$$

   The optimal values for the decision variables will not change as long as the objective function
   coefficients stay in these intervals.

g.   For b_1

$$4 + \Delta b_1 (1) \geq 0 \rightarrow \Delta b_1 \geq -4$$
$$1/2 + \Delta b_1 (-1/4) \geq 0 \rightarrow \Delta b_1 \leq 2$$
$$3/2 + \Delta b_1 (-3/4) \geq 0 \rightarrow \Delta b_1 \leq 2$$

   therefore $-4 \leq \Delta b_1 \leq 2$

   Range: $0 \leq b_1 \leq 6$

   For b_2

$$4 + \Delta b_2 (0) \geq 0 \rightarrow \text{no restriction}$$
$$1/2 + \Delta b_2 (1/2) \geq 0 \rightarrow \Delta b_2 \geq -1$$
$$3/2 + \Delta b_2 (-1/2) \geq 0 \rightarrow \Delta b_2 \leq 3$$

   therefore $-1 \leq \Delta b_2 \leq 3$

   Range: $2 \leq b_2 \leq 6$

For b_3

$$4 \; + \; \Delta b_3 \,(0) \; \geq \; 0 \; \rightarrow \; \text{no restriction}$$
$$1/2 \; + \; \Delta b_3 \,(0) \; \geq \; 0 \; \rightarrow \; \text{no restriction}$$
$$3/2 \; + \; \Delta b_3 \,(1) \; \geq \; 0 \; \rightarrow \; \Delta b_3 \geq -3/2$$

therefore $-3/2 \leq \Delta b_3$

Range: $4\,{}^1\!/_2 \leq b_3$

The dual prices accurately predict the rate of change of the objective function with respect to an increase in the right-hand side as long as the right-hand side remains within its range of feasibility.

16. a. After converting to a maximization problem by multiplying the objective function by (-1) and solving we obtain the optimal simplex tableau shown.

Basis	c_B	x_1 -8	x_2 -3	s_1 0	s_2 0	s_3 0	
s_3	0	0	0	1/60	1/6	1	7,000
x_1	-8	1	0	-1/75	-1/3	0	4,000
x_2	-3	0	1	1/60	1/6	0	10,000
z_j		-8	-3	17/300	13/6	0	-62,000
$c_j - z_j$		0	0	-17/300	-13/6	0	

Total Risk = 62,000

b. The dual price for the second constraint is $-13/6 = -2.167$. So, every \$1 increase in the annual income requirement increases the total risk of the portfolio by 2.167.

c.

$$7000 \; - \; \Delta b_2 \,(1/6) \; \geq \; 0 \; \rightarrow \; \Delta b_2 \; \leq \; 42,000$$
$$4000 \; - \; \Delta b_2 \,(-1/3) \; \geq \; 0 \; \rightarrow \; \Delta b_2 \; \geq \; -12,000$$
$$10,000 \; - \; \Delta b_2 \,(1/6) \; \geq \; 0 \; \rightarrow \; \Delta b_2 \; \leq \; 60,000$$

So, $-12,000 \leq \Delta b_2 \leq 42,000$

and $48,000 \leq b_2 \leq 102,000$

d. The new optimal solution and its value are

$$s_3 \; = \; 7000 \; - \; 5000(1/6) \; = \; 37000/6 \; = \; 6,166.667$$
$$x_1 \; = \; 4000 \; - \; 5000(-1/3) \; = \; 17,000/3 \; = \; 5,666.667$$
$$x_2 \; = \; 10,000 \; - \; 5000(1/6) \; = \; 55,000/6 \; = \; 9,166.67$$

Value $= -62,000 - 5000(13/6) = -437,000/6 = -72,833.33$

Since, this is a min problem being solved as a max, the new optimal value is 72,833.33

e. There is no upper limit in the range of optimality for the objective function coefficient of the stock fund. Therefore, the solution will not change. But, its value will increase to:

$$9(4,000) + 3(10,000) = 66,000$$

17. a. The dual is given by:

$$
\begin{array}{lrcrcrcl}
\text{Min} & 550u_1 & + & 700u_2 & + & 200u_3 \\
\text{s.t.} \\
& 1.5u_1 & + & 4u_2 & + & 2u_3 & \geq & 4 \\
& 2u_1 & + & 1u_2 & + & 3u_3 & \geq & 6 \\
& 4u_1 & + & 2u_2 & + & 1u_3 & \geq & 3 \\
& 3u_1 & + & 1u_2 & + & 2u_3 & \geq & 1 \\
& & & u_1,\ u_2,\ u_3, & \geq 0
\end{array}
$$

b. Optimal solution: $u_1 = 3/10$, $u_2 = 0$, $u_3 = 54/30$

The z_j values for the four surplus variables of the dual show $x_1 = 0$, $x_2 = 25$, $x_3 = 125$, and $x_4 = 0$.

c. Since $u_1 = 3/10$, $u_2 = 0$, and $u_3 = 54/30$, machines A and C ($u_j > 0$) are operating at capacity. Machine C is the priority machine since each hour is worth 54/30.

18. The dual is given by:

$$
\begin{array}{lrcrcrcl}
\text{Max} & 5u_1 & + & 5u_2 & + & 24u_3 \\
\text{s.t.} \\
& 15u_1 & + & 4u_2 & + & 12u_3 & \leq & 2800 \\
& 15u_1 & + & 8u_2 & & & \leq & 6000 \\
& u_1 & & & + & 8u_3 & \leq & 1200 \\
& & & u_1, u_2, u_3 \geq 0
\end{array}
$$

19. The canonical form is

$$
\begin{array}{lrcrcrcrcl}
\text{Max} & 3x_1 & + & x_2 & + & 5x_3 & + & 3x_4 \\
\text{s.t.} \\
& 3x_1 & + & 1x_2 & + & 2x_3 & & & \leq & 30 \\
& -3x_1 & - & 1x_2 & - & 2x_3 & & & \leq & -30 \\
& -2x_1 & - & 1x_2 & - & 3x_3 & - & x_4 & \leq & -15 \\
& & & 2x_2 & & & + & 3x_4 & \leq & 25 \\
& & & x_1,\ x_2,\ x_3,\ x_4, & \geq 0.
\end{array}
$$

The dual is

$$
\begin{array}{lrcrcrcrcl}
\text{Max} & 30u_1' & - & 30u_1'' & - & 15u_2 & + & 25u_3 \\
\text{s.t.} \\
& 3u_1' & - & 3u_1'' & - & 2u_2 & & & \geq & 3 \\
& u_1' & - & u_1'' & - & u_2 & + & 2u_3 & \geq & 1 \\
& 2u_1' & - & 20u_1'' & - & 3u_2 & & & \geq & 5 \\
& & & & - & u_2 & + & 3u_3 & \geq & 3 \\
& & & u_1',\ u_1'',\ u_2, u_3 \geq 0
\end{array}
$$

20. a.

$$\text{Max} \quad 30u_1 + 20u_2 + 80u_3$$

s.t.

$$u_1 \qquad\qquad + \quad u_3 \leq 1$$
$$\qquad\quad u_2 + 2u_3 \leq 1$$
$$u_1, u_2, u_3 \geq 0$$

b. The final simplex tableau for the dual problem is given by

Basis	c_B	u_1 30	u_2 20	u_3 80	s_1 0	s_2 0	
u_1	30	1	-1/2	0	1	-1/2	1/2
u_3	80	0	1/2	1	0	1/2	1/2
z_j		30	25	80	30	25	55
$c_j - z_j$		0	-5	0	-30	-25	

The z_j values for the two slack variables indicate $x_1 = 30$ and $x_2 = 25$.

c. With $u_3 = 1/2$, the relaxation of that constraint by one unit would reduce costs by $.50.

21. a.

$$\text{Max} \quad 15u_1 + 30u_2 + 20u_3$$

s.t.

$$u_1 \qquad\qquad + \quad u_3 \leq 4$$
$$0.5u_1 + 2u_2 + \quad u_3 \leq 3$$
$$u_1 + \quad u_2 + 2u_3 \leq 6$$
$$u_1, u_2, u_3 \geq 0$$

b. The optimal simplex tableau for the dual is

Basis	c_B	u_1 15	u_2 30	u_3 20	s_1 0	s_2 0	s_3 0	
u_1	15	1	0	1	1	0	0	4
u_2	30	0	1	1/4	-1/4	1/2	0	1/2
s_3	0	0	0	3/4	-3/4	-1/2	1	3/2
z_j		15	30	45/2	15/2	15	0	75
$c_j - z_j$		0	0	-5/2	-15/2	-15	0	

c. From the z_j values for the surplus variables we see that the optimal primal solution is $x_1 = 15/2$, $x_2 = 15$, and $x_3 = 0$.

d. The optimal value for the dual is shown in part b to equal 75. Substituting $x_1 = 15/2$ and $x_2 = 15$ into the primal objective function, we find that it gives the same value.

$$4(15/2) + 3(15) = 75$$

22. a.

$$\text{Max} \quad 10x_1 + 5x_2$$

s.t.

$$
\begin{array}{rcl}
x_1 & \geq & 20 \\
x_2 & \geq & 20 \\
x_1 & \leq & 100 \\
x_2 & \leq & 100 \\
3x_1 + x_2 & \leq & 175
\end{array}
$$

$$x_1, \ x_2 \geq 0$$

b.   The dual problem is

$$\text{Min} \quad -20u_1 - 20u_2 + 100u_3 \ 100u_4 + 175u_5$$

s.t.

$$
\begin{array}{rcl}
-u_1 \qquad + \ u_3 \qquad + \ 3u_5 & \geq & 10 \\
- \ u_2 \qquad u_4 + \ u_5 & \geq & 5
\end{array}
$$

$$u_1, \ u_2, \ u_3, \ u_4, \ u_5 \ \geq 0$$

The optimal solution to this problem is given by:

$$u_1 = 0, \ u_2 = 0, \ u_3 = 0, \ u_4 = 5/3, \text{ and } u_5 = 10/3.$$

c.   The optimal number of calls is given by the negative of the dual prices for the dual: $x_1 = 25$ and $x_2 = 100$.
Commission = $750.

d. $u_4 = 5/3$: $1.67 commission increase for an additional call for product 2.

$u_5 = 10/3$: $3.33 commission increase for an additional hour of selling time per month.

23. a.   Extreme point 1: $x_1 = 0, x_2 = 0$ value = 0

Extreme point 2: $x_1 = 5, x_2 = 0$ value = 15

Extreme point 3: $x_1 = 4, x_2 = 2$ value = 16

b.   Dual problem:

$$\text{Min} \quad 8u_1 + 10u_2$$

$$
\begin{array}{rcl}
\text{s.t.} \quad u_1 + 2u_2 & \geq & 3 \\
2u_1 + u_2 & \geq & 2
\end{array}
$$

$$u_1, \ u_2, \ \geq 0$$

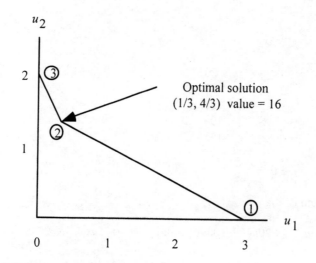

c. Extreme Point 1: $u_1 = 3$, $u_2 = 0$ value = 24

Extreme Point 2: $u_1 = 1/3$, $u_2 = 4/3$ value = 16

Extreme Point 3: $u_1 = 0$, $u_2 = 2$ value = 20

d. Each dual extreme point solution yields a value greater-than-or-equal-to each primal extreme point solution.

e. No. The value of any feasible solution to the dual problem provides an upper bound on the value of any feasible primal solution.

24. a. If the current optimal solution satisfies the new constraints, it is still optimal. Checking, we find

$$6(10) + 4(30) - 15 = 165 \leq 170 \quad \text{ok}$$

$$^1/_4(10) + 30 = 32.5 \geq 25 \quad \text{ok}$$

Both of the omitted constraints are satisfied.
Therefore, the same solution is optimal.

Chapter 7
Transportation, Assignment, and Transshipment Problems

Learning Objectives

1. Be able to identify the special features of the transportation problem.

2. Become familiar with the types of problems that can be solved by applying a transportation model.

3. Be able to develop network and linear programming models of the transportation problem.

4. Know how to handle the cases of (1) unequal supply and demand, (2) unacceptable routes, and (3) maximization objective for a transportation problem.

5. Be able to identify the special features of the assignment problem.

6. Become familiar with the types of problems that can be solved by applying an assignment model.

7. Be able to develop network and linear programming models of the assignment problem.

8. Be familiar with the special features of the transshipment problem.

9. Become familiar with the types of problems that can be solved by applying a transshipment model.

10 Be able to develop network and linear programming models of the transshipment problem.

11. Be able to utilize the minimum-cost method to find an initial feasible solution to a transportation problem.

12. Be able to utilize the transportation simplex method to find the optimal solution to a transportation problem.

13. Be able to utilize the Hungarian algorithm to solve an assignment problem.

14. Understand the following terms.

transportation problem	modified distribution (MODI) method
origin	assignment problem
destination	Hungarian method
network flow problem	opportunity loss
transportation tableau	transshipment problem
minimum cost method	capacitated transshipment problem
stepping-stone path	

Solutions:

1. The network model is shown.

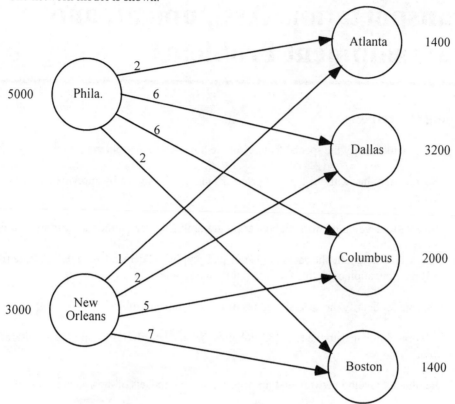

2. a.

    Let x_{11} : Amount shipped from Jefferson City to Des Moines
    x_{12} : Amount shipped from Jefferson City to Kansas City
    •
    •
    •
    x_{23} : Amount shipped from Omaha to St. Louis

    Min $14x_1 + 9x_{12} + 7x_{13} + 8x_{21} + 10x_{22} + 5x_{23}$

    s.t.

    $$x_{11} + x_{12} + x_{13} \qquad\qquad\qquad\qquad \le 30$$
    $$x_{21} + x_{22} + x_{23} \le 20$$
    $$x_{11} \qquad\qquad + x_{21} \qquad\qquad = 25$$
    $$x_{12} \qquad\qquad + x_{22} \qquad = 15$$
    $$x_{13} \qquad\qquad + x_{23} = 10$$

    $$x_{11}, \ x_{12}, \ x_{13}, \ x_{21}, \ x_{22}, \ x_{23}, \ \ge 0$$

    b. Optimal Solution:

	Amount	Cost
Jefferson City - Des Moines	5	70
Jefferson City - Kansas City	15	135
Jefferson City - St. Louis	10	70
Omaha - Des Moines	20	160
Total		435

3.   a. & b.
     The linear programming formulation and optimal solution as printed by The Management
     Scientist are shown below. The first two letters in the variable names identify the "from" node
     for the shipping route and the last two identify the "to" node. Also, The Management Scientist
     prints '<' for '≤.'

LINEAR PROGRAMMING PROBLEM

MIN 2PHAT + 6PHDA + 6PHCO + 2PHBO + 1NOAT + 2NODA + 5NOCO + 7NOBO

        S.T.

            1)   PHAT + PHDA + PHCO + PHBO < 5000
            2)   NOAT + NODA + NOCO + NOBO < 3000
            3)   PHAT + NOAT = 1400
            4)   PHDA + NODA = 3200
            5)   PHCO + NOCO = 2000
            6)   PHBO + NOBO = 1400

OPTIMAL SOLUTION

Objective Function Value =   24800.000

        Variable   Value   Reduced Costs
     --------------   ---------------   ------------------
        PHAT   1400.000   0.000
        PHDA   200.000   0.000
        PHCO   2000.000   0.000
        PHBO   1400.000   0.000
        NOAT   0.000   3.000
        NODA   3000.000   0.000
        NOCO   0.000   3.000
        NOBO   0.000   9.000

     Note that the Philadelphia port satisfies all the demand at Atlanta, Columbus, and Boston as
     well as the portion of the Dallas demand exceeding the New Orleans capacity.

4.   a.

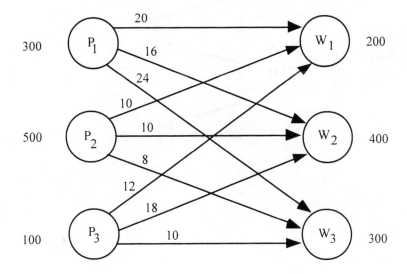

b. Let x_{ij} = Amount shipped from plant i to warehouse j

$$\text{Min} \quad 20x_1 + 16x_{12} + 24x_{13} + 10x_{21} + 10x_{22} + 8x_{23} + 12x_{31} + 18x_{32} + 10x_{33}$$

s.t.

$$
\begin{array}{llllllllll}
x_{11} & + & x_{12} & + & x_{13} & & & & & & & & & & & \le 300 \\
& & & & & x_{21} & + & x_{22} & + & x_{23} & & & & & & \le 500 \\
& & & & & & & & & & x_{31} & + & x_{32} & + & x_{33} & \le 100 \\
x_{11} & & & & & + & x_{21} & & & & + & x_{31} & & & & = 200 \\
& & x_{12} & & & & & + & x_{22} & & & & + & x_{32} & & = 400 \\
& & & & x_{13} & & & & & + & x_{23} & & & & + & x_{33} = 300
\end{array}
$$

$$x_{ij} \ge 0 \quad i = 1, 2, 3; \; j = 1, 2, 3$$

Optimal Solution:

	Amount	Cost
$P_1 - W_2$	300	4800
$P_2 - W_1$	100	1000
$P_2 - W_2$	100	1000
$P_2 - W_3$	300	2400
$P_3 - W_1$	100	1200
		10,400

c. The only change necessary, if the data are profit values, is to change the objective to one of maximization.

5. a.

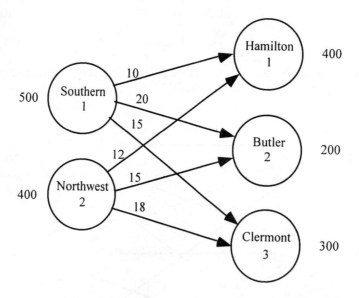

b.   Let x_{ij} = amount shipped from supply node i to demand node j.

$$\text{Min} \quad 10x_{11} + 20x_{12} + 15x_{13} + 12x_{21} + 15x_{22} + 18x_{23}$$

s.t.

$$
\begin{array}{lcl}
x_{11} + x_{12} + x_{13} & \leq & 500 \\
x_{21} + x_{22} + x_{23} & \leq & 400 \\
x_{11} \qquad\quad + x_{21} & = & 400 \\
x_{12} \qquad\qquad\quad + x_{22} & = & 200 \\
x_{13} \qquad\qquad\qquad\quad + x_{23} & = & 300
\end{array}
$$

$$x_{ij} \geq 0 \;\text{ for all }\; i, j$$

c.   Optimal Solution

	Amount	Cost
Southern - Hamilton	200	$ 2000
Southern - Clermont	300	4500
Northwest - Hamilton	200	2400
Northwest - Butler	200	3000
Total Cost		$11,900

d.   To answer this question the simplest approach is to increase the Butler County demand to 300 and to increase the supply by 100 at both Southern Gas and Northwest Gas.

The new optimal solution is:

	Amount	Cost
Southern - Hamilton	300	$ 3000
Southern - Clermont	300	4500
Northwest - Hamilton	100	1200
Northwest - Butler	300	4500
Total Cost		$13,200

From the new solution we see that Tri-County should contract with Southern Gas for the additional 100 units.

6.   a.

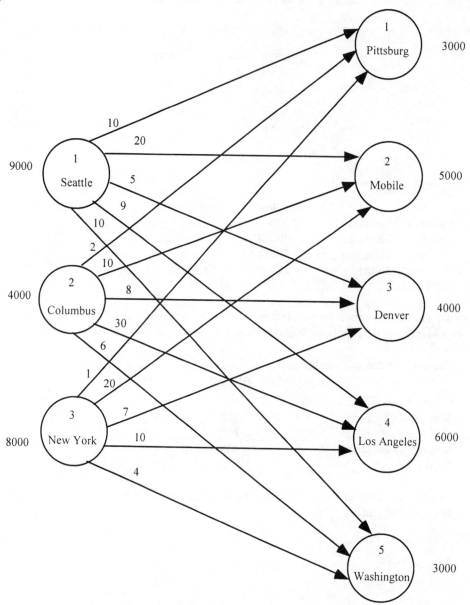

b.   The linear programming formulation and optimal solution as printed by *The Management Scientist* are shown. The first two letters of the variable name identify the "from" node and the second two letters identify the "to" node. Also, The Management Scientist prints "<" for "≤."

LINEAR PROGRAMMING PROBLEM

MIN 10SEPI + 20SEMO + 5SEDE + 9SELA + 10SEWA + 2COPI + 10COMO + 8CODE
+ 30COLA + 6COWA + 1NYPI + 20NYMO + 7NYDE + 10NYLA + 4NYWA

S.T.

```
1)  SEPI + SEMO + SEDE + SELA + SEWA < 9000
2)  COPI + COMO + CODE + COLA + COWA < 4000
3)  NYPI + NYMO + NYDE + NYLA + NYWA < 8000
4)  SEPI + COPI + NYPI = 3000
5)  SEMO + COMO + NYMO = 5000
6)  SEDE + CODE + NYDE = 4000
7)  SELA + COLA + NYLA = 6000
8)  SEWA + COWA + NYWA = 3000
```

OPTIMAL SOLUTION

Objective Function Value =   150000.000

Variable	Value	Reduced Costs
SEPI	0.000	10.000
SEMO	0.000	1.000
SEDE	4000.000	0.000
SELA	5000.000	0.000
SEWA	0.000	7.000
COPI	0.000	11.000
COMO	4000.000	0.000
CODE	0.000	12.000
COLA	0.000	30.000
COWA	0.000	12.000
NYPI	3000.000	0.000
NYMO	1000.000	0.000
NYDE	0.000	1.000
NYLA	1000.000	0.000
NYWA	3000.000	0.000

c. The new optimal solution actually shows a decrease of $9000 in shipping cost. It is summarized.

Optimal Solution	Units	Cost
Seattle - Denver	4000	$ 20,000
Seattle - Los Angeles	5000	45,000
Columbus - Mobile	5000	50,000
New York - Pittsburgh	4000	4,000
New York - Los Angeles	1000	10,000
New York - Washington	3000	12,000
	Total:	$141,000

7.　a.

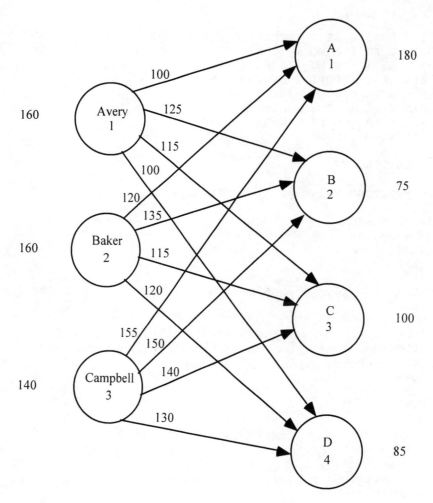

b.　Let x_{ij} = number of hours from consultant i assigned to client j.

$$
\begin{aligned}
\text{Max} \quad & 100x_{11} + 125x_{12} + 115x_{13} + 100x_{14} + 120x_{21} + 135x_{22} + 115x_{23} \\
\text{s.t.} \quad & \qquad\quad\;\; + 120x_{24} + 155x_{31} + 150x_{32} + 140x_{33} + 130x_{34}
\end{aligned}
$$

x_{11}	+	x_{12}	+	x_{13}	+	x_{14}				$\leq$ 160
				x_{21}	+	x_{22}	+	x_{23}	+ x_{24}	$\leq$ 160
						x_{31}	+	x_{32}	+ x_{33} + x_{34}	$\leq$ 140
x_{11}				+ x_{21}			+	x_{31}		= 180
		x_{12}		+ x_{22}			+	x_{32}		= 75
				x_{13}	+	x_{23}		+	x_{33}	= 100
				x_{14}		+	x_{24}		+ x_{34}	= 85

$$x_{ij} \geq 0 \quad \text{for all} \;\; i, j$$

Optimal Solution

	Hours Assigned	Billing
Avery - Client B	40	$ 5,000
Avery - Client C	100	11,500
Baker - Client A	40	4,800
Baker - Client B	35	4,725
Baker - Client D	85	10,200
Campbell - Client A	140	21,700
	Total Billing:	$57,925

c. New Optimal Solution

	Hours Assigned	Billing
Avery - Client A	40	$ 4,000
Avery - Client C	100	11,500
Baker - Client B	75	10,125
Baker - Client D	85	10,200
Campbell - Client A	140	21,700
	Total Billing:	$57,525

8. The network model, the linear programming formulation, and the optimal solution are shown. Note that the third constraint corresponds to the dummy origin. The variables x_{31}, x_{32}, x_{33}, and x_{34} are the amounts shipped out of the dummy origin; they do not appear in the objective function since they are given a coefficient of zero.

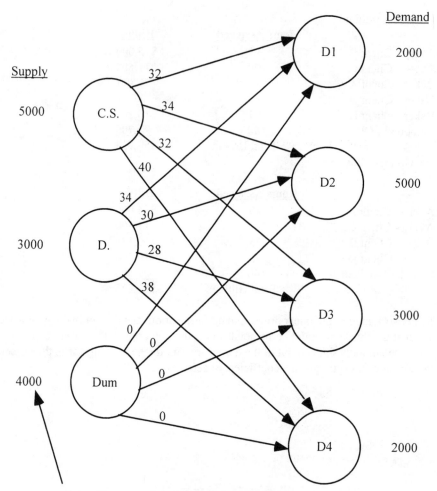

Note: Dummy origin has supply of 4000.

Max $32x_{11} + 34x_{12} + 32x_{13} + 40x_{14} + 34x_{21} + 30x_{22} + 28x_{23} + 38x_{24}$
s.t.

$$
\begin{array}{rcl}
x_{11} + x_{12} + x_{13} + x_{14} & \leq & 5000 \\
x_{21} + x_{22} + x_{23} + x_{24} & \leq & 3000 \\
x_{31} + x_{32} + x_{33} + x_{34} & \leq & 4000 \quad \text{Dummy} \\
x_{11} + x_{21} + x_{31} & = & 2000 \\
x_{12} + x_{22} + x_{32} & = & 5000 \\
x_{13} + x_{23} + x_{33} & = & 3000 \\
x_{14} + x_{24} + x_{34} & = & 2000
\end{array}
$$

$x_{ij} \geq 0$ for all i, j

Optimal Solution	Units	Cost
Clifton Springs - D2	4000	$136,000
Clifton Springs - D4	1000	40,000
Danville - D1	2000	68,000
Danville - D4	1000	38,000
	Total Cost:	$282,000

Customer 2 demand has a shortfall of 1000

Customer 3 demand of 3000 is not satisfied.

9.   We show a linear programming formulation. The cost of shipping from Martinsville is incremented by \$29.50 to every destination, the cost of shipping from Plymouth is incremented by \$31.20, and the cost of shipping from Franklin is incremented by \$30.35.

Let x_{ij} = amount produced at plant i and shipped to distributor j

Note that no variable is included for the unacceptable Plymouth to Dallas route.

$$\text{Min } 30.95x_{11} + 31.10x_{12} + 30.90x_{13} + 32.30x_2 + 31.80x_{23} + 31.55x_{31} + 31.55x_{32} + 32.15x_{33}$$

s.t.

$$
\begin{array}{llllllll}
x_{11} + & x_{12} + & x_{13} & & & & & \le 400 \\
 & & & x_{21} + & x_{23} & & & \le 600 \\
 & & & & & x_{31} + & x_{32} + & x_{33} \le 300 \\
x_{11} & & & + & x_{21} & + & x_{31} & = 400 \\
 & x_{12} & & & & + & x_{32} & = 400 \\
 & & x_{13} & + & & x_{23} & + & x_{33} = 400
\end{array}
$$

$$x_{ij} \ge 0 \text{ for all } i, j$$

Optimal Plan:

Martinsville to Chicago:	300
Martinsville to Dallas:	100
Plymouth to Chicago:	100
Plymouth to New York:	400
Franklin to Dallas:	300

Total Cost = \$37,810

Note: Plymouth has excess supply of 100.

10.   The linear programming formulation and optimal solution are shown.

Let x_{1A} = Units of product A on machine 1
x_{1B} = Units of product B on machine 1
.
.
.
x_{3C} = Units of product C on machine 3

$$\text{Max } x_{1A} + 1.2x_{1B} + 0.9x_{1C} + 1.3x_{2A} + 1.4x_{2B} + 1.2x_{2C} + 1.1x_{3A} + x_{3B} + 1.2x_{3C}$$

s.t.

$$
\begin{array}{lllllllll}
x_{1A} + & x_{1B} + & x_{1C} & & & & & & \le 1500 \\
 & & & x_{2A} + & x_{2B} + & x_{2C} & & & \le 1500 \\
 & & & & & & x_{3A} + & x_{3B} + & x_{3C} \le 1000 \\
x_{1A} & & & + & x_{2A} & & + & x_{3A} & = 2000 \\
 & x_{1B} & & & + & x_{2B} & & + & x_{3B} = 500 \\
 & & x_{1C} & & & + & x_{2C} & & + & x_{3C} = 1200
\end{array}
$$

$$x_{ij} \ge 0 \text{ for all } i, j$$

Optimal Solution	Units	Cost
1 - A	300	$ 300
1 - C	1200	1080
2 - A	1200	1560
3 - A	500	550
3 - B	500	500
	Total:	$3990

Note: There is an unused capacity of 300 units on machine 2.

11. a.

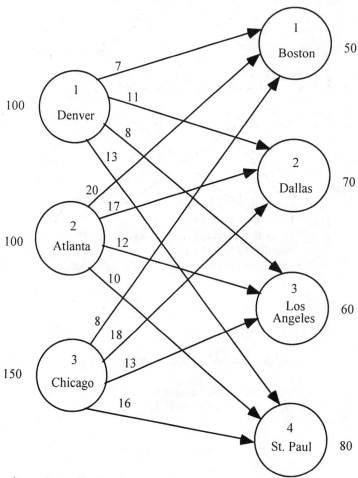

b. There are alternative optimal solutions.

Solution #1		Solution # 2	
Denver to St. Paul:	10	Denver to St. Paul:	10
Atlanta to Boston:	50	Atlanta to Boston:	50
Atlanta to Dallas:	50	Atlanta to Los Angeles:	50
Chicago to Dallas:	20	Chicago to Dallas:	70
Chicago to Los Angeles:	60	Chicago to Los Angeles:	10
Chicago to St. Paul:	70	Chicago to St. Paul:	70

Total Profit: $4240

If solution #1 is used, Forbelt should produce 10 motors at Denver, 100 motors at Atlanta, and 150 motors at Chicago. There will be idle capacity for 90 motors at Denver.

If solution #2 is used, Forbelt should adopt the same production schedule but a modified shipping schedule.

12. a.

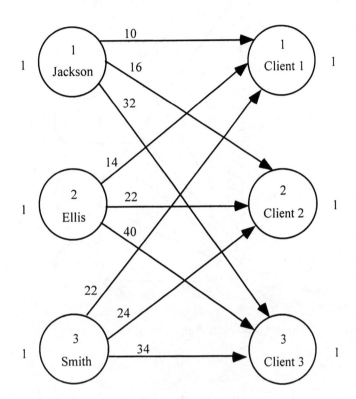

b.

$$\text{Min } 10x_{11} + 16x_{12} + 32x_{13} + 14x_{21} + 22x_{22} + 40x_{23} + 22x_{31} + 24x_{32} + 34x_{33}$$

s.t.

$$
\begin{array}{llllllll}
x_{11} + & x_{12} + & x_{13} & & & & & \leq 1 \\
& & & x_{21} + & x_{22} + & x_{23} & & \leq 1 \\
& & & & & & x_{31} + x_{32} + x_{33} \leq 1 \\
x_{11} & & & + x_{21} & & + x_{31} & & = 1 \\
& x_{12} & & + x_{22} & & + x_{32} & & = 1 \\
& & x_{13} & & + x_{23} & & + x_{33} & = 1
\end{array}
$$

$$x_{ij} \geq 0 \text{ for all } i, j$$

Solution $x_{12} = 1$, $x_{21} = 1$, $x_{33} = 1$ Total completion time = 64

13. a. Optimal assignment: Jackson to 1, Smith to 3, and Burton to 2. Time requirement is 62 days.

b. Considering Burton has saved 2 days.

c. Ellis.

14. a.

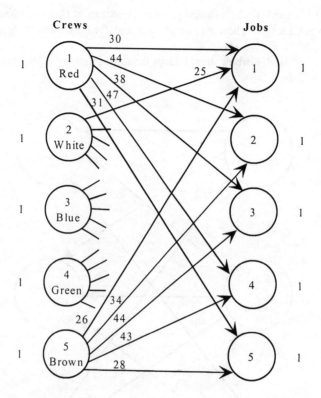

b.

Min $30x_{11} + 44x_{12} + 38x_{13} + 47x_{14} + 31x_{15} + 25x_{21} + \cdots + 28x_{55}$
s.t.

$$
\begin{array}{llllllllll}
x_{11} & + & x_{12} & + & x_{13} & + & x_{14} & + & x_{15} & & & & & & \leq & 1 \\
& & x_{21} & + & x_{22} & + & x_{23} & + & x_{24} & + & x_{25} & & & & \leq & 1 \\
& & x_{31} & + & x_{32} & + & x_{33} & + & x_{34} & + & x_{35} & & & & \leq & 1 \\
& & x_{41} & + & x_{42} & + & x_{43} & + & x_{44} & + & x_{45} & & & & \leq & 1 \\
& & x_{51} & + & x_{52} & + & x_{53} & + & x_{54} & + & x_{55} & & & & \leq & 1 \\
x_{11} & + & x_{21} & + & x_{31} & + & x_{41} & + & x_{51} & & & & & & = & 1 \\
& & x_{12} & + & x_{22} & + & x_{32} & + & x_{42} & + & x_{52} & & & & = & 1 \\
& & x_{13} & + & x_{23} & + & x_{33} & + & x_{43} & + & x_{53} & & & & = & 1 \\
& & x_{14} & + & x_{24} & + & x_{34} & + & x_{44} & + & x_{54} & & & & = & 1 \\
& & x_{15} & + & x_{25} & + & x_{35} & + & x_{45} & + & x_{55} & & & & = & 1 \\
\end{array}
$$

$x_{ij} \geq 0, \; i = 1, 2, .., 5; \; j = 1, 2, .., 5$

Optimal Solution:

Green to Job 1	$26
Brown to Job 2	34
Red to Job 3	38
Blue to Job 4	39
White to Job 5	25
	$162

Since the data is in hundreds of dollars, the total installation cost for the 5 contracts is $16,200.

15.   Optimal Solution:

Terry: Client 2 (15 days)
Carle: Client 3 (5 days)
McClymonds: Client 1 (6 days)
Higley: Not accepted
Total time = 26 days

Note: An alternative optimal solution is Terry: Client 2, Carle: unassigned, McClymonds: Client 3, and Higley: Client 1.

16. a.

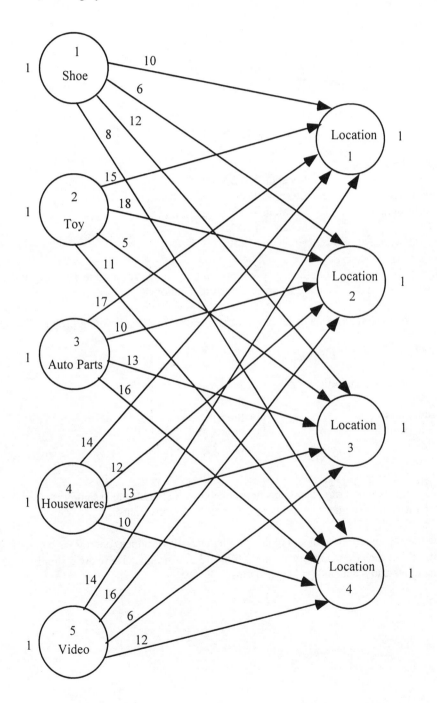

b. Let $x_{ij} = \begin{cases} 1 \text{ if department } i \text{ is assigned location } j \\ 0 \text{ otherwise} \end{cases}$

$$\begin{aligned}
\text{Max} \quad & 10x_{11} + 6x_{12} + 12x_{13} + 8x_{14} + 15x_{21} + 18x_{22} + 5x_{23} + 11x_{24} \\
& + 17x_{31} + 10x_{32} + 13x_{33} + 16x_{34} + 14x_{41} + 12x_{42} + 13x_{43} + 10x_{44} \\
& + 14x_{51} + 16x_{52} + 6x_{53} + 12x_{54}
\end{aligned}$$

s.t.

$$\begin{aligned}
x_{11} + x_{12} + x_{13} + x_{14} & \leq 1 \\
x_{21} + x_{22} + x_{23} + x_{24} & \leq 1 \\
x_{31} + x_{32} + x_{33} + x_{34} & \leq 1 \\
x_{41} + x_{42} + x_{43} + x_{44} & \leq 1 \\
x_{51} + x_{52} + x_{53} + x_{54} & \leq 1 \\
x_{11} + x_{21} + x_{31} + x_{41} + x_{51} & = 1 \\
x_{12} + x_{22} + x_{32} + x_{42} + x_{52} & = 1 \\
x_{13} + x_{23} + x_{33} + x_{43} + x_{53} & = 1 \\
x_{14} + x_{24} + x_{34} + x_{44} + x_{54} & = 1
\end{aligned}$$

$$x_{ij} \geq 0 \text{ for all } i, j$$

Optimal Solution:
Toy: Location 2
Auto Parts: Location 4
Housewares: Location 3
Video: Location 1
   Profit: 61

17. a. Simply delete 2 arcs from the network representation in the solution to 16 part (a): the arc from Toy to location 2 and the arc from Auto Parts to location 4.

   b. Add two constraints to the linear programming model in the solution to problem 16 part (b).

      $x_{22} = 0$ and $x_{34} = 0$

      Revised optimal solution:
      Toy: Location 4
      Auto Parts: Location 1
      Housewares: Location 3
      Video: Location 2
         Profit: 57

18. a. This is the variation of the assignment problem in which multiple assignments are possible. Each distribution center may be assigned up to 3 customer zones.

      The linear programming model of this problem has 40 variables (one for each combination of distribution center and customer zone). It has 13 constraints. There are 5 supply (≤ 3) constraints and 8 demand ($= 1$) constraints.

The problem can also be solved using the Transportation module of *The Management Scientist*. The optimal solution is given below.

	Assignments	Cost ($1000s)
Plano:	Kansas City, Dallas	34
Flagstaff:	Los Angeles	15
Springfield:	Chicago, Columbus, Atlanta	70
Boulder:	Newark, Denver	97
	Total Cost -	$216

b.   the Nashville distribution center is not used.

c.   All the distribution centers are used. Columbus is switched from Springfield to Nashville. Total cost increases by $11,000 to $227,000.

19.   A linear programming formulation and the optimal solution are given. For the variables, we let the first letter of the sales representatives name be the first subscript and the sales territory be the second subscript.

$$\text{Max}\quad 44x_{WA} + 80x_{WB} + 52x_{WC} + 60x_{WD} + 60x_{BA} + 56x_{BB} + 40x_{BC}$$
$$+ 72x_{BD} + 36x_{FA} + 60x_{FB} + 48x_{FC} + 48x_{FD} + 52x_{HA}$$
$$+ 76x_{HB} + 36x_{HC} + 40x_{HD}$$

s.t.

$$x_{WA} + x_{WB} + x_{WC} + x_{WD} \leq 1$$
$$x_{BA} + x_{BB} + x_{BC} + x_{BD} \leq 1$$
$$x_{FA} + x_{FB} + x_{FC} + x_{FD} \leq 1$$
$$x_{HA} + x_{HB} + x_{HC} + x_{HD} \leq 1$$
$$x_{WA} + x_{BA} + x_{FA} + x_{HA} = 1$$
$$x_{WB} + x_{BB} + x_{FB} + x_{HB} = 1$$
$$x_{WC} + x_{BC} + x_{FC} + x_{HC} = 1$$
$$x_{WD} + x_{BD} + x_{FD} + x_{HD} = 1$$

$$x_{ij} \geq 0 \text{ for all } i, j$$

Optimal Solution	Sales
Washington - B	80
Benson - D	72
Fredricks - C	48
Hodson - A	52
Total	252

20. A linear programming formulation of this problem can be developed as follows. Let the first letter of each variable name represent the professor and the second two the course. Note that a DPH variable is not created because the assignment is unacceptable.

$$\text{Max} \quad 2.8AUN + 2.2AMB + 3.3AMS + 3.0APH + 3.2BUN + \ldots + 2.5DMS$$

s.t.

AUN +	AMB +	AMS +	APH				≤ 1
	BUN +	BMB +	BMS +	BPH			≤ 1
		CUN +	CMB +	CMS +	CPH		≤ 1
			DUN +	DMB +	DMS		≤ 1
AUN +	BUN +	CUN +	DUN				$= 1$
	AMB +	BMB +	CMB +	DMB			$= 1$
		AMS +	BMS +	CMS +	DMS		$= 1$
			APH +	BPH +	CPH		$= 1$

All Variables ≥ 0

Optimal Solution:	Rating
A to MS course	3.3
B to Ph.D. course	3.6
C to MBA course	3.2
D to Undergraduate course	3.2
Max Total Rating	13.3

21. a.

$$\begin{aligned}
\text{Min} \quad & 150x_{11} + 210x_{12} + 270x_{13} \\
& + 170x_{21} + 230x_{22} + 220x_{23} \\
& + 180x_{31} + 230x_{32} + 225x_{33} \\
& + 160x_{41} + 240x_{42} + 230x_{43}
\end{aligned}$$

s.t.

$x_{11} +$	$x_{12} +$	x_{13}			≤ 1
	$x_{21} +$	$x_{22} +$	x_{23}		≤ 1
		$x_{31} +$	$x_{32} +$	x_{33}	≤ 1
			$x_{41} +$	$x_{42} + x_{43}$	≤ 1
x_{11}	$+x_{21}$	$+x_{31}$	$+x_{41}$		$= 1$
x_{12}	$+x_{22}$	$+x_{32}$	$+x_{42}$		$= 1$
x_{13}	$+x_{23}$	$+x_{33}$	$+x_{43}$		$= 1$

$$x_{ij} \geq \text{ for all } i, j$$

Optimal Solution: $x_{12} = 1$, $x_{23} = 1$, $x_{41} = 1$

Total hours required: 590

Note: statistician 3 is not assigned.

b. The solution will not change, but the total hours required will increase by 5. This is the extra time required for statistician 4 to complete the job for client A.

c. The solution will not change, but the total time required will decrease by 20 hours.

d. The solution will not change; statistician 3 will not be assigned. Note that this occurs because increasing the time for statistician 3 makes statistician 3 an even less attractive candidate for assignment.

22. a. The total cost is the sum of the purchase cost and the transportation cost. We show the calculation for Division 1 - Supplier 1 and present the result for the other Division-Supplier combinations.

Division 1 - Supplier 1

Purchase cost (40,000 x $12.60)	$504,000
Transportation Cost (40,000 x $2.75)	110,000
Total Cost:	$614,000

Cost Matrix ($1,000s)

Supplier

	1	2	3	4	5	6
1	614	660	534	680	590	630
2	603	639	702	693	693	630
3	865	830	775	850	900	930
4	532	553	511	581	595	553
5	720	648	684	693	657	747

Division

b. Optimal Solution:

Supplier 1 - Division 2	$603
Supplier 2 - Division 5	648
Supplier 3 - Division 3	775
Supplier 5 - Division 1	590
Supplier 6 - Division 4	553
Total	$3,169

23. a. Network Model

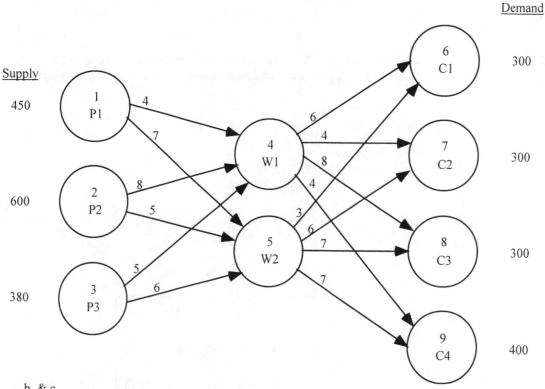

b. & c.
The linear programming formulation and solution as printed by *The Management Scientist* is shown.

LINEAR PROGRAMMING PROBLEM

MIN 4X14 + 7X15 + 8X24 + 5X25 + 5X34 + 6X35 + 6X46 + 4X47 + 8X48 + 4X49 + 3X56 + 6X57 + 7X58 + 7X59

    S.T.

       1)   X14 + X15 < 450
       2)   X24 + X25 < 600
       3)   X34 + X35 < 380
       4)   X46 + X47 + X48 + X49 - X14 - X24 - X34 = 0
       5)   X56 + X57 + X58 + X59 - X15 - X25 - X35 = 0
       6)   X46 + X56 = 300
       7)   X47 + X57 = 300
       8)   X48 + X58 = 300
       9)   X49 + X59 = 400

OPTIMAL SOLUTION

Objective Function Value =   11850.000

Variable	Value	Reduced Costs
X14	450.000	0.000
X15	0.000	3.000
X24	0.000	3.000
X25	600.000	0.000
X34	250.000	0.000
X35	0.000	1.000
X46	0.000	3.000
X47	300.000	0.000
X48	0.000	1.000
X49	400.000	0.000
X56	300.000	0.000
X57	0.000	2.000
X58	300.000	0.000
X59	0.000	3.000

There is an excess capacity of 130 units at plant 3.

24. a. Three arcs must be added to the network model in problem 23a. The new network is shown.

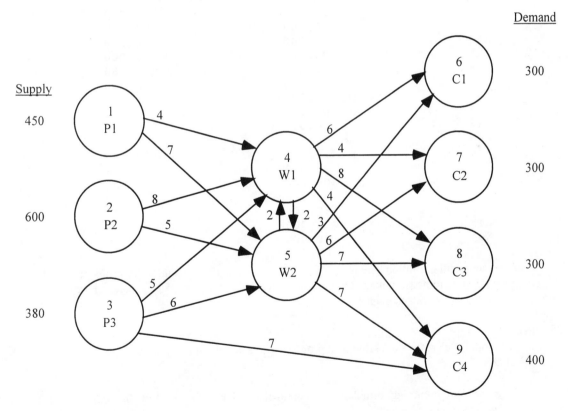

b.&c.

The linear programming formulation and optimal solution as printed by The management Scientist follow:

LINEAR PROGRAMMING PROBLEM

MIN 4X14 + 7X15 + 8X24 + 5X25 + 5X34 + 6X35 + 6X46 + 4X47 + 8X48 + 4X49 + 3X56 + 6X57 + 7X58 + 7X59 + 7X39 + 2X45 + 2X54

    S.T.

       1) X14 + X15 < 450
       2) X24 + X25 < 600
       3) X34 + X35 + X39 < 380
       4) X45 + X46 + X47 + X48 + X49 - X14 - X24 - X34 - X54 = 0
       5) X54 + X56 + X57 + X58 + X59 - X15 - X25 - X35 - X45 = 0
       6) X46 + X56 = 300
       7) X47 + X57 = 300
       8) X48 + X58 = 300
       9) X39 + X49 + X59 = 400

OPTIMAL SOLUTION

Objective Function Value =   11220.000

Variable	Value	Reduced Costs
X14	320.000	0.000
X15	0.000	2.000
X24	0.000	4.000
X25	600.000	0.000
X34	0.000	2.000
X35	0.000	2.000
X46	0.000	2.000
X47	300.000	0.000
X48	0.000	0.000
X49	20.000	0.000
X56	300.000	0.000
X57	0.000	3.000
X58	300.000	0.000
X59	0.000	4.000
X39	380.000	0.000
X45	0.000	1.000
X54	0.000	3.000

The value of the solution here is $630 less than the value of the solution for problem 23. The new shipping route from plant 3 to customer 4 has helped ($x_{39} = 380$). There is now excess capacity of 130 units at plant 1.

25. a&b

To model, we create a transshipment problem with a supply of one at node 1 and a demand of 1 at node 7.

The linear programming formulation and optimal solution as provided by *The Management Scientist* are shown below.

LINEAR PROGRAMMING PROBLEM

MIN 35X12+30X13+12X23+18X24+39X27+15X35+12X45+16X47+9X56+18X67

S.T.

1) 1X12+1X13=1
2) -1X12+1X23+1X24+1X27=0
3) -1X13-1X23+1X35=0
4) -1X24+1X45+1X47=0
5) -1X35-1X45+1X56=0
6) -1X56+1X67=0
7) +1X27+1X47+1X67=1

OPTIMAL SOLUTION

Objective Function Value =   69.000

Variable	Value	Reduced Costs
X12	1.000	0.000
X13	0.000	0.000
X23	0.000	17.000
X24	1.000	0.000
X27	0.000	5.000
X35	0.000	0.000
X45	0.000	20.000
X47	1.000	0.000
X56	0.000	0.000
X67	0.000	3.000

Constraint	Slack/Surplus	Dual Prices
1	0.000	-1.000
2	0.000	34.000
3	0.000	29.000
4	0.000	52.000
5	0.000	44.000
6	0.000	53.000
7	0.000	-68.000

c. Allowing for 8 minutes to get to node 1 and 69 minutes to go from node 1 to node 7, we expect to take 77 minutes for the delivery. With a 10% safety margin, we can guarantee a delivery in 85 minutes - that is at 1:25 p.m.

26. a.

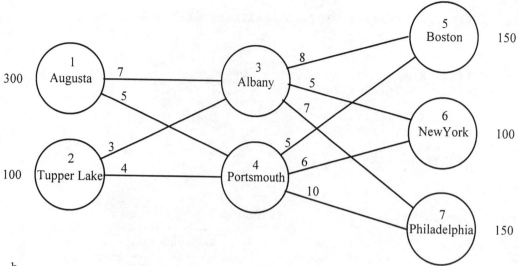

b.

$$\text{Min} \quad 7x_{13} + 5x_{14} + 3x_{23} + 4x_{24} + 8x_{35} + 5x_{36} + 7x_{37} + 5x_{45} + 6x_{46} + 10x_{47}$$
s.t.

$$
\begin{array}{llllllllll}
x_{13} & + & x_{14} & & & & & & & \leq 300 \\
 & & & x_{23} & + & x_{24} & & & & \leq 100 \\
x_{13} & - & & - & x_{23} & & + x_{35} & + x_{36} & + x_{37} & = 0 \\
 & - & x_{14} & & - & x_{24} & & & + x_{45} & + x_{46} & + x_{47} & = 0 \\
 & & & & & & x_{35} & & + x_{45} & & = 150 \\
 & & & & & & & + x_{36} & & + x_{46} & = 100 \\
 & & & & & & & x_{37} & & + x_{47} & = 150 \\
\end{array}
$$

$$x_{ij} \geq 0 \text{ for all } i \text{ and } j$$

c. Optimal Solution:

Variable	Value
x_{13}	50
x_{14}	250
x_{23}	100
x_{24}	0
x_{35}	0
x_{36}	0
x_{37}	150
x_{45}	150
x_{46}	100
x_{47}	0

Objective Function: 4300

27. a.

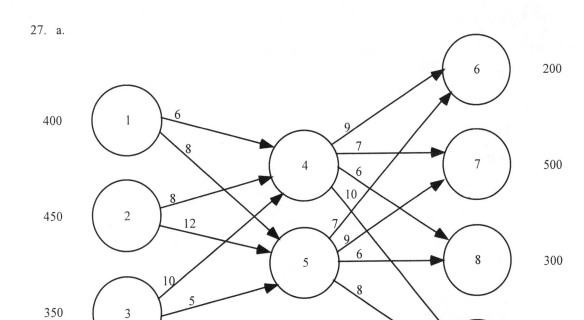

b.

Min

$$6x_{14}+8x_{15}+8x_{24}+12x_{25}+10x_{34}+5x_{35}+9x_{46}+7x_{47}+6x_{48}+10x_{49}+7x_{56}+9x_{57}+6x_{58}+8x_{59}$$

s.t.

$$
\begin{aligned}
x_{14}+x_{15} &\le 400 \\
x_{24}+x_{25} &\le 450 \\
x_{34}+x_{35} &\le 350 \\
-x_{14}-x_{24}-x_{34}+x_{46}+x_{47}+x_{48}+x_{49} &= 0 \\
-x_{15}-x_{25}-x_{35}+x_{56}+x_{57}+x_{58}+x_{59} &= 0 \\
x_{46}+x_{56} &= 200 \\
x_{47}+x_{57} &= 500 \\
x_{48}+x_{58} &= 300 \\
x_{49}+x_{59} &= 200
\end{aligned}
$$

$$x_{ij} \ge 0 \text{ for all } i, j$$

c. Optimal Solution

Variable	Value
x_{14}	400
x_{15}	0
x_{24}	450
x_{25}	0
x_{34}	0
x_{35}	350
x_{46}	0
x_{47}	500
x_{48}	300
x_{49}	50
x_{56}	200
x_{57}	0
x_{58}	0
x_{59}	150

Value of optimal solution: 16150

28.

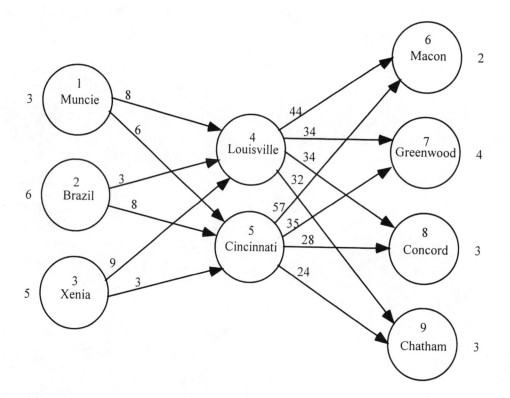

A linear programming model is

Min

$$8x_{14} + 6x_{15} + 3x_{24} + 8x_{25} + 9x_{34} + 3x_{35} + 44x_{46} + 34x_{47} + 34x_{48} + 32x_{49} + 57x_{56} + 35x_{57} + 28x_{58} + 24x_{59}$$

s.t.

$$
\begin{array}{llll}
x_{14} + x_{15} & & & \leq 3 \\
x_{24} + x_{25} & & & \leq 6 \\
x_{34} + x_{35} & & & \leq 5 \\
-x_{14} - x_{24} - x_{34} + x_{46} + x_{47} + x_{48} + x_{49} & & & = 0 \\
-x_{15} - x_{25} - x_{35} + x_{56} + x_{57} + x_{58} + x_{59} & & & = 0 \\
x_{46} + x_{56} & & & = 2 \\
x_{47} + x_{57} & & & = 4 \\
x_{48} + x_{58} & & & = 3 \\
x_{49} + x_{59} & & & = 3
\end{array}
$$

$$x_{ij} \geq 0 \text{ for all } i, j$$

Optimal Solution	Units Shipped	Cost
Muncie to Cincinnati	1	6
Cincinnati to Concord	3	84
Brazil to Louisville	6	18
Louisville to Macon	2	88
Louisville to Greenwood	4	136
Xenia to Cincinnati	5	15
Cincinnati to Chatham	3	72
		419

Two rail cars must be held at Muncie until a buyer is found.

29. a.

Min $20x_{12} + 25x_{15} + 30x_{25} + 45x_{27} + 20x_{31} + 35x_{36}$
$+ 30x_{42} + 25x_{53} + 15x_{54} + 28x_{56} + 12x_{67} + 27x_{74}$

s.t.

$$
\begin{array}{l}
x_{31} - x_{12} - x_{15} = 8 \\
x_{25} + x_{27} - x_{12} - x_{42} = 5 \\
x_{31} + x_{36} - x_{53} = 3 \\
x_{54} + x_{74} - x_{42} = 3 \\
x_{53} + x_{54} + x_{56} - x_{15} - x_{25} = 2 \\
x_{36} + x_{56} - x_{67} = 5 \\
x_{74} - x_{27} - x_{67} = 6
\end{array}
$$

$$x_{ij} \geq 0 \text{ for all } i, j$$

b. $x_{12} = 0$ $x_{53} = 5$

     $x_{15} = 0$ $x_{54} = 0$

     $x_{25} = 8$ $x_{56} = 5$

     $x_{27} = 0$ $x_{67} = 0$

     $x_{31} = 8$ $x_{74} = 6$

     $x_{36} = 0$

     $x_{42} = 3$

Total cost of redistributing cars = \$917

30.

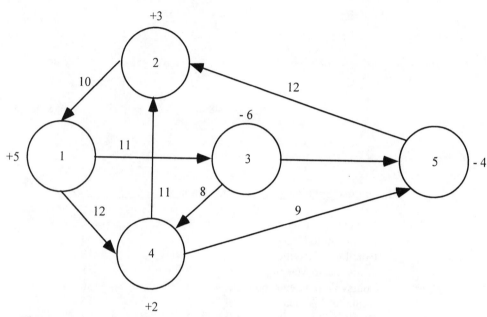

The positive numbers by nodes indicate the amount of supply at that node. The negative numbers by nodes indicate the amount of demand at the node.

31. a. Modify Figure 7.12 by adding two nodes and two arcs. Let node 0 be a beginning inventory node with a supply of 50 and an arc connecting it to node 5 (period 1 demand). Let node 9 be an ending inventory node with a demand of 100 and an arc connecting node 8 (period 4 demand to it).

     b.

Min $+ \ 2x_{15} \ + \ 5x_{26} \ + \ 3x_{3:} \ + \ 3x_{48} \ + \ 0.25x_{56} \ + \ 0.25x_{67} \ + \ 0.25x_{78} \ + \ 0.25x_{89}$

s.t.

$$
\begin{array}{llllllllr}
x_{05} & & & & & & & & = & 50 \\
& x_{15} & & & & & & & \leq & 600 \\
& & x_{26} & & & & & & \leq & 300 \\
& & & x_{3:} & & & & & \leq & 500 \\
& & & & x_{48} & & & & \leq & 400 \\
x_{05} \ + & x_{15} & & & & - & x_{56} & & = & 400 \\
& & x_{26} & & & + & x_{56} \ - & x_{67} & = & 500 \\
& & & x_{3:} & & & + & x_{67} \ - & x_{78} & = & 400 \\
& & & & x_{48} & & & + & x_{78} \ - & x_{89} & = & 400 \\
& & & & & & & & x_{89} & = & 100 \\
\end{array}
$$

$x_{ij} \geq 0$ for all i and j

Optimal Solution:

$x_{05} = 50$ $x_{56} = 250$
$x_{15} = 600$ $x_{67} = 0$
$x_{26} = 250$ $x_{78} = 100$
$x_{37} = 500$ $x_{89} = 100$
$x_{48} = 400$

Total Cost = $5262.50

32. a. Let R1, R2, R3   represent regular time production in months 1, 2, 3
            O1, O2, O3   represent overtime production in months 1, 2, 3
            D1, D2, D3   represent demand in months 1, 2, 3

Using these 9 nodes, a network model is shown.

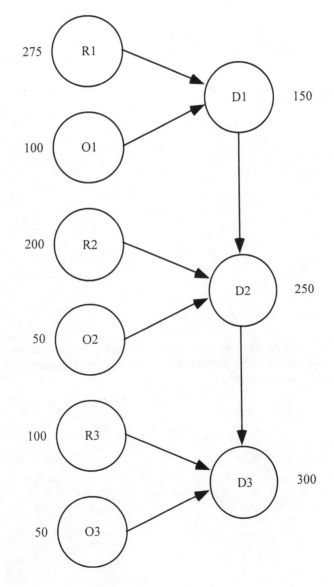

b. Use the following notation to define the variables: first two letters designates the "from node" and the second two letters designates the "to node" of the arc. For instance, R1D1 is amount of regular time production available to satisfy demand in month 1, O1D1 is amount of overtime production in month 1 available to satisfy demand in month 1, D1D2 is the amount of inventory carried over from month 1 to month 2, and so on.

```
MIN 50R1D1 + 80O1D1 + 20D1D2 + 50R2D2 + 80O2D2 + 20D2D3 + 60R3D3 +
10OO3D3

    S.T.

        1)   R1D1 ≤ 275
        2)   O1D1 ≤ 100
        3)   R2D2 ≤ 200
        4)   O2D2 ≤ 50
        5)   R3D3 ≤ 100
        6)   O3D3 ≤ 50
        7)   R1D1 + O1D1 - D1D2                 = 150
        8)   R2D2 + O2D2 + D1D2 - D2D3          = 250
        9)   R3D3 + O3D3 + D2D3                 = 300
```

c. Optimal Solution:

Variable	Value
R1D1	275.000
O1D1	25.000
D1D2	150.000
R2D2	200.000
O2D2	50.000
D2D3	150.000
R3D3	100.000
O3D3	50.000

Value = $46,750

Note: Slack variable for constraint 2 = 75.

d. The values of the slack variables for constraints 1 through 6 represent unused capacity. The only nonzero slack variable is for constraint 2; its value is 75. Thus, there are 75 units of unused overtime capacity in month 1.

33. a.

v_j

u_i	5	5	10	4	Supply
0	5 25	7 ②	10 50	5 ①	75
-2	6 ③	5 ②	8 100	2 75	175
1	6 100	6 ⓪	12 ①	7 ②	100
0	8 ③	5 100	14 ④	4 50	150
Demand	125	100	150	125	

This is the minimum cost solution since $e_{ij} \geq 0$ for all i, j.

Solution:

Shipping Route (Arc)	Units	Unit Cost	Arc Shipping Cost
O1 - D1	25	5	$ 125
O1 - D3	50	10	500
O2 - D3	100	8	800
O2 - D4	75	2	150
O3 - D1	100	6	600
O4 - D2	100	5	500
O4 - D4	50	4	200
		Total Transportation Cost:	$2875

b. Yes, $e_{32} = 0$. This indicates that we can ship over route O3 - D2 without increasing the cost. To find the alternative optimal solution identify cell (3, 2) as the incoming cell and make appropriate adjustments on the stepping stone path.

The increasing cells on the path are O4 - D4, O2 - D3, and O1 - D1. The decreasing cells on the path are O4 - D2, O2 - D4, O1 - D3, and O3 - D1. The decreasing cell with the smallest number of units is O1 - D3 with 50 units. Therefore, 50 units is assigned to O3 - D2. After making the appropriate increases and decreases on the stepping stone path the following alternative optimal solution is identified.

v_j

u_i	5	5	10	4	Supply
0	⑤ ② 75	⑦ ②	⑩ ⓪	⑤ ①	75
-2	⑥ ③	⑤ ②	⑧ 150	② 25	175
1	⑥ 50	⑥ 50	⑫ ①	⑦ ②	100
0	⑧ ③	⑤ 50	⑭ ④	④ 100	150
Demand	125	100	150	125	

Note that all $e_{ij} \geq 0$ indicating that this solution is also optimal. Also note that $e_{13} = 0$ indicating there is an alternative optimal solution with cell (1, 3) in solution. This is the solution we found in part (a).

34. a. An initial solution is given below.

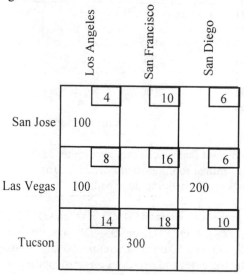

	Los Angeles	San Francisco	San Diego
San Jose	4 100	10	6
Las Vegas	8 100	16	6 200
Tucson	14	18 300	10

Total Cost: $7800

b. Note that the initial solution is degenerate. A zero is assigned to the cell in row 3 and column 1 so that the row and column indices can be computed.

u_i	v_j = 4	v_j = 8	v_j = 2
	[4]	[10] ②	[6] ④
0	100		
	[8]	[16] ④	[6]
4	100		200
	[14]	[18]	[10] ⊝2
10	0	300	0

Cell in row 3 and column 3 is identified as an incoming cell.

	4	10	6
	100		
	+ [8]	[16]	- [6]
	100		200
	- [14]	[18]	[10]
	0	300	

Stepping-stone path shows cycle of adjustments. Outgoing cell is in row 3 and column 1.

u_i	v_j = 4	v_j = 10	v_j = 2
	[4]	[10] ⓪	[6] ④
0	100		
	[8]	[16] ②	[6]
4	100		200
	[14] ②	[18]	[10]
8		300	0

Solution is recognized as optimal. It is degenerate.

Thus, the initial solution turns out to be the optimal solution; total cost = $7800.

c. To begin with we reduce the supply at Tucson by 100 and the demand at San Diego by 100; the
    new solution is shown below:

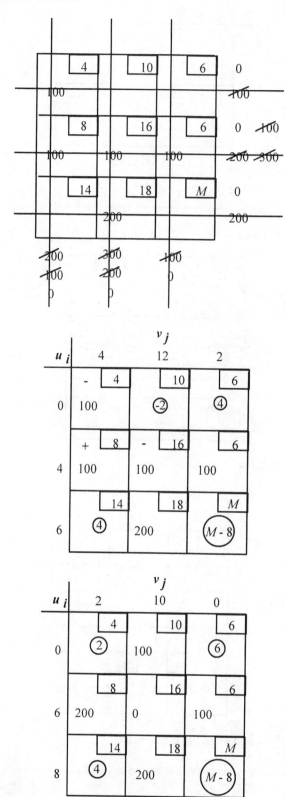

Optimal Solution: recall, however, that the 100 units shipped from Tucson to San Diego must be added to obtain the total cost.

San Jose to San Francisco:	100
Las Vegas to Los Angeles:	200
Las Vegas to San Diego:	100
Tucson to San Francisco:	200
Tucson to San Diego:	100
Total Cost: $7800	

Note that this total cost is the same as for part (a); thus, we have alternative optima.

d. The final transportation tableau is shown below. The total transportation cost is $8,000, an increase of $200 over the solution to part (a).

u_i \ v_j	2	10	2	
0	[4] (2)	[10] 100	[6] (4)	100
6	[8] 200	[16] 100	[M] (M - 8)	300
8	[14] (4)	[18] 100	[10] 200	300
	200	300	200	700

35. a.

	Des Moines	Kansas City	St. Louis	
Jefferson City	[14]	[9]	[7]	30
Omaha	[8]	[10]	[5]	20
	25	15	10	

b.

	14	9	7	
				30
	8	10	5	
			0	~~20~~ 10
	25	15	0	

	14	9	7	
				30
	8	10	5	
~~10~~		0	~~20 10~~ 0	
~~25~~ 15	15	0		

	14	9	7	
	15	15		30
	8	10	5	
	10		10	20
	25	15	10	

This is an initial feasible solution with a total cost of $475.

36.   An initial feasible solution found by the minimum cost method is given below.

	W_1	W_2	W_3
P_1	20 100	16 200	24
P_2	10	10 200	8 300
P_3	12 100	18	10

Computing row and column indexes and evaluating the unoccupied cells one identifies the cell in row 2 and column 1 as the incoming cell.

u_i \ v_j	20	16	14
0	$-$ [20] 100	$+$ [16] 200	[24] ⑩
-6	[10] ④	$-$ [10] 200	[8] 300
-8	[12] 100	[18] ⑩	[10] ④

The +'s and -'s above show the cycle of adjustments necessary on the stepping-stone path as flow is allocated to the cell in row 2 and column 1. The cell in row 1 and column 1 is identified as corresponding to the outgoing arc. The new solution follows.

u_i \ v_j	16	16	14
0	[20] ④	[16] 300	[24] ⑩
-6	[10] 100	[10] 100	[8] 300
-4	[12] 100	[18] ⑥	[10] ⓪

Since all per-unit costs are ≥ 0, this solution is optimal. However, an alternative optimal solution can be found by shipping 100 units over the P_3 - W_3 route.

37. a. Initial Solution:

	D_1	D_2	D_3
O_1	[6] 150	[8] 100	[8]
O_2	[18]	[12] 100	[14] 50
O_3	[8]	[12]	[10] 100

Total Cost: $4600

b.

v_j

u_i	6	8	10
0	6 — 150	— 8 — 100	8 (-2)
4	18 (8)	+ 12 + 100	14 — 50
0	8 (2)	12 (4)	10 100

Incoming arc: $O_1 - D_3$

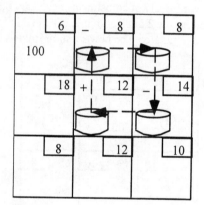

Outgoing arc: $O_2 - D_3$

v_j

u_i	6	8	8
0	6 150	8 50	8 50
4	18 (8)	12 150	14 (2)
2	8 (0)	12 (2)	10 100

Since all cell evaluations are non-negative, the solution is optimal; Total Cost: $4500.

c. At the optimal solution found in part (b), the cell evaluation for $O_3 - D_1 = 0$. Thus, additional units can be shipped over the $O_3 - D_1$ route with no increase in total cost.

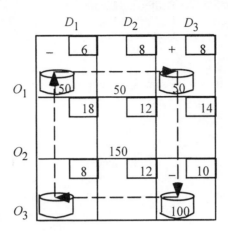

Thus, an alternative optimal solution is

	D_1	D_2	D_3
O_1	50 / 6	50 / 8	150 / 8
O_2	18	150 / 12	14
O_3	100 / 8	12	10

38. a.

	Boston	Chicago	St. Louis	Lexington
Cleveland	1001 ~~1000~~ / 3	3999 ~~4000~~ / 2	7	6
Bedford	2499 ~~2500~~ / 7	1 / 5	2000 / 2	1500 / 3
York	2500 / 2	5	4	5

Changes:			Effect on Cost
Add	1 unit	York to Lexington	+ 5
Reduce	1 unit	Bedford to Lexington	- 3
Add	1 unit	Bedford to Boston	+ 7
Reduce	1 unit	York to Boston	- 2
		Net Effect	+ 7

We note that the net effect is the same as the per-unit cost change obtained using the MODI method.

b.

Changes:			Effect on Cost
Add	1 unit	York to Lexington	+ 5
Reduce	1 unit	Bedford to Lexington	- 3
Add	1 unit	Bedford to Boston	+ 7
Reduce	1 unit	York to Boston	- 2
		Net Effect	+ 7

Again the net effect is the same as $e_{34} = +7$ computed using the MODI method

39. a.

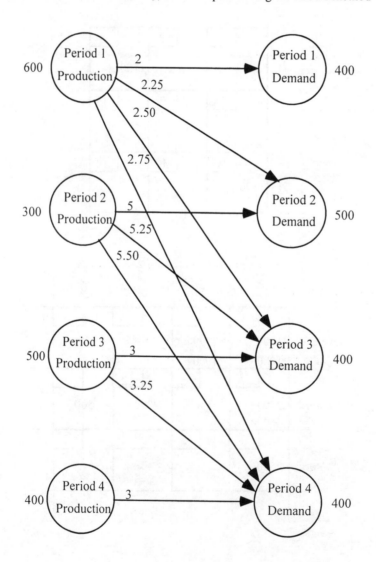

b. All of the cells corresponding to production in one period being used to satisfy demand in a previous period are assigned a "big M" cost.

The initial solution found using the minimum cost method is optimal.

	2	2.25	2.50	2.75	
	400	200			600
	M	5	5.25	5.50	
		300			300
	M	M	3	3.25	
			400		500
	M	M	M	3	
				400	400
	400	500	400	400	

40. Subtract 10 from row 1, 14 from row 2, and 22 from row 3 to obtain:

	1	2	3
Jackson	0	6	22
Ellis	0	8	26
Smith	0	2	12

Subtract 0 from column 1, 2 from column 2, and 12 from column 3 to obtain:

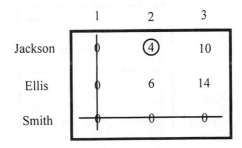

	1	2	3
Jackson	0	④	10
Ellis	0	6	14
Smith	0	0	0

Two lines cover the zeros. The minimum unlined element is 4. Step 3 yields:

	1	2	3
Jackson	0	[0]	6
Ellis	[0]	2	10
Smith	0	0	[0]

Optimal Solution:

Jackson - 2
Ellis   - 1
Smith   - 3

Time requirement is 64 days.

41. Subtract 30 from row 1, 25 from row 2, 23 from row 3, 26 from row 4, and 26 from row 5 to obtain:

	1	2	3	4	5
Red	0	14	8	17	1
White	0	7	20	19	0
Blue	0	17	14	16	6
Green	0	12	11	19	2
Brown	0	8	18	17	2

Subtract 0 from column 1, 7 from column 2, 8 from column 3, 16 from column 4, and 0 from column 5 to obtain:

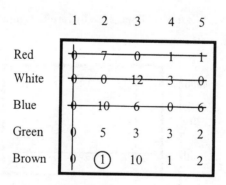

	1	2	3	4	5
Red	0	7	0	1	1
White	0	0	12	3	0
Blue	0	10	6	0	6
Green	0	5	3	3	2
Brown	0	(1)	10	1	2

Four lines cover the zeroes. The minimum unlined element is 1. Step 3 of the Hungarian algorithm yields:

	1	2	3	4	5
Red	1	7	[0]	1	1
White	1	0	12	3	[0]
Blue	1	10	6	[0]	6
Green	[0]	4	2	2	1
Brown	0	[0]	9	0	1

Optimal Solution:

Green to Job 1	$26
Brown to Job 2	34
Red to Job 3	38
Blue to Job 4	39
White to Job 5	25
	$162

Total cost is $16,200.

42. After adding a dummy column, we get an initial assignment matrix.

10	15	9	0
9	18	5	0
6	14	3	0
8	16	6	0

Applying Steps 1 and 2 we obtain:

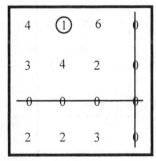

Applying Step 3 followed by Step 2 results in:

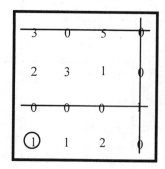

Finally, application of Step's 3 and 2 lead to the optimal solution shown below.

3	0	5	1
1	2	0	0
0	0	0	2
0	0	1	0

Terry: Client 2 (15 days)
Carle: Client 3 (5 days)
McClymonds: Client 1 (6 days)
Higley: Not accepted

                    Total time = 26 days

Note: An alternative optimal solution is Terry: Client 2, Carle: unassigned, McClymonds: Client 3, and Higley: Client 1.

43.   We start with the opportunity loss matrix.

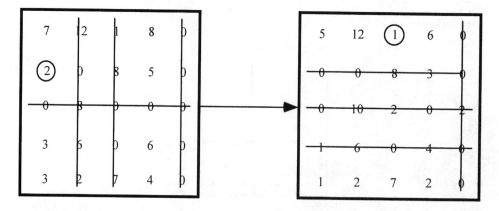

	1	2	3	4	Dummy
Shoe	4	11	0	5	[0]
Toy	0	[0]	8	3	1
Auto	0	10	2	[0]	3
Houseware	1	6	[0]	4	1
Video	[0]	1	6	1	0

Optimal Solution		Profit
Toy :	2	18
Auto :	4	16
Houseware :	3	13
Video :	1	14
		61

44. Subtracting each element from the largest element in its column leads to the opportunity loss matrix.

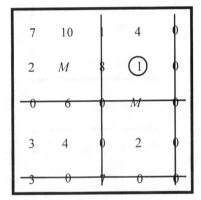

	1	2	3	4	Dummy
Shoe	6	9	1	3	[0]
Toy	1	M	8	[0]	0
Auto	[0]	6	1	M	1
Houseware	2	3	[0]	1	0
Video	3	[0]	8	0	1

Optimal Solution		Profit
Toy :	4	11
Auto :	1	17
Houseware :	3	13
Video :	2	16
		57

45.   Original problem:

44	80	52	60
60	56	40	72
36	60	48	48
52	76	36	40

Opportunity loss matrix;

14	0	0	12
0	24	12	0
24	20	4	24
8	4	16	32

Step 1 (row reduction) and lining out zeros.

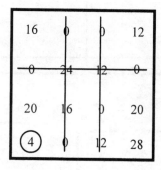

Step 3 followed by Step 2 results in the optimal solution

12	[0]	0	8
0	28	16	[0]
16	16	[0]	16
[0]	0	12	24

Optimal Solution:

Washington to B:	80
Benson to D:	72
Fredricks to C:	48
Hodson to A:	<u>52</u>
Total Sales	252

Chapter 8
Integer Linear Programming

Learning Objectives

1. Be able to recognize the types of situations where integer linear programming problem formulations are desirable.

2. Know the difference between all-integer and mixed integer linear programming problems.

3. Be able to solve small integer linear programs with a graphical solution procedure.

4. Be able to formulate and solve fixed charge, capital budgeting, distribution system, and product design problems as integer linear programs.

5. See how zero-one integer linear variables can be used to handle special situations such as multiple choice, k out of n alternatives, and conditional constraints.

6. Be familiar with the computer solution of MILPs.

7. Understand the following terms:

all-integer	mutually exclusive constraint
mixed integer	k out of n alternatives constraint
zero-one variables	conditional constraint
LP relaxation	co-requisite constraint
multiple choice constraint	

Solutions:

1. a. This is a mixed integer linear program. Its LP Relaxation is

$$\text{Max} \quad 30x_1 + 25x_2$$

s.t.

$$
\begin{aligned}
3x_1 + 1.5x_2 &\leq 400 \\
1.5x_1 + 2x_2 &\leq 250 \\
x_1 + x_2 &\leq 150
\end{aligned}
$$

$$x_1, \; x_2 \geq 0$$

    b. This is an all-integer linear program. Its LP Relaxation just requires dropping the words "and integer" from the last line.

2. a.

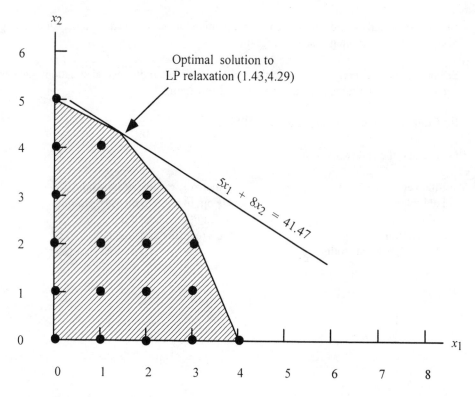

    b. The optimal solution to the LP Relaxation is given by $x_1 = 1.43$, $x_2 = 4.29$ with an objective function value of 41.47.

        Rounding down gives the feasible integer solution $x_1 = 1$, $x_2 = 4$. Its value is 37.

c.

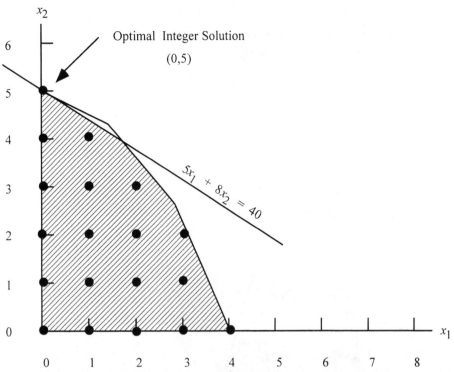

The optimal solution is given by $x_1 = 0$, $x_2 = 5$. Its value is 40. This is not the same solution as that found by rounding down. It provides a 3 unit increase in the value of the objective function.

3.   a.

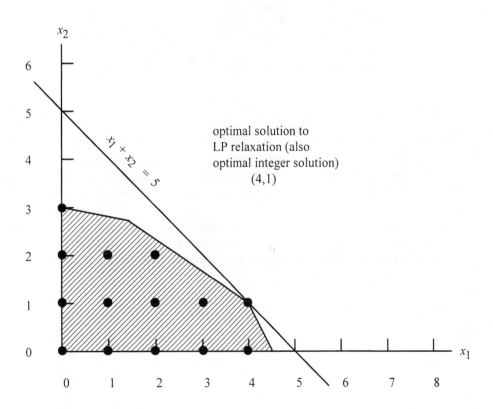

b. The optimal solution to the LP Relaxation is shown on the above graph to be $x_1 = 4$, $x_2 = 1$. Its value is 5.

c. The optimal integer solution is the same as the optimal solution to the LP Relaxation. This is always the case whenever all the variables take on integer values in the optimal solution to the LP Relaxation.

4. a.

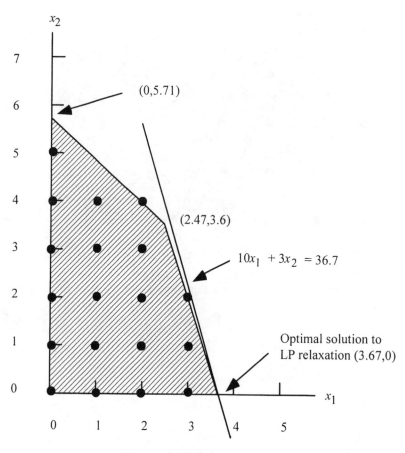

The value of the optimal solution to the LP Relaxation is 36.7 and it is given by $x_1 = 3.67$, $x_2 = 0.0$. Since we have all less-than-or-equal-to constraints with positive coefficients, the solution obtained by "rounding down" the values of the variables in the optimal solution to the LP Relaxation is feasible. The solution obtained by rounding down is $x_1 = 3$, $x_2 = 0$ with value 30.

Thus a lower bound on the value of the optimal solution is given by this feasible integer solution with value 30. An upper bound is given by the value of the LP Relaxation, 36.7. (Actually an upper bound of 36 could be established since no integer solution could have a value between 36 and 37.)

b.

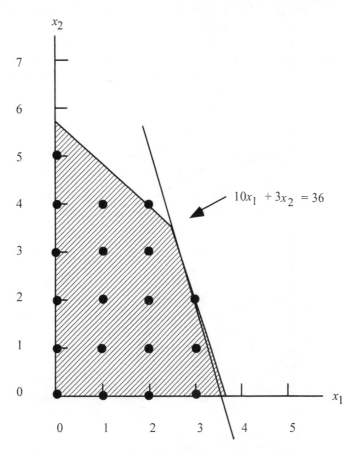

The optimal solution to the ILP is given by $x_1 = 3$, $x_2 = 2$. Its value is 36. The solution found by "rounding down" the solution to the LP relaxation had a value of 30. A 20% increase in this value was obtained by finding the optimal integer solution - a substantial difference if the objective function is being measured in thousands of dollars.

c.

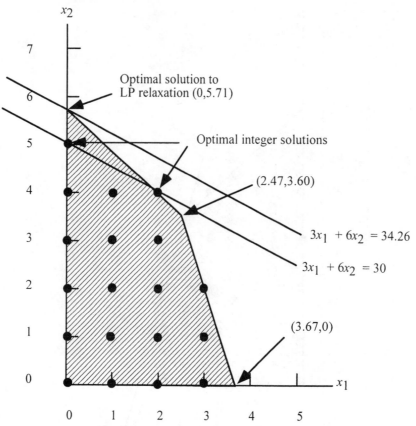

The optimal solution to the LP Relaxation is $x_1 = 0$, $x_2 = 5.71$ with value = 34.26. The solution obtained by "rounding down" is $x_1 = 0$, $x_2 = 5$ with value 30. These two values provide an upper bound of 34.26 and a lower bound of 30 on the value of the optimal integer solution.

There are alternative optimal integer solutions given by $x_1 = 0$, $x_2 = 5$ and $x_1 = 2$, $x_2 = 4$; value is 30. In this case rounding the LP solution down does provide the optimal integer solution.

5. a.

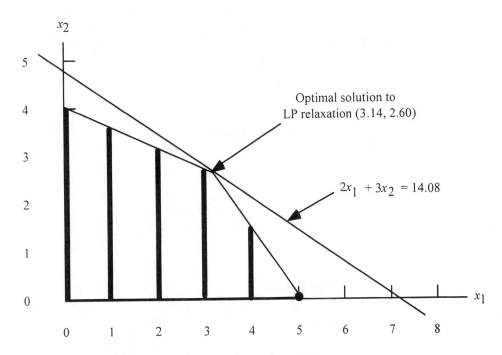

Optimal solution to
LP relaxation (3.14, 2.60)

$2x_1 + 3x_2 = 14.08$

The feasible mixed integer solutions are indicated by the boldface vertical lines in the graph above.

b. The optimal solution to the LP relaxation is given by $x_1 = 3.14$, $x_2 = 2.60$. Its value is 14.08. Rounding the value of x_1 down to find a feasible mixed integer solution yields $x_1 = 3$, $x_2 = 2.60$ with a value of 13.8. This solution is clearly not optimal. With $x_1 = 3$ we can see from the graph that x_2 can be made larger without violating the constraints.

c.

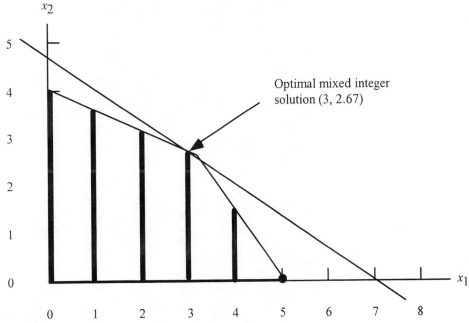

Optimal mixed integer
solution (3, 2.67)

The optimal solution to the MILP is given by $x_1 = 3$, $x_2 = 2.67$. Its value is 14.

6. a.

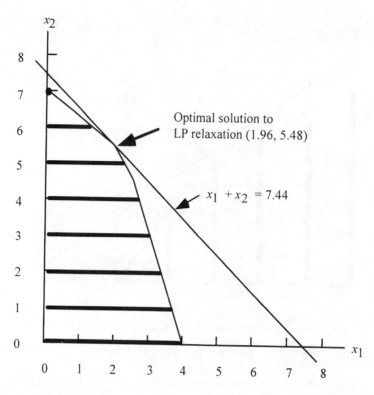

b. The optimal solution to the LP Relaxation is given by $x_1 = 1.96$, $x_2 = 5.48$. Its value is 7.44. Thus an upper bound on the value of the optimal is given by 7.44.

Rounding the value of x_2 down yields a feasible solution of $x_1 = 1.96$, $x_2 = 5$ with value 6.96. Thus a lower bound on the value of the optimal solution is given by 6.96.

c.

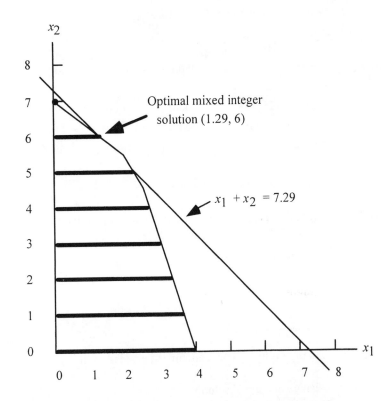

The optimal solution to the MILP is $x_1 = 1.29$, $x_2 = 6$. Its value is 7.29.

The solution $x_1 = 2.22$, $x_2 = 5$ is almost as good. Its value is 7.22.

7. a. $x_1 + x_3 + x_5 + x_6 = 2$

    b. $x_3 - x_5 = 0$

    c. $x_1 + x_4 = 1$

    d. $x_4 \leq x_1$

        $x_4 \leq x_3$

    e. $x_4 \leq x_1$

        $x_4 \leq x_3$

        $x_4 \geq x_1 + x_3 - 1$

8.   a.   Let $x_i = \begin{cases} 1 \text{ if investment alternative } i \text{ is selected} \\ 0 \text{ otherwise} \end{cases}$

$$\max \quad 4000x_1 + 6000x_2 + 10500x_3 + 4000x_4 + 8000x_5 + 3000x_6$$

s.t.

$$3000x_1 + 2500x_2 + 6000x_3 + 2000x_4 + 5000x_5 + 1000x_6 \leq 10,500$$
$$1000x_1 + 3500x_2 + 4000x_3 + 1500x_4 + 1000x_5 + 500x_6 \leq 7,000$$
$$4000x_1 + 3500x_2 + 5000x_3 + 1800x_4 + 4000x_5 + 900x_6 \leq 8,750$$

$$x_1, x_2, x_3, x_4, x_5, x_6 = 0, 1$$

Optimal Solution found using *The Management Scientist* or LINDO

$$x_3 = 1$$
$$x_4 = 1$$
$$x_6 = 1$$

Value = 17,500

b.   The following mutually exclusive constraint must be added to the model.

$x_1 + x_2 \leq 1$ No change in optimal solution.

c.   The following co-requisite constraint must be added to the model in b.

$x_3 - x_4 = 0.$ No change in optimal solution.

9.   a. $x_4 \leq 8000 s_4$

b. $x_6 \leq 6000 s_6$

c. $x_4 \leq 8000 s_4$
$x_6 \leq 6000 s_6$
$s_4 + s_6 = 1$

d.   Min $15 x_4 + 18 x_6 + 2000 s_4 + 3500 s_6$

10. a. Let $x_i = 1$ if a substation is located at site i, 0 otherwise

$$
\begin{array}{l}
\min \quad x_A + x_B + x_C + x_D + x_E + x_F + x_G \\
\text{s.t.}
\end{array}
$$

$x_A +$	$x_B +$	x_C				$+ x_G \geq$	(area 1 covered)
	x_B	$+ x_D$				$\geq$	(area 2 covered)
		x_C	$+ x_E$			$\geq$	(area 3 covered)
			$x_D + x_E +$	x_F		$\geq$	(area 4 covered)
$x_A +$	$x_B +$	$x_C + x_D$		$+ x_F + x_G$		$\geq$	(area 5 covered)
			$x_E +$	$x_F + x_G$		$\geq$	(area 6 covered)
$x_A +$	x_B			$+ x_G$		$\geq$	(area 7 covered)

b. Choose locations B and E.

11. a. Let $P_i =$ units of product i produced

$$
\begin{array}{l}
\text{Max} \quad 25P_1 + 28P_2 + 30P_3 \\
\text{s.t.}
\end{array}
$$

$$
\begin{array}{rcrcrcl}
1.5P_1 &+& 3P_2 &+& 2P_3 &\leq& 450 \\
2P_1 &+& 1P_2 &+& 2.5P_3 &\leq& 350 \\
.25P_1 &+& .25P_2 &+& .25P_3 &\leq& 50 \\
\end{array}
$$

$$P_1,\ P_2,\ P_3 \geq 0$$

b. The optimal solution is

$$
\begin{array}{l}
P_1 = 60 \\
P_2 = 80 \qquad \text{Value} = 5540 \\
P_3 = 60
\end{array}
$$

This solution provides a profit of $5540.

c. Since the solution in part (b) calls for producing all three products, the total setup cost is

$$\$1550 = \$400 + \$550 + \$600.$$

Subtracting the total setup cost from the profit in part (b), we see that

$$\text{Profit} = \$5540 - 1550 = \$3990$$

d. We introduce a 0-1 variable y_i that is one if any quantity of product i is produced and zero otherwise.

With the maximum production quantities provided by management, we obtain 3 new constraints:

$$
\begin{array}{l}
P_1 \leq 175y_1 \\
P_2 \leq 150y_2 \\
P_3 \leq 140y_3
\end{array}
$$

Bringing the variables to the left-hand side of the constraints, we obtain the following fixed charge formulation of the Hart problem.

$$\text{Max} \quad 25P_1 + 28P_2 + 30P_3 - 400y_1 - 550y_2 - 600y_3$$

s.t.

$$
\begin{array}{rcl}
1.5P_1 + 3P_2 + 2P_3 & \le & 450 \\
2P_1 + 1P_2 + 2.5P_3 & \le & 350 \\
.25P_1 + .25P_2 + .25P_3 & \le & 50 \\
P_1 \qquad\qquad - 175y_1 & \le & 0 \\
P_2 \qquad\qquad - 150y_2 & \le & 0 \\
P_3 \qquad\qquad - 140y_3 & \le & 0
\end{array}
$$

$$P_1, P_2, P_3 \ge 0; \quad y_1, y_2, y_3 = 0, 1$$

e. The optimal solution using The Management Scientist is

$$
\begin{array}{lll}
P_1 = 100 & y_1 = 1 & \\
P_2 = 100 & y_2 = 1 & \text{Value} = 4350 \\
P_3 = 0 & y_3 = 0 &
\end{array}
$$

The profit associated with this solution is \$4350. This is an improvement of \$360 over the solution in part (c).

12. a. Constraints

$$
\begin{array}{l}
P \le 15 + 15Y_P \\
D \le 15 + 15Y_D \\
J \le 15 + 15Y_J \\
Y_P + Y_D + Y_J \le 1
\end{array}
$$

b. We must add a constraint requiring 60 tons to be shipped and an objective function.

$$\text{Min} \quad 100Y_P + 85Y_D + 50Y_J$$

s.t.

$$
\begin{array}{rcl}
P + D + J & = & 60 \\
P & \le & 15 + 15Y_P \\
D & \le & 15 + 15Y_D \\
J & \le & 15 + 15Y_J \\
Y_P + Y_D + Y_J & \le & 1
\end{array}
$$

$$P, D, J \ge 0$$
$$Y_P, Y_D, Y_J = 0, 1$$

Optimal Solution: $P = 15, D = 15, J = 30$
$$Y_P = 0, Y_D = 0, Y_J = 1$$
$$\text{Value} = 50$$

13. a. One just needs to add the following multiple choice constraint to the problem.

$$y_1 + y_2 = 1$$

New Optimal Solution: $y_1 = 1$, $y_3 = 1$, $x_{12} = 10$, $x_{31} = 30$, $x_{52} = 10$, $x_{53} = 20$

Value $= 940$

b. Since one plant is already located in St. Louis, it is only necessary to add the following constraint to the model

$$y_3 + y_4 \leq 1$$

New Optimal Solution: $y_4 = 1$, $x_{42} = 20$, $x_{43} = 20$, $x_{51} = 30$

Value $= 860$

14. a. Let 1 denote the Michigan plant
2 denote the first New York plant
3 denote the second New York plant
4 denote the Ohio plant
5 denote the California plant

It is not possible to meet needs by modernizing only one plant.

The following table shows the options which involve modernizing two plants.

		Plant			Transmission Capacity	Engine Block Capacity	Feasible ?	Cost
1	2	3	4	5				
√	√				700	1300	No	
√		√			1100	900	Yes	60
√			√		900	1400	Yes	65
√				√	600	700	No	
	√	√			1200	1200	Yes	70
	√		√		1000	1700	Yes	75
	√			√	700	1000	No	
		√	√		1400	1300	Yes	75
		√		√	1100	600	No	
			√	√	900	1100	Yes	60

b. Modernize plants 1 and 3 or plants 4 and 5.

c. Let $x_i = \begin{cases} 1 \text{ if plant } i \text{ is modernized} \\ 0 \text{ if plant } i \text{ is not modernized} \end{cases}$

$$\begin{array}{llllllllll} \text{Min} & 25x_1 & + & 35x_2 & + & 35x_3 & + & 40x_4 & + & 25x_5 \\ \text{s.t.} \end{array}$$

$$\begin{array}{llllllllllll} 300x_1 & + & 400x_2 & + & 800x_3 & + & 600x_4 & + & 300x_5 & \geq & 900 & \text{Transmissions} \\ 500x_1 & + & 800x_2 & + & 400x_3 & + & 900x_4 & + & 200x_5 & \geq & 900 & \text{Engine Blocks} \end{array}$$

d. Optimal Solution: $x_1 = x_3 = 1$.

15. a. Let $x_i = \begin{cases} 1 \text{ if a principal place of business in in county } i \\ 0 \text{ otherwise} \end{cases}$

$y_i = \begin{cases} 1 \text{ if county } i \text{ is not served} \\ 0 \text{ if county } i \text{ is served} \end{cases}$

The objective function for an integer programming model calls for minimizing the population not served.

$$\min \quad 195y_1 + 96y_2 + \bullet\bullet\bullet + 175\, y_{13}$$

There are 13 constraints needed; each is written so that y_i will be forced to equal one whenever it is not possible to do business in county i.

$$\begin{array}{lllllllllllllll} \text{Constraint 1:} & x_1 & + & x_2 & + & x_3 & & & & & & & + & y_1 & \geq & 1 \\ \text{Constraint 2:} & x_1 & + & x_2 & + & x_3 & + & x_4 & + & x_6 & + & x_7 & + & y_2 & \geq & 1 \\ & \bullet & & & & & & & & \bullet & & & & \bullet \\ & \bullet & & & & & & & & \bullet & & & & \bullet \\ & \bullet & & & & & & & & \bullet & & & & \bullet \\ \text{Constraint 13:} & & & x_{11} & + & x_{12} & + & x_{13} & & & & & + & y_{13} & \geq & 1 \end{array}$$

One more constraint must be added to reflect the requirement that only one principal place of business may be established.

$$x_1 + x_2 + \bullet\bullet\bullet + x_{13} = 1$$

The optimal solution has a principal place of business in County 11 with an optimal value of 739,000. A population of 739,000 cannot be served by this solution. Counties 1-5 and 10 will not be served.

b. The only change necessary in the integer programming model for part a is that the right-hand side of the last constraint is increased from 1 to 2.

$$x_1 + x_2 + \bullet\bullet\bullet + x_{13} = 2.$$

The optimal solution has principal places of business in counties 3 and 11 with an optimal value of 76,000. Only County 10 with a population of 76,000 is not served.

c. It is not the best location if only one principal place of business can be established; 1,058,000 customers in the region cannot be served. However, 642,000 can be served and if there is no opportunity to obtain a principal place of business in County 11, this may be a good start. Perhaps later there will be an opportunity in County 11.

16. a.

$$\min \; 105x_9 + 105x_{10} + 105x_{11} + 32y_9 + 32y_{10} + 32y_{11} + 32y_{12} + 32y_1 + 32y_2 + 32y_3$$

$$
\begin{aligned}
x_9 && + && y_9 &&&&&&&&&&&& \ge 6 \\
x_9 + && x_{10} && + && y_9 + && y_{10} &&&&&&&&&&& \ge 4 \\
x_9 + && x_{10} + && x_{11} + && y_9 + && y_{10} + && y_{11} &&&&&&&& \ge 8 \\
x_9 + && x_{10} + && x_{11} + && y_9 + && y_{10} + && y_{11} + && y_{12} &&&&&& \ge 10 \\
&& x_{10} + && x_{11} && + && y_{10} + && y_{11} + && y_{12} + && y_1 &&&& \ge 9 \\
x_9 && && x_{11} && && + && y_{11} + && y_{12} + && y_1 + && y_2 && \ge 6 \\
x_9 + && x_{10} && && && && + && y_{12} + && y_1 + && y_2 + && y_3 \ge 4 \\
x_9 + && x_{10} + && x_{11} && && && && + && y_1 + && y_2 + && y_3 \ge 7 \\
&& x_{10} + && x_{11} && && && && && + && y_2 + && y_3 \ge 6 \\
&& && x_{11} && && && && && && && + && y_3 \ge 6
\end{aligned}
$$

$x_i, \; y_j \ge 0$ and integer for $i = 9, 10, 11$ and $j = 9, 10, 11, 12, 1, 2, 3$

b. Solution to LP Relaxation obtained using LINDO/PC:

$y_9 = 6$	$y_{12} = 6$	$y_3 = 6$	All other variables = 0.
$y_{11} = 2$	$y_1 = 1$		Cost: $672.

c. The solution to the LP Relaxation is integral therefore it is the optimal solution to the integer program.

A difficulty with this solution is that only part-time employees are used; this may cause problems with supervision, etc. The large surpluses from 5, 12-1 (4 employees), and 3-4 (9 employees) indicate times when the tellers are not needed for customer service and may be reassigned to other tasks.

d. Add the following constraints to the formulation in part (a).

$$x_9 \ge 1$$
$$x_{11} \ge 1$$
$$x_9 + x_{10} + x_{11} \ge 5$$

The new optimal solution, which has a daily cost of $909 is

$x_9 = 1$	$y_9 = 5$
$x_{11} = 4$	$y_{12} = 5$
	$y_3 = 2$

There is now much less reliance on part-time employees. The new solution uses 5 full-time employees and 12 part-time employees; the previous solution used no full-time employees and 21 part-time employees.

17. a. Let $x_1 = 1$ if PPB is Lorain, 0 otherwise
   $x_2 = 1$ if PPB is Huron, 0 otherwise
   $x_3 = 1$ if PPB is Richland, 0 otherwise
   $x_4 = 1$ if PPB is Ashland, 0 otherwise
   $x_5 = 1$ if PPB is Wayne, 0 otherwise
   $x_6 = 1$ if PPB is Medina, 0 otherwise
   $x_7 = 1$ if PPB is Knox, 0 otherwise

Min $\quad x_1 + x_2 + x_3 + x_4 + x_5 + x_6 + x_7$
s.t.

$x_1 + x_2 + x_4 + x_6$	≥ 1	(Lorain)
$x_1 + x_2 + x_3 + x_4$	≥ 1	(Huron)
$x_2 + x_3 + x_4 + x_7$	≥ 1	(Richland)
$x_1 + x_2 + x_3 + x_4 + x_5 + x_6 + x_7$	≥ 1	(Ashland)
$x_4 + x_5 + x_6$	≥ 1	(Wayne)
$x_1 + x_4 + x_5 + x_6$	≥ 1	(Medina)
$x_3 + x_4 + x_7$	≥ 1	(Knox)

b. Locating a principal place of business in Ashland county will permit Ohio Trust to do business in all 7 counties.

18. a. Add the part-worths for Antonio's Pizza for each consumer in the Salem Foods' consumer panel.

Consumer	Overall Preference for Antonio's
1	$2 + 6 + 17 + 27 = 52$
2	$7 + 15 + 26 + 1 = 49$
3	$5 + 8 + 7 + 16 = 36$
4	$20 + 20 + 14 + 29 = 83$
5	$8 + 6 + 20 + 5 = 39$
6	$17 + 11 + 30 + 12 = 70$
7	$19 + 12 + 25 + 23 = 79$
8	$9 + 4 + 16 + 30 = 59$

b. Let $l_{ij} = 1$ if level i is chosen for attribute j, 0 otherwise
   $y_k = 1$ if consumer k chooses the Salem brand, 0 otherwise

Max $\quad y_1 + y_2 + y_3 + y_4 + y_5 + y_6 + y_7 + y_8$
s.t.

$$11l_{11} + 2l_{21} + 6l_{12} + 7l_{22} + 3l_{13} + 17l_{23} + 26l_{14} + 27l_{24} + 8l_{34} - 52y_1 \geq 1$$
$$11l_{11} + 7l_{21} + 15l_{12} + 17l_{22} + 16l_{13} + 26l_{23} + 14l_{14} + 1l_{24} + 10l_{34} - 49y_2 \geq 1$$
$$7l_{11} + 5l_{21} + 8l_{12} + 14l_{22} + 16l_{13} + 7l_{23} + 29l_{14} + 16l_{24} + 19l_{34} - 36y_3 \geq 1$$
$$13l_{11} + 20l_{21} + 20l_{12} + 17l_{22} + 17l_{13} + 14l_{23} + 25l_{14} + 29l_{24} + 10l_{34} - 83y_4 \geq 1$$
$$2l_{11} + 8l_{21} + 6l_{12} + 11l_{22} + 30l_{13} + 20l_{23} + 15l_{14} + 5l_{24} + 12l_{34} - 39y_5 \geq 1$$
$$12l_{11} + 17l_{21} + 11l_{12} + 9l_{22} + 2l_{13} + 30l_{23} + 22l_{14} + 12l_{24} + 20l_{34} - 70y_6 \geq 1$$
$$9l_{11} + 19l_{21} + 12l_{12} + 16l_{22} + 16l_{13} + 25l_{23} + 30l_{14} + 23l_{24} + 19l_{34} - 79y_7 \geq 1$$
$$5l_{11} + 9l_{21} + 4l_{12} + 14l_{22} + 23l_{13} + 16l_{23} + 16l_{14} + 30l_{24} + 3l_{34} - 59y_8 \geq 1$$
$$l_{11} + l_{21} = 1$$
$$l_{12} + l_{22} = 1$$
$$l_{13} + l_{23} = 1$$
$$l_{14} + l_{24} + l_{34} = 1$$

The optimal solution shows $l_{21} = l_{22} = l_{23} = l_{24} = 1$. This calls for a pizza with a thick crust, a cheese blend, a chunky sauce, and medium sausage. With $y_1 = y_2 = y_3 = y_5 = y_7 = y_8 = 1$, we see that 6 of the 8 people in the consumer panel will prefer this pizza to Antonio's.

19. a. Let $l_{ij} = 1$ if level i is chosen for attribute j, 0 otherwise
            $y_k = 1$ if child k prefers the new cereal design, 0 otherwise

The share of choices problem to solve is given below:

Max $y_1 + y_2 + y_3 + y_4 + y_5 + y_6$
s.t.

$$
\begin{array}{rrrrrrrrl}
15l_{11} + & 35l_{21} + & 30l_{12} + & 40l_{22} + & 25l_{32} + & 15l_{13} + & 9l_{23} - & 75y_1 & \geq 1 \\
30l_{11} + & 20l_{21} + & 40l_{12} + & 35l_{22} + & 25l_{32} + & 8l_{13} + & 11l_{23} - & 75y_2 & \geq 1 \\
40l_{11} + & 25l_{21} + & 20l_{12} + & 40l_{22} + & 10l_{32} + & 7l_{13} + & 14l_{23} - & 75y_3 & \geq 1 \\
35l_{11} + & 30l_{21} + & 25l_{12} + & 20l_{22} + & 30l_{32} + & 15l_{13} + & 18l_{23} - & 75y_4 & \geq 1 \\
25l_{11} + & 40l_{21} + & 40l_{12} + & 20l_{22} + & 35l_{32} + & 18l_{13} + & 14l_{23} - & 75y_5 & \geq 1 \\
20l_{11} + & 25l_{21} + & 20l_{12} + & 35l_{22} + & 30l_{32} + & 9l_{13} + & 16l_{23} - & 75y_6 & \geq 1 \\
30l_{11} + & 15l_{21} + & 25l_{12} + & 40l_{22} + & 40l_{32} + & 20l_{13} + & 11l_{23} - & 75y_7 & \geq 1 \\
l_{11} + & l_{21} & & & & & & & = 1 \\
& & l_{12} + & l_{22} + & l_{32} & & & & = 1 \\
& & & & & l_{13} + & l_{23} & & = 1 \\
\end{array}
$$

The optimal solution obtained using LINDO on Excel shows $l_{11} = l_{32} = l_{13} = 1$. This indicates that a cereal with a low wheat/corn ratio, artificial sweetener, and no flavor bits will maximize the share of choices.

The optimal solution also has $y_4 = y_5 = y_7 = 1$ which indicates that children 4, 5, and 7 will prefer this cereal.

    b. The coefficients for the y_i variable must be changed to -70 in constraints 1-4 and to -80 in constraints 5-7.

The new optimal solution has $l_{21} = l_{12} = l_{23} = 1$. This is a cereal with a high wheat/corn ratio, a sugar sweetener, and no flavor bits. Four children will prefer this design: 1, 2, 4, and 5.

20. a. Objective function changes to

        Min $25x_1 + 40x_2 + 40x_3 + 40x_4 + 25x_5$

    b. $x_4 = x_5 = 1$; modernize the Ohio and California plants.

    c. Add the constraint $x_2 + x_3 = 1$

    d. $x_1 = x_3 = 1$; modernize the Michigan plant and the first New York plant.

21. a. Let $x_i = \begin{cases} 1 \text{ if a camera is located at opening } i \\ 0 \text{ if not} \end{cases}$

$$\min x_1 + x_2 + x_3 + x_4 + x_5 + x_6 + x_7 + x_8 + x_9 + x_{10} + x_{11} + x_{12} + x_{13}$$
s.t.

$$
\begin{array}{lll}
x_1 + x_4 + x_6 & \geq 1 & \text{Room 1} \\
x_6 + x_8 + x_{12} & \geq 1 & \text{Room 2} \\
x_1 + x_2 + x_3 & \geq 1 & \text{Room 3} \\
x_3 + x_4 + x_5 + x_7 & \geq 1 & \text{Room 4} \\
x_7 + x_8 + x_9 + x_{10} & \geq 1 & \text{Room 5} \\
x_{10} + x_{12} + x_{13} & \geq 1 & \text{Room 6} \\
x_2 + x_5 + x_9 + x_{11} & \geq 1 & \text{Room 7} \\
x_{11} + x_{13} & \geq 1 & \text{Room 8}
\end{array}
$$

b. $x_1 = x_5 = x_8 = x_{13} = 1$. Thus, cameras should be located at 4 openings: 1, 5, 8, and 13.
An alternative optimal solution is $x_1 = x_7 = x_{11} = x_{12} = 1$.

c. Change the constraint for room 7 to $x_2 + x_5 + x_9 + x_{11} \geq 2$

d. $x_3 = x_6 = x_9 = x_{11} = x_{12} = 1$. Thus, cameras should be located at openings 3, 6, 9, 11, and 12.

An alternate optimal solution is $x_2 = x_4 = x_6 = x_{10} = x_{11} = 1$. Optimal Value = 5

22. Note that Team Size $= x_1 + x_2 + x_3$

The following two constraints will guarantee that the team size will be 3, 5, or 7.

$$
\begin{array}{l}
x_1 + x_2 + x_3 = 3y_1 + 5y_2 + 7y_3 \\
y_1 + y_2 + y_3 = 1
\end{array}
$$

Of course, the variables in the first constraint will need to be brought to the left hand side if a computer solution is desired.

23. a. A mixed integer linear program can be set up to solve this problem. Binary variables are used to indicate whether or not we setup to produce the subassemblies.

Let SB   = 1 if bases are produced; 0 if not
     STVC   = 1 if TV cartridges are produced; 0 if not
     SVCRC = 1 if VCR cartridges are produced; 0 if not
     STVP   = 1 if TV keypads are produced; 0 if not
     SVCRP = 1 if VCR keypads are produced; 0 if not
     BM   = No. of bases manufactured
     BP   = No. of bases purchased
     TVCM   = No. of TV cartridges made

     •
     •
     •

     VCRPP = No. of VCR keypads purchased

A mixed integer linear programming model for solving this problem follows. There are 11 constraints. Constraints (1) to (5) are to satisfy demand. Constraint (6) reflects the limitation on manufacturing time. Finally, constraints (7) - (11) are constraints not allowing production unless the setup variable equals 1. Variables SB, STVC, SVCRC, STVP, and SVCRP must be specified as 0/1.

```
LINEAR PROGRAMMING PROBLEM

MIN
0.4BM+2.9TVCM+3.15VCRCM+0.3TVPM+0.55VCRPM+0.65BP+3.45TVCP+3.7VCRCP+
0.5TVPP+0
.7VCRPP+1000SB+1200STVC+1900SVCRC+1500STVP+1500SVCRP

    S.T.

        1)   1BM+1BP=12000
        2)   +1TVCM+1TVCP=7000
        3)   +1VCRCM+1VCRCP=5000
        4)   +1TVPM+1TVPP=7000
        5)   +1VCRPM+1VCRPP=5000
        6)   0.9BM+2.2TVCM+3VCRCM+0.8TVPM+1VCRPM<30000
        7)   1BM-12000SB<0
        8)   +1TVCM-7000STVC<0
        9)   +1VCRCM-5000SVCRC<0
        10)  +1TVPM-7000STVP<0
        11)  +1VCRPM-5000SVCRP<0

OPTIMAL SOLUTION

Objective Function Value =     52800.00

        Variable              Value
        --------------        ---------------
              BM              12000.000
            TVCM               7000.000
           VCRCM                  0.000
            TVPM                  0.000
           VCRPM                  0.000
              BP                  0.000
            TVCP                  0.000
           VCRCP               5000.000
            TVPP               7000.000
           VCRPP               5000.000
              SB                  1.000
            STVC                  1.000
           SVCRC                  0.000
            STVP                  0.000
           SVCRP                  0.000
```

Constraint	Slack/Surplus
1	0.000
2	0.000
3	0.000
4	0.000
5	0.000
6	3800.000
7	0.000
8	0.000
9	0.000
10	0.000
11	0.000

b. This part can be solved by changing appropriate coefficients in the formulation for part (a). The coefficient of SVCRC becomes 3000 and the coefficient of VCRCM becomes 2.6 in the objective function. Also, the coefficient of VCRCM becomes 2.5 in constraint (6). The new optimal solution is shown below.

OPTIMAL SOLUTION

Objective Function Value =   52300.00

Variable	Value
BM	0.000
TVCM	7000.000
VCRCM	5000.000
TVPM	0.000
VCRPM	0.000
BP	12000.000
TVCP	0.000
VCRCP	0.000
TVPP	7000.000
VCRPP	5000.000
SB	0.000
STVC	1.000
SVCRC	1.000
STVP	0.000
SVCRP	0.000

Constraint	Slack/Surplus
1	0.000
2	0.000
3	0.000
4	0.000
5	0.000
6	2100.000
7	0.000
8	0.000
9	0.000
10	0.000
11	0.000

24. a. Variable for movie 1: $x_{111}, x_{112}, x_{121}$

 b. Only 1 schedule for movie 1: $x_{111} + x_{112} + x_{121} \leq 1$

 c. Only 1 schedule for movie 5: $x_{531} + x_{532} + x_{533} + x_{541} + x_{542} + x_{543} + x_{551} + x_{552} + x_{561} \leq 1$

 d. Only 2-screens are available at the theater.

 Week 1 constraint: $x_{111} + x_{112} + x_{211} + x_{212} + x_{311} \leq 2$

 e. Week 3 constraint:

 $$x_{213} + x_{222} + x_{231} + x_{422} + x_{431} + x_{531} + x_{532} + x_{533} + x_{631} + x_{632} + x_{633} \leq 2$$

25. a. Let $x_i = \begin{cases} 1 \text{ if a service facility is located in city } i \\ 0 \text{ otherwise} \end{cases}$

 $$\min \quad x_1 + x_2 + x_3 + x_4 + x_5 + x_6 + x_7 + x_8 + x_9 + x_{10} + x_{11} + x_{12}$$

 s.t.

(Boston)	$x_1 + x_2 + x_3$	≥ 1
(New York)	$x_1 + x_2 + x_3 + x_4 + x_5 + x_6$	≥ 1
(Philadelphia)	$x_1 + x_2 + x_3 + x_4 + x_5 + x_6 + x_7$	≥ 1
(Baltimore)	$x_2 + x_3 + x_4 + x_5 + x_6 + x_7$	≥ 1
(Washington)	$x_2 + x_3 + x_4 + x_5 + x_6 + x_7$	≥ 1
(Richmond)	$x_2 + x_3 + x_4 + x_5 + x_6 + x_7 + x_8$	≥ 1
(Raleigh)	$x_3 + x_4 + x_5 + x_6 + x_7 + x_8 + x_9$	≥ 1
(Florence)	$x_6 + x_7 + x_8 + x_9 + x_{10}$	≥ 1
(Savannah)	$x_7 + x_8 + x_9 + x_{10} + x_{11}$	≥ 1
(Jacksonville)	$x_8 + x_9 + x_{10} + x_{11}$	≥ 1
(Tampa)	$x_9 + x_{10} + x_{11} + x_{12} \geq 1$	
(Miami)	$x_{11} + x_{12} \geq 1$	

 $x_i = 0, 1$

 b. 3 service facilities: Philadelphia, Savannah and Tampa.

 Note: alternate optimal solution is New York, Richmond and Tampa.

 c. 4 service facilities: New York, Baltimore, Savannah and Tampa.

 Note: alternate optimal solution: Boston, Philadelphia, Florence and Tampa.

Chapter 9
Network Models

Learning Objectives

1. Know the basic characteristics of the shortest route problem.

2. Know the basic characteristics of the minimal spanning tree problem.

3. Know the basic characteristics of the maximal flow problem.

4. Be able to use network-based algorithms to solve shortest route, and minimal spanning tree problems.

5. Be able to formulate and solve a maximal flow problem as a linear program.

6. Understand the following terms:

   shortest route
   tentative label
   permanent label
   spanning tree
   minimal spanning tree
   maximal flow
   source node
   sink node
   arc flow capacities

Solutions:

1.

Node	Shortest Route From Node 1	Distance
2	1-2	7
3	1-3	9
4	1-2-5-64	17
5	1-2-5	12
6	1-2-5-6	14
7	1-2-5-67	17

2.

Node	Shortest Route From Node 7	Distance
1	7-6-5-21	17
2	7-6-5-2	10
3	7-6-5-3	9
4	7-6-4	6
5	7-6-5	5
6	7-6	3

3.

Node	Shortest Route From Node 1	Time
2	-2	20
3	1-3	16
4	1-2-4	32
5	1-3-5	31
6	1-3-5-6	36
7	1-2-4-7	43

4.

Node	Shortest Route From Node 1	Distance
2	-2	3
3	1-3	4
4	1-4	3
5	1-4-5	6
6	1-4-5-6	8
7	1-4-5-67	11
8	1-4-5-6-8	10

5.   Shortest route: 1-3-5-8-10
       Total Distance: 19.

6.

Node	Shortest Route From Node C	Distance
1	C-1	35
2	C-2	20
3	C-3	20
4	C-4	30
5	C-3-5	55
6	C-3-6	50
7	C-3-8-7	100
8	C-3-8	80
9	C-4-109	85
10	C-4-10	70

7.   Shortest route: 1-5-4-6-7-10

Time = 10 + 4 + 3 + 4 + 4 = 25 minutes

8.   Shortest route: 1-2-8-10-11

Value = 15

Note: an alternative optimal solution is: 1-4-3-7-6-9-11

9.   Shortest route or minimum-cost policy: 0-2-3-4

Total cost is $2500

10.

Start Node	End Node	Distance
1	6	2
6	7	3
7	8	1
7	10	2
10	9	3
9	4	2
9	3	3
3	2	1
4	5	3
7	11	4
8	13	4
14	15	2
15	12	3
14	13	4

Total length = 37

11.

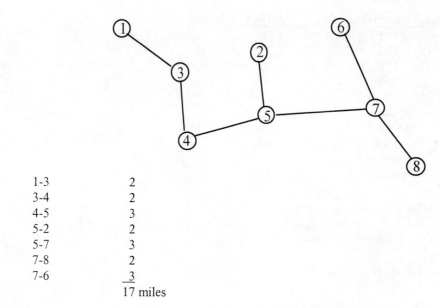

1-3	2
3-4	2
4-5	3
5-2	2
5-7	3
7-8	2
7-6	3
	17 miles

12.

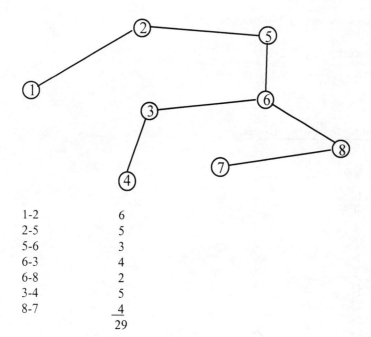

1-2	6
2-5	5
5-6	3
6-3	4
6-8	2
3-4	5
8-7	4
	29

13.

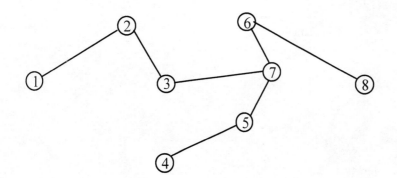

Minimum length of connections = 2 + 0.5 + 1 + 1 + 2 + 0.5 + 1 = 8
8000 feet

14.

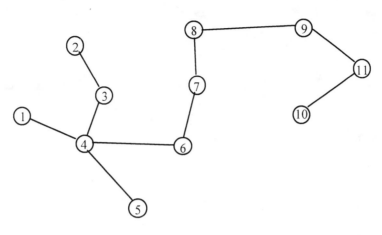

Minimum length of cable lines = 2 + 2 + 2 + 3 + 3 + 2 + 3 + 3 + 4 + 4 = 28 miles

15.   The capacitated transshipment problem to solve is given:

Max x_{61}
s.t.

$$x_{12} + x_{13} + x_{14} - x_{61} = 0$$
$$x_{24} + x_{25} - x_{12} - x_{42} = 0$$
$$x_{34} + x_{36} - x_{13} - x_{43} = 0$$
$$x_{42} + x_{43} + x_{45} + x_{46} - x_{14} - x_{24} - x_{34} - x_{54} = 0$$
$$x_{54} + x_{56} - x_{25} - x_{45} = 0$$
$$x_{61} - x_{36} + x_{46} - x_{56} = 0$$

$$x_{12} \le 2 \qquad x_{13} \le 6 \qquad x_{14} \le 3$$
$$x_{24} \le 1 \qquad x_{25} \le 4$$
$$x_{34} \le 3 \qquad x_{36} \le 2$$
$$x_{42} \le 1 \qquad x_{43} \le 3 \qquad x_{45} \le 1 \qquad x_{46} \le 3$$
$$x_{54} \le 1 \qquad x_{56} \le 6$$

$x_{ij} \ge 0$ for all i, j

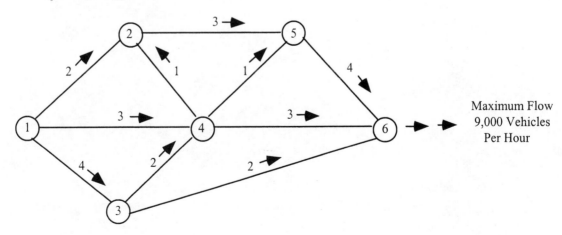

Maximum Flow
9,000 Vehicles
Per Hour

The system cannot accommodate a flow of 10,000 vehicles per hour.

16.

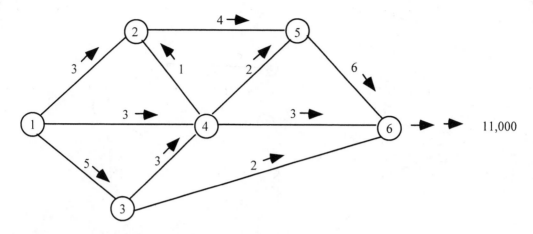

17. The maximum number of messages that may be sent is 10,000.

18. a. 10,000 gallons per hour or 10 hours

   b. Flow reduced to 9,000 gallons per hour; 11.1 hours.

19. Current Max Flow = 6,000 vehicles/hour.

   With arc 3-4 at a 3,000 unit/hour flow capacity, total system flow is increased to 8,000 vehicles/hour. Increasing arc 3-4 to 2,000 units/hour will also increase system to 8,000 vehicles/hour. Thus a 2,000 unit/hour capacity is recommended for this arc.

20. Maximal Flow = 23 gallons / minute. Five gallons will flow from node 3 to node 5.

Chapter 10
Project Scheduling: PERT/CPM

Learning Objectives

1.   Understand the role and application of PERT/CPM for project scheduling.

2.   Learn how to define a project in terms of activities such that a network can be used to describe the project.

3.   Know how to compute the critical path and the project completion time.

4.   Know how to convert optimistic, most probable, and pessimistic time estimates into expected activity time estimates.

5.   With uncertain activity times, be able to compute the probability of the project being completed by a specific time.

6.   Understand the concept and need for crashing.

7.   Be able to formulate the crashing problem as a linear programming model.

8.   Learn how to schedule and control project costs with PERT/Cost.

9.   Understand the following terms:

network	beta distribution
PERT/CPM	path
activities	critical path
event	critical activities
optimistic time	slack
most probable time	crashing
pessimistic time	

Solutions:

1.

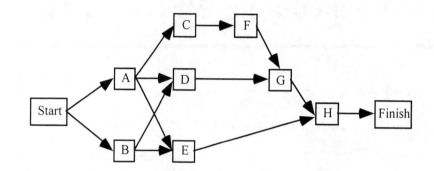

2.

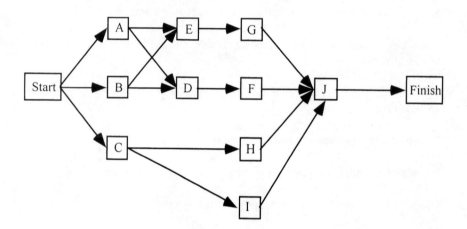

3.

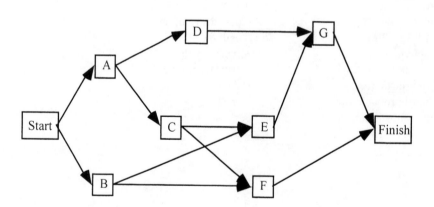

4. a.

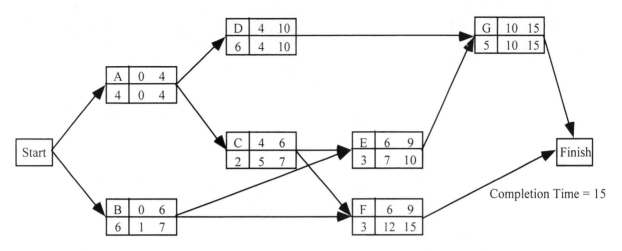

Critical Path: A-D-G

b. The critical path activities require 15 months to complete. Thus the project should be completed in 1-1/2 years.

5.

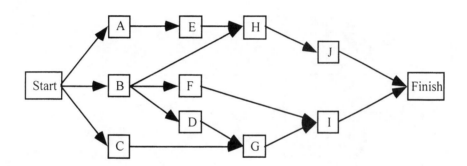

6.

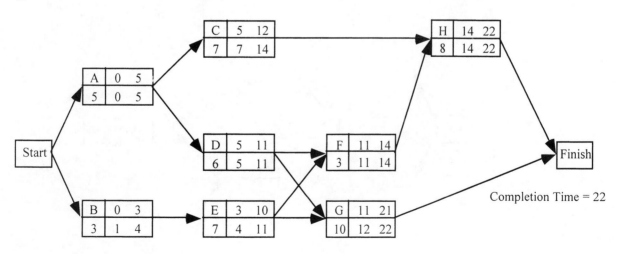

a. Critical path: A-D-F-H

b. 22 weeks

c. No, it is a critical activity

d. Yes, 2 weeks

e. Schedule for activity E:

Earliest Start	3
Latest Start	4
Earliest Finish	10
Latest Finish	11

7. a.

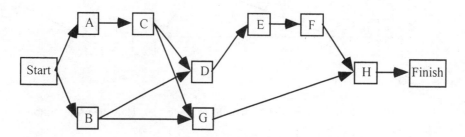

b. B-D-E-F-H

c. 21 weeks

Activity	Earliest Start	Latest Start	Earliest Finish	Latest Finish	Slack	Critical Activity
A	0	1	3	4	1	
B	0	0	6	6	0	Yes
C	3	4	5	6	1	
D	6	6	11	11	0	Yes
E	11	11	15	15	0	Yes
F	15	15	18	18	0	Yes
G	6	9	15	18	3	
H	18	18	21	21	0	Yes

8. a.

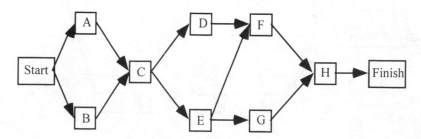

b. B-C-E-F-H

c.

Activity	Earliest Start	Latest Start	Earliest Finish	Latest Finish	Slack	Critical Activity
A	0	2	6	8	2	
B	0	0	8	8	0	Yes
C	8	8	20	20	0	Yes
D	20	22	24	26	2	
E	20	20	26	26	0	Yes
F	26	26	41	41	0	Yes
G	26	29	38	41	3	
H	41	41	49	49	0	Yes

d. Yes. Project Completion Time 49 weeks.

9. a. A-C-E-H-I

b.

Activity	Earliest Start	Latest Start	Earliest Finish	Latest Finish	Slack	Critical Activity
A	0	0	9	9	0	Yes
B	0	9	6	15	9	
C	9	9	15	15	0	Yes
D	9	12	12	15	3	
E	15	15	15	15	0	Yes
F	15	16	18	19	1	
G	18	19	20	21	1	
H	15	15	21	21	0	Yes
I	21	21	24	24	0	Yes

c. Project completion 24 weeks. The park can open within the 6 months (26 weeks) after the project is

10. a.

Activity	Optimistic	Most Probable	Pessimistic	Expected Times	Variance
A	4	5	6	5.00	0.11
B	8	9	10	9.00	0.11
C	7	7.5	11	8.00	0.44
D	6	9	10	8.83	0.25
E	6	7	9	7.17	0.25
F	5	6	7	6.00	0.11

b. Critical activities: B-D-F

Expected project completion time: 9.00 + 8.83 + 6.00 = 23.83.

Variance of projection completion time: 0.11 + 0.25 + 0.11 = 0.47

11.

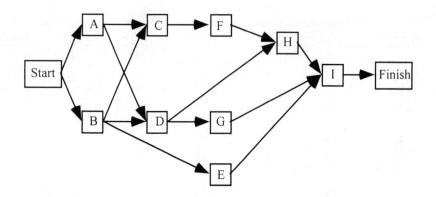

12. a.

Activity	Expected Time	Variance
A	4.83	0.25
B	4.00	0.44
C	6.00	0.11
D	8.83	0.25
E	4.00	0.44
F	2.00	0.11
G	7.83	0.69
H	8.00	0.44
I	4.00	0.11

Activity	Earliest Start	Latest Start	Earliest Finish	Latest Finish	Slack	Critical Activity
A	0.00	0.00	4.83	4.83	0.00	Yes
B	0.00	0.83	4.00	4.83	0.83	
C	4.83	5.67	10.83	11.67	0.83	
D	4.83	4.83	13.67	13.67	0.00	Yes
E	4.00	17.67	8.00	21.67	13.67	
F	10.83	11.67	12.83	13.67	0.83	
G	13.67	13.83	21.50	21.67	0.17	
H	13.67	13.67	21.67	21.67	0.00	Yes
I	21.67	21.67	25.67	25.67	0.00	Yes

Critical Path: A-D-H-I

b. $E(T) = t_A + t_D + t_H + t_I$
$= 4.83 + 8.83 + 8 + 4 = 25.66$ days

c.
$\sigma^2 = \sigma_A^2 + \sigma_D^2 + \sigma_H^2 + \sigma_I^2$
$= 0.25 + 0.25 + 0.44 + 0.11 = 1.05$

Using the normal distribution,

$$z = \frac{25 - E(T)}{\sigma} = \frac{25 - 25.66}{\sqrt{1.05}} = -0.65$$

From Appendix, area for $z = -0.65$ is 0.2422.

Probability of 25 days or less = 0.5000 - 0.2422 = 0.2578

13.

Activity	Expected Time	Variance
A	5	0.11
B	3	0.03
C	7	0.11
D	6	0.44
E	7	0.44
F	3	0.11
G	10	0.44
H	8	1.78

From problem 6, A-D-F-H is the critical path.

$$E(T) = 5 + 6 + 3 + 8 = 22$$

$$\sigma^2 = 0.11 + 0.44 + 0.11 + 1.78 = 2.44$$

$$z = \frac{Time - E(T)}{\sigma} = \frac{Time - 22}{\sqrt{2.44}}$$

a.

		From Appendix
		Area
Time = 21	$z = -0.64$	0.2389
		$P(21\ weeks) = 0.5000 - 0.2389 = 0.2611$

b.

		Area
Time = 22	$z = 0$	0.0000
		$P(22\ weeks) = 0.5000$

c.

		Area
Time = 25	$z = +1.92$	0.4726
		$P(22\ weeks) = 0.5000 + 0.4726 = 0.9726$

14. a.

Activity	Expected Time	Variance
A	6.0	0.11
B	11.0	1.78
C	8.0	0.44
D	9.0	1.00
E	7.0	1.78
F	7.5	0.25
G	7.0	1.00

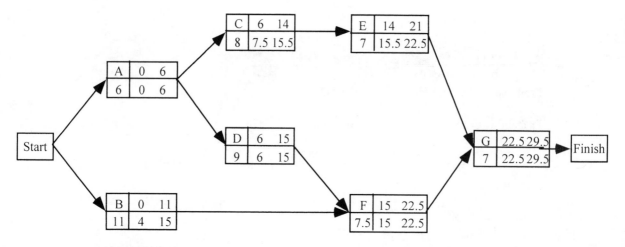

Critical Path: A-D-F-G   Time = 29.5

b. Activity C:
    Slack = LS - ES = 7.5 - 6 = 1.5 days

c. $E(T) = t_A + t_D + t_F + t_G$
    $= 6 + 9 + 7.5 + 7 = 29.5$ days

    $\sigma^2 = \sigma_A^2 + \sigma_D^2 + \sigma_F^2 + \sigma_G^2$
    $= 0.11 + 1.00 + 0.25 + 1.00 = 2.36$

d.   Area

$$z = \frac{30 - E(T)}{\sigma} = \frac{30 - 29.5}{\sqrt{2.36}} = 0.33$$

                                                                      0.1293
                     $P(30 \text{ days}) = 0.5000 + 0.1293 = 0.6293$

15. a.

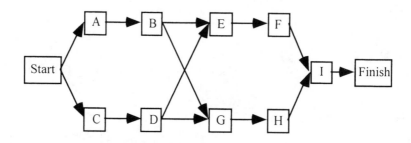

b.

Activity	Expected Time	Variance
A	2	0.03
B	3	0.44
C	2	0.11
D	2	0.03
E	1	0.03
F	2	0.11
G	4	0.44
H	4	0.11
I	2	0.03

Activity	Earliest Start	Latest Start	Earliest Finish	Latest Finish	Slack	Critical Activity
A	0	0	2	2	0	Yes
B	2	2	5	5	0	Yes
C	0	1	2	3	1	
D	2	3	4	5	1	
E	5	10	6	11	5	
F	6	11	8	13	5	
G	5	5	9	9	0	Yes
H	9	9	13	13	0	Yes
I	13	13	15	15	0	Yes

c. Critical Path: A-B-G-H-I

$E(T) = 2 + 3 + 4 + 4 + 2 = 15$ weeks

d. Variance on critical path

$\sigma^2 = 0.03 + 0.44 + 0.44 + 0.11 + 0.03 = 1.05$

From Appendix, we find 0.99 probability occurs at $z = +2.33$. Thus

$$z = \frac{T - E(T)}{\sigma} = \frac{T - 15}{\sqrt{1.05}} = 2.33$$

or

$$T = 15 + 2.33\sqrt{1.05} = 17.4 \text{ weeks}$$

16. a. A-D-G-J

$$E(T) = 6 + 5 + 3 + 2 = 16$$
$$\sigma^2 = 1.78 + 1.78 + 0.25 + 0.11 = 3.92$$

A-C-F-J

$$E(T) = 6 + 3 + 2 + 2 = 13$$
$$\sigma^2 = 1.78 + 0.11 + 0.03 + 0.11 = 2.03$$

B-H-I-J

$$E(T) = 2 + 4 + 2 + 2 = 10$$
$$\sigma^2 = 0.44 + 0.69 + 0.03 + 0.11 = 1.27$$

b. A-D-G-J

$$z = \frac{20 - 16}{\sqrt{3.92}} = 2.02 \quad \text{Area} = 0.4783 + 0.5000 = 0.9783$$

A-C-F-J

$$z = \frac{20 - 13}{\sqrt{2.03}} = 4.91 \quad \text{Area is approximately } 1.0000$$

B-H-I-J

$$z = \frac{20 - 10}{\sqrt{1.27}} = 8.87 \quad \text{Area is approximately } 1.0000$$

c. Critical path is the longest path and generally will have the lowest probability of being completed by the desired time. The noncritical paths should have a higher probability of being completed on time.

It may be desirable to consider the probability calculation for a noncritical path if the path activities have little slack, if the path completion time is almost equal to the critical path completion time, or if the path activity times have relatively high variances. When all of these situations occur, the noncritical path may have a probability of completion on time that is less than the critical path.

17. a.

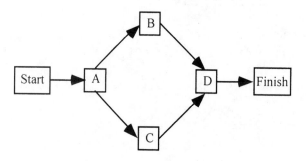

b. Critical Path A-B-D
Expected Time = 4.5 + 8.0 + 6.0 = 18.5 weeks

c. Material Cost = $3000 + $5000 = $8000

Best Cost (Optimistic Times) 3 + 5 + 2 + 4 = 14 days
Total Cost = $8000 + 14($400) = $12,800

Worst Case (Pessimistic Times) 8 + 11 + 6 + 12 = 37 days
Total Cost = $8000 + 37($400) = $22,800

d. Bid Cost = $8000 + 18.5($400) = $15,400
.50 probability time and cost will exceed the expected time and cost.

e. $\sigma = \sqrt{3.47} = 1.86$

Bid = $16,800 = $8,000 + Days ($400)
400 Days = 16,800 - 8000 = 8,800
Days = 22

The project must be completed in 22 days or less.

The probability of a loss = P (T > 22)

$$z = \frac{22 - 18.5}{1.86} = 1.88$$

From Appendix, Area = .5000 - .4699 = .0301

18. a.

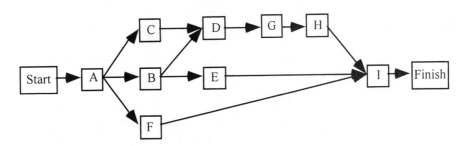

b.

Activity	Expected Time	Variance
A	1.17	0.03
B	6.00	0.44
C	4.00	0.44
D	2.00	0.11
E	3.00	0.11
F	2.00	0.11
G	2.00	0.11
H	2.00	0.11
I	1.00	0.00

Activity	Earliest Start	Latest Start	Earliest Finish	Latest Finish	Slack	Critical Activity
A	0.00	0.00	1.17	1.17	0.00	Yes
B	1.17	1.17	7.17	7.17	0.00	Yes
C	1.17	3.17	5.17	7.17	2.00	
D	7.17	7.17	9.17	9.17	0.00	Yes
E	7.17	10.17	10.17	13.17	3.00	
F	1.17	11.17	3.17	13.17	10.00	
G	9.17	9.17	11.17	11.17	0.00	Yes
H	11.17	11.17	13.17	13.17	0.00	Yes
I	13.17	13.17	14.17	14.17	0.00	Yes

c. Critical Path: A-B-D-G-H-I

Expected Project Completion Time = 1.17 + 6 + 2 + 2 + 2 + 1 = 14.17 weeks

d. Compute the probability of project completion in 13 weeks or less.

$$\sigma^2 = \sigma_A^2 + \sigma_B^2 + \sigma_D^2 + \sigma_G^2 + \sigma_H^2 + \sigma_I^2$$

$$= 0.03 + 0.44 + 0.11 + 0.11 + 0.11 + 0.00 = 0.80$$

$$z = \frac{13 - E(T)}{\sigma} = \frac{13 - 14.17}{\sqrt{0.80}} = -1.31$$

Area
0.4049 P(13 weeks) = 0.5000 - 0.4049 = 0.0951

With this low probability, the manager should start prior to February 1.

19. a.

Activity	Expected Time	Variance
A	4	0.11
B	4	0.44
C	5	0.11
D	3	0.11
E	10	1.78
F	9	0.69
G	6	0.25
H	7	1.78
I	3	0.44
J	5	0.11

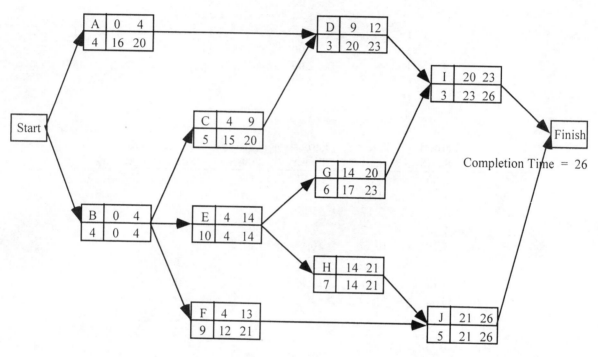

Completion Time = 26

Activity	Earliest Start	Latest Start	Earliest Finish	Latest Finish	Slack	Critical Activity
A	0	16	4	20	16	
B	0	0	4	4	0	Yes
C	4	15	9	20	11	
D	9	20	12	23	11	
E	4	4	14	14	0	Yes
F	4	12	13	21	8	
G	14	17	20	23	3	
H	14	14	21	21	0	Yes
I	20	23	23	26	3	
J	21	21	26	26	0	Yes

Critical Path: B-E-H-J

b.

$$E(T) = t_B + t_E + t_H + t_J = 4 + 10 + 7 + 5 = 26$$

$$\sigma^2 = \sigma_B^2 + \sigma_E^2 + \sigma_H^2 + \sigma_J^2 = 0.44 + 1.78 + 1.78 + 0.11 = 4.11$$

$$z = \frac{T - E(T)}{\sigma}$$

$$z = \frac{25 - 26}{\sqrt{4.11}} = -0.49 \quad P \text{ (25 weeks)} = 0.5000 - 0.1879 = 0.3121$$

$$z = \frac{30 - 26}{\sqrt{4.11}} = 1.97 \quad P \text{ (30 weeks)} = 0.5000 + 0.756 = 0.9756$$

20. a.

Activity	Maximum Crash	Crash Cost/Week
A	2	400
B	3	667
C	1	500
D	2	300
E	1	350
F	2	450
G	5	360
H	1	1000

Min $\quad 400Y_A + 667Y_B + 500Y_C + 300Y_D + 350Y_E + 450Y_F + 360Y_G + 1000Y_H$

s.t.

$$x_A + y_A \geq 3 \qquad x_E + y_E - x_D \geq 4 \qquad x_H + y_H - x_G \geq 3$$
$$x_B + y_B \geq 6 \qquad x_F + y_F - x_E \geq 3 \qquad x_H \leq 16$$
$$x_C + y_C - x_A \geq 2 \qquad x_G + y_G - x_C \geq 9$$
$$x_D + y_D - x_C \geq 5 \qquad x_G + y_G - x_B \geq 9$$
$$x_D + y_D - x_B \geq 5 \qquad x_H + y_H - x_F \geq 3$$

Maximum Crashing:

$$y_A \leq 2$$
$$y_B \leq 3$$
$$y_C \leq 1$$
$$y_D \leq 2$$
$$y_E \leq 1$$
$$y_F \leq 2$$
$$y_G \leq 5$$
$$y_H \leq 1$$

b. Linear Programming Solution

Activity	Crash Time	New Time	Crash Cost
A	0	3	—
B	1	5	667
C	0	2	—
D	2	3	600
E	1	3	350
F	1	2	450
G	1	8	360
H	0	3	—
		Total Crashing Cost	$2,427

c.

Activity	Earliest Start	Latest Start	Earliest Finish	Latest Finish	Slack	Critical Activity
A	0	0	3	3	0	Yes
B	0	0	5	5	0	Yes
C	3	3	5	5	0	Yes
D	5	5	8	8	0	Yes
E	8	8	11	11	0	Yes
F	11	11	13	13	0	Yes
G	5	5	13	13	0	Yes
H	13	13	16	16	0	Yes

All activities are critical.

21. a.

Activity	Earliest Start	Latest Start	Earliest Finish	Latest Finish	Slack	Critical Activity
A	0	0	3	3	0	Yes
B	0	1	2	3	1	
C	3	3	8	8	0	Yes
D	2	3	7	8	1	
E	8	8	14	14	0	Yes
F	8	10	10	12	2	
G	10	12	12	14	2	

Critical Path: A-C-E

Project Completion Time $= t_A + t_C + t_E = 3 + 5 + 6 = 14$ days

b. Total Cost = $8,400

22. a.

Activity	Max Crash Days	Crash Cost/Day
A	1	600
B	1	700
C	2	400
D	2	400
E	2	500
F	1	400
G	1	500

Min $\quad 600y_A + 700y_B + 400y_C + 400y_D + 500y_E + 400y_F + 400y_G$

s.t.

$$x_A + y_A \geq 3$$
$$x_B + y_B \geq 2$$
$$x_C + y_C - x_A \geq 5$$
$$x_D + y_D - x_B \geq 5$$
$$x_E + y_E - x_C \geq 6$$
$$x_E + y_E - x_D \geq 6$$
$$x_F + y_F - x_C \geq 2$$
$$x_F + y_F - x_D \geq 2$$
$$x_G + y_G - x_F \geq 2$$
$$x_{FIN} - x_E \geq 0$$
$$x_{FIN} - x_G \geq 0$$
$$x_{FIN} \leq 12$$
$$y_A \leq 1$$
$$y_B \leq 1$$
$$y_C \leq 2$$
$$y_D \leq 2$$
$$y_E \leq 2$$
$$y_F \leq 1$$
$$y_G \leq 1$$

All $x, y \geq 0$

b.

Activity	Crash	Crashing Cost
C	1 day	$400
E	1 day	500
	Total	$900

c. Total Cost = Normal Cost + Crashing Cost
= $8,400 + $900 = $9,300

23. a. This problem involves the formulation of a linear programming model that will determine the length of the critical path in the network. Since x_I, the completion time of activity I, is the project completion time, the objective function is:

Min x_I

Constraints are needed for the completion times for all activities in the project. The optimal solution will determine x_I which is the length of the critical path.

Activity	
A	$x_A \geq \tau_A$
B	$x_B \geq \tau_B$
C	$x_C - x_A \geq \tau_C$
D	$x_D - x_A \geq \tau_D$
E	$x_E - x_A \geq \tau_E$
F	$x_F - x_E \geq \tau_F$
G	$x_G - x_D \geq \tau_G$
	$x_G - x_F \geq \tau_G$
H	$x_H - x_B \geq \tau_H$
	$x_H - x_C \geq \tau_H$
I	$x_I - x_G \geq \tau_I$
	$x_I - x_H \geq \tau_I$

All $x \geq 0$

24. a.

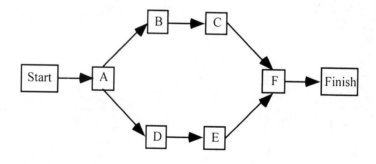

b.

Activity	Earliest Start	Latest Start	Earliest Finish	Latest Finish	Slack
A	0	0	10	10	0
B	10	10	18	18	0
C	18	18	28	28	0
D	10	11	17	18	1
E	17	18	27	28	1
F	28	28	31	31	0

c. Activities A, B, C, and F are critical. The expected project completion time is 31 weeks.

d.

Crash Activities	Number of Weeks	Cost
A	2	$ 40
B	2	30
C	1	20
D	1	10
E	1	12.5
		$ 112.5

e.

Activity	Earliest Start	Latest Start	Earliest Finish	Latest Finish	Slack
A	0	0	8	8	0
B	8	8	14	14	0
C	14	14	23	23	0
D	8	8	14	14	0
E	14	14	23	23	0
F	23	23	26	26	0

All activities are critical.

f.   Total added cost due to crashing $112,500 (see part d.)

Chapter 11
Inventory Models

Learning Objectives

1. Learn where inventory costs occur and why it is important for managers to make good inventory policy decisions.

2. Learn the economic order quantity (EOQ) model.

3. Know how to develop total cost models for specific inventory systems.

4. Be able to use the total cost model to make how-much-to-order and when-to-order decisions.

5. Extend the basic approach of the EOQ model to inventory systems involving production lot size, planned shortages, and quantity discounts.

6. Be able to make inventory decisions for single-period inventory models.

7. Know how to make order quantity and reorder point decisions when demand must be described by a probability distribution.

8. Learn about lead time demand distributions and how they can be used to meet acceptable service levels.

9. Be able to develop order quantity decisions for periodic review inventory systems.

10. Understand the following terms:

inventory holding costs	backorder
cost of capital	quantity discounts
ordering costs	goodwill costs
economic order quantity (EOQ)	probabilistic demand
constant demand rate	lead time demand distribution
reorder point	service level
lead time	single-period inventory model
lead time demand	periodic review
cycle time	
safety stock	

Solutions:

1. a. $Q^* = \sqrt{\dfrac{2DC_o}{C_h}} = \sqrt{\dfrac{2(3600)(20)}{0.25(3)}} = 438.18$

    b. $r = dm = \dfrac{3600}{250}(5) = 72$

    c. $T = \dfrac{250Q^*}{D} = \dfrac{250(438.18)}{3600} = 30.43$ days

    d. $TC = \dfrac{1}{2}QC_h + \dfrac{D}{Q}C_o = \dfrac{1}{2}(438.18)(0.25)(3) + \dfrac{3600}{438.18}(20) = \$328.63$

2. Annual Holding Cost

    $\dfrac{1}{2}QC_h = \dfrac{1}{2}(438.18)(0.25)(3) = \$164.32$

    Annual Ordering Cost

    $\dfrac{D}{Q}C_o = \dfrac{3600}{438.18}(20) = 164.32$

    Total Cost = \$328.64.

3. $Q^* = \sqrt{\dfrac{2DC_o}{C_h}} = \sqrt{\dfrac{2(5000)(32)}{2}} = 400$

    $d = \dfrac{D}{250} = \dfrac{5000}{250} = 20$ units per day

    a. $r = dm = 20(5) = 100$

    Since $r \le Q^*$, both inventory position and inventory on hand equal 100.

    b. $r = dm = 20(15) = 300$

    Since $r \le Q^*$, both inventory position and inventory on hand equal 300.

    c. $r = dm = 20(25) = 500$

    Inventory position reorder point = 500. One order of $Q^* = 400$ is outstanding. The on-hand inventory reorder point is 500 - 400 = 100.

    d. $r = dm = 20(45) = 900$

    Inventory position reorder point = 900. Two orders of $Q^* = 400$ are outstanding. The on-hand inventory reorder point is 900 - 2(400) = 100.

4. a. $Q^* = \sqrt{\dfrac{2DC_o}{C_h}} = \sqrt{\dfrac{2(12,000)(25)}{(0.20)(2.50)}} = 1095.45$

    b. $r = dm = \dfrac{1200}{250}(5) = 240$

    c. $T = \dfrac{250Q^*}{D} = \dfrac{250(1095.45)}{12,000} = 22.82$

    d. Holding $\dfrac{1}{2}QC_h = \dfrac{1}{2}(1095.45)(0.20)(2.50) = \$278.86$

        Ordering $\dfrac{D}{Q}C_o = \dfrac{12,000}{1095.45}(25) = 273.86$

        Total Cost $= \$547.72$

5. For $Q = 1000$

    $TC = 1/2(1000)(0.20)(2.50) + (12,000/1000)(25) = 250 + 300 = \$550$

    The cost increase of using $Q = 1000$ is only $\$550 - \$547.72 = \$2.28$. Thus the order quantity of 1000 is acceptable.

    $r = dm = \dfrac{12,000}{250}(50) = 240$ (Unchanged)

6. a. $D = 12 \times 20 = 240$

        $Q^* = \sqrt{\dfrac{2DC_o}{C_h}} = \sqrt{\dfrac{2(240)(70)}{(0.22)(600)}} = 15.95$

    b. Holding $\dfrac{1}{2}QC_h = \dfrac{1}{2}(15.95)(0.22)(600) = \$1,053.00$

        Ordering $\dfrac{D}{Q}C_o = \dfrac{240}{15.95}(70) = \$1,053.00$

        Total Cost $= \$2,106.00$

    c. $D/Q = 240/15.95 = 15.04$

    d. $T = \dfrac{250Q^*}{D} = \dfrac{250(240)}{15.95} = 16.62$ days

7. $$Q^* = \sqrt{\frac{2DC_o}{C_h}} = \sqrt{\frac{2DC_o}{IC}} \quad Q'\sqrt{\frac{2DC_o}{I'C}}$$

Where Q' is the revised order quantity for the new carrying charge I'. Thus

$$Q'/Q^* = \frac{\sqrt{2DC_o/I'C}}{\sqrt{2DC_o/IC}} = \sqrt{\frac{I}{I'}}$$

$$\therefore Q' = \sqrt{\frac{I}{I'}}Q^*$$

$$Q' = \sqrt{\frac{0.22}{0.27}}(80) = 72$$

8. Annual Demand D = (5/month)(12 months) = 60
   Ordering Cost = Fixed Cost per class = \$22,000
   Holding Cost = (\$1,600/month)(12 months) = \$19,200 per year for one driver

   $$Q^* = \sqrt{\frac{2DC_o}{C_h}} = \sqrt{\frac{2(60)(22,000)}{(19,200)}} = 11.73$$

   Use 12 as the class size.

   $$D/Q^* = 60/12 = 5 \text{ classes per year}$$

   Driver holding cost $= \frac{1}{2}QC_h = \frac{1}{2}(12)(19,200) = \$115,200$

   Class holding cost $= (D/Q)C_O = (60/12)(22,000) = 110,000$

   Total cost = \$225,200

9. a. $$Q^* = \sqrt{\frac{2DC_o}{C_h}} = \sqrt{\frac{2(5000)(80)}{(0.25)(20)}} = 400$$

   b. $$r = dm = \frac{5000}{250}(12) = 240$$

   c. $$r = dm = \frac{5000}{250}(35) = 700$$

   d. Since $r = 700$ and $Q^* = 400$, one order will be outstanding when the reorder point is reached. Thus the inventory on hand at the time of reorder will be 700 - 400 = 300.

10. This is a production lot size model. However, the operation is only six months rather than a full year. The basis for analysis may be for periods of one month, 6 months, or a full year. The inventory policy will be the same. In the following analysis we use a monthly basis.

$$Q^* = \sqrt{\frac{2DC_o}{(1 - D/P)C_h}} = \sqrt{\frac{2(1000)(150)}{\left(1 - \dfrac{1000}{4000}\right)(0.02)(10)}} = 1414.21$$

$$T = \frac{20Q}{D} = \frac{20(1414.21)}{1000} = 28.28 \text{ days}$$

Production run length = $\dfrac{Q}{P/20} = \dfrac{1414.21}{4000/20} = 7.07$ days

11. $\quad Q^* = \sqrt{\dfrac{2DC_o}{(1 - D/P)C_h}} = \sqrt{\dfrac{2(6400)(100)}{\left(1 - \dfrac{6400}{P}\right)2}}$

$P = 8,000$	$Q^* = 1789$
$P = 10,000$	$Q^* = 1333$
$P = 32,000$	$Q^* = 894$
$P = 100,000$	$Q^* = 827$

EOQ Model:

$$Q^* = \sqrt{\frac{2DC_o}{C_h}} = \sqrt{\frac{2(6400)(100)}{2}} = 800$$

Production Lot Size Q^* is always greater than the EOQ Q^* with the same D, C_0, and C_h values.

As the production rate P increases, the recommended Q^* decreases, but always remains greater than the EOQ Q^*.

12. $\quad Q^* = \sqrt{\dfrac{2DC_o}{(1 - D/P)C_h}} = \sqrt{\dfrac{2(2000)(300)}{\left(1 - \dfrac{2000}{8000}\right)1.60}} = 1000$

Current total cost using $Q = 500$ is as follows:

$$TC = \frac{1}{2}\left(1 - \frac{D}{P}\right)QC_h + \left(\frac{D}{Q}\right)C_o = \frac{1}{2}\left(1 - \frac{2000}{8000}\right)500(1.60) + \frac{2000}{500}300 = 300 + 1200 = \$1500$$

Proposed Total Cost using $Q^* = 1000$ is as follows:

$$TC = \frac{1}{2}\left(1 - \frac{2000}{8000}\right)1000(160) + \frac{2000}{1000}300 = 600 + 600 = \$1200$$

Savings of \$300/year
300/1500 = 20% of current policy.
$\therefore$ Make change to $Q^* = 1000$.

13. a. $Q^* = \sqrt{\dfrac{2DC_o}{(1-D/P)C_h}} = \sqrt{\dfrac{2(7200)(150)}{\left(1-\dfrac{7200}{25000}\right)(0.18)(14.50)}} = 1078.12$

   b. Number of production runs $= D/Q^* = 7200/1078.12 = 6.68$

   c. $T = \dfrac{250Q}{D} = \dfrac{250(1078.12)}{7200} = 37.43 \text{ days}$

   d. Production run length $= \dfrac{Q}{P/250} = \dfrac{1078.12}{25000/250} = 10.78 \text{ days}$

   e. Maximum Inventory

$$\left(1-\frac{D}{P}\right)Q = \left(1-\frac{7200}{25000}\right)(1078.12) = 767.62$$

   f. Holding Cost

$$\frac{1}{2}\left(1-\frac{D}{P}\right)QC_h = \frac{1}{2}\left(1-\frac{7200}{25000}\right)(1078.12)(0.18)(14.50) = \$1001.74$$

$$\text{Ordering cost} = \frac{D}{Q}C_o = \frac{7200}{1078.12}(150) = \$1001.74$$

Total Cost $= \$2,003.48$

   g. $r = dm = \left(\dfrac{D}{250}\right)m = \dfrac{7200}{250}(15) = 432$

14. C = current cost per unit
      $C' = 1.23\,C$ new cost per unit

$$Q^* = \sqrt{\frac{2DC_o}{(1-D/P)C_h}} = \sqrt{\frac{2DC_o}{(1-D/P)IC}} = 5000$$

Let Q' = new optimal production lot size

$$Q' = \sqrt{\frac{2DC_o}{(1-D/P)IC'}}$$

$$\frac{Q'}{Q^*} = \frac{\sqrt{\dfrac{2DC_o}{(1-D/P)IC'}}}{\sqrt{\dfrac{2DC_o}{(1-D/P)IC}}} = \frac{\sqrt{\dfrac{1}{C'}}}{\sqrt{\dfrac{1}{C}}} = \sqrt{\frac{C}{C'}} = \sqrt{\frac{C}{1.23C}} = \sqrt{\frac{1}{1.23}} = 0.9017$$

$Q' = 0.9017(Q^*) = 0.9017(5000) = 4509$

15. a. $Q^* = \sqrt{\dfrac{2DC_o}{C_h}\left(\dfrac{C_h + C_b}{C_b}\right)} = \sqrt{\dfrac{2(1200)(25)}{0.50}\left(\dfrac{0.50 + 5}{0.50}\right)} = 1148.91$

   b. $S^* = Q^*\left(\dfrac{C_h}{C_h + C_b}\right) = 1148.91\left(\dfrac{0.50}{0.50 + 5}\right) = 104.45$

   c. Max inventory $= Q^* - S^* = 1044.46$

   d. $T = \dfrac{250Q^*}{D} = \dfrac{250(1148.91)}{12000} = 23.94$

   e. Holding: $\dfrac{(Q-S)^2}{2Q}C_h = \$237.38$

   Ordering: $\dfrac{D}{Q}C_o = 261.12$

   Backorder: $\dfrac{S^2}{2Q}C_b = 23.74$

   Total Cost: $522.24

   The total cost for the EOQ model in problem 4 was $547.72. Allowing backorders reduces the total cost.

16. $r = dm = \left(\dfrac{12000}{250}\right)5 = 240$

   With backorder allowed the reorder point should be revised to

   $r = dm - S = 240 - 104.45 = 135.55$

   The reorder point will be smaller when backorders are allowed.

17. EOQ Model

   $Q^* = \sqrt{\dfrac{2DC_o}{C_h}} = \sqrt{\dfrac{2(800)(150)}{3}} = 282.84$

   Total Cost $= \dfrac{1}{2}QC_h + \dfrac{D}{Q}C_0 = \left(\dfrac{282.84}{2}\right)3 + \dfrac{800}{282.84}(150) = \$848.53$

   Planned Shortage Model

   $Q^* = \sqrt{\dfrac{2DC_o}{C_h}\left(\dfrac{C_h + C_b}{C_b}\right)} = \sqrt{\dfrac{2(800)(150)}{3}\left(\dfrac{3 + 20}{20}\right)} = 303.32$

$$S* = Q*\left(\frac{C_h}{C_h + C_b}\right) = 303.32\left(\frac{3}{3+20}\right) = 39.56$$

$$\text{Total Cost} = \frac{(Q-S)^2}{2Q}C_h + \frac{D}{Q}C_o + \frac{S^2}{2Q}C_b = 344.02 + 395.63 + 51.60 = \$791.25$$

Cost Reduction with Backorders allowed

$848.53 - 791.25 = \$57.28$ (6.75%)

Both constraints are satisfied:

1. $S/Q = 39.56/303.32 = 0.13$

Only 13% of units will be backordered.

2. Length of backorder period $= S/d = 39.56/(800/250) = 12.4$ days

18. Reorder points:

EOQ Model: $r = dm = \left(\frac{800}{250}\right)20 = 64$

Backorder Model: $r = dm - S = 24.44$

19. a. $Q* = \sqrt{\frac{2DC_o}{C_h}} = \sqrt{\frac{2(480)(15)}{(0.20)(60)}} = 34.64$

Total Cost: $= \frac{1}{2}QC_h + \frac{D}{Q}C_o = 207.85 + 207.85 = \$415.70$

b. $Q* = \sqrt{\frac{2DC_o}{C_h}\left(\frac{C_h + C_b}{C_b}\right)} = \sqrt{\frac{2(480)(15)}{(0.20)(60)}\left(\frac{0.20(60)+45}{45}\right)} = 39$

$$S* = Q*\left(\frac{C_h}{C_h + C_b}\right) = 8.21$$

$$\text{Total Cost} = \frac{(Q-S)^2}{2}C_h + \frac{D}{Q}C_o + \frac{S^2}{2Q}C_b = 145.80 + 184.68 + 38.88 = \$369.36$$

c. Length of backorder period $= \dfrac{S}{d} = \dfrac{8.21}{480/300} = 5.13$ days

d. Backorder case since the maximum wait is only 5.13 days and the cost savings is

$415.70 - 369.36 = \$46.34$ (11.1%)

e. EOQ: $r = dm = \left(\dfrac{480}{300}\right)6 = 9.6$

Backorder: $r = dm - S = 1.39$

20. $Q = \sqrt{\dfrac{2DC_o}{C_h}}$

$Q_1 = \sqrt{\dfrac{2(120)(20)}{0.25(30)}} = 25.30 \quad Q_1 = 25$

$Q_2 = \sqrt{\dfrac{2(120)(20)}{0.25(28.5)}} = 25.96 \quad Q_2 = 50$ to obtain 5% discount

$Q_3 = \sqrt{\dfrac{2(120)(20)}{0.25(27)}} = 26.67 \quad Q_3 = 100$ to obtain 10% discount

Category	Unit Cost	Order Quantity	Holding Cost	Order Cost	Purchase Cost	Total Cost
1	30.00	25	93.75	96	3600	$3,789.75
2	28.50	50	178.13	48	3420	$3,646.13
3	27.00	100	337.50	24	3240	$3,601.50

$Q = 100$ to obtain the lowest total cost.

The 10% discount is worthwhile.

21. $Q = \sqrt{\dfrac{2DC_o}{C_h}}$

$Q_1 = \sqrt{\dfrac{2(500)(40)}{0.20(10)}} = 141.42$

$Q_2 = \sqrt{\dfrac{2(500)(40)}{0.20(9.7)}} = 143.59$

Since Q_1 is over its limit of 99 units, Q_1 cannot be optimal (see problem 23). Use $Q_2 = 143.59$ as the optimal order quantity.

Total Cost: $= \dfrac{1}{2}QC_h + \dfrac{D}{Q}C_o + DC = 139.28 + 139.28 + 4,850.00 = \$5,128.56$

22. $D = 4(500) = 2,000$ per year
$C_o = \$30$
$I = 0.20$
$C = \$28$

Annual cost of current policy: ($Q = 500$ and $C = \$28$)

$$TC = 1/2(Q)(C_h) + (D/Q)C_o + DC$$
$$= 1/2(500)(0.2)(28) + (2000/500)(30) + 2000(28)$$
$$= 1400 + 120 + 56{,}000 = 57{,}520$$

Evaluation of Quantity Discounts

$$Q^* = \sqrt{\frac{2DC_o}{C_h}}$$

Order Quantity	C_h	Q^*	Q to obtain Discount	TC
0-99	$(0.20)(36) = 7.20$	129	*	—
100-199	$(0.20)(32) = 6.40$	137	137	64,876
200-299	$(0.20)(30) = 6.00$	141	200	60,900
300 or more	$(0.20)(28) = 5.60$	146	300	57,040

*Cannot be optimal since $Q^* > 99$.

Reduce Q to 300 pairs/order. Annual savings is $480; note that shoes will still be purchased at the lowest possible cost ($28/pair).

23. $$TC = \frac{1}{2}QIC + \frac{D}{Q}C_o + DC$$

At a specific Q (and given I, D, and C_0), since C of category 2 is less than C of category 1, the TC for 2 is less than TC for 1.

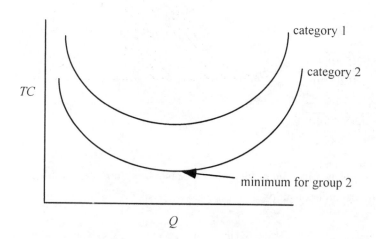

Thus, if the minimum cost solution for category 2 is feasible, there is no need to search category 1. From the graph we can see that all TC values of category 1 exceed the minimum cost solution of category 2.

24. a. $c_o = 1.50$

$c_u = 3.00 - 1.50 = 1.50$

$$P(D \le Q^*) = \frac{c_u}{c_u + c_o} = \frac{1.50}{1.50 + 1.50} = 0.50$$

Order the mean demand of 500

b. $c_o = 1.50 - 1.00 = 0.50$

$$P(D \le Q^*) = \frac{c_u}{c_u + c_o} = \frac{1.50}{1.50 + 0.50} = 0.75$$

For area 0.25, $z = 0.67$

$Q = 500 + 0.67(120) = 580.4$

25. a. $c_o = 80 - 50 = 30$

$c_u = 125 - 80 = 45$

$$P(D \le Q^*) = \frac{c_u}{c_u + c_o} = \frac{45}{45 + 30} = 0.60$$

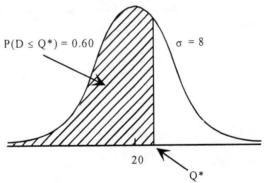

For an area of 0.60 below Q^*, $z = 0.25$

$Q^* = 20 + 0.25(8) = 22$

b. $P(\text{Sell All}) = P(D \ge Q^*) = 1 - 0.60 = 0.40$

26. a. $c_o = \$150$

b. The city would have liked to have planned for more additional officers at the $150 per officer rate. However, overtime at $240 per officer will have to be used.

$c_u = \$240 - \$150 = \$90$

c. $P(\text{Demand} \le Q^*) = \dfrac{c_u}{c_u + c_o} = \dfrac{90}{90 + 150} = 0.375$

$z = -0.32$

$\therefore Q^* = \mu + z\sigma = 50 - 0.32(10) = 46.8$

Recommend 47 additional officers

d. $P(\text{Overtime}) = 1 - 0.375 = 0.625$

27. a. $c_o = 1.19 - 1.00 = 0.19$

$c_u = 1.65 - 1.19 = 0.46$

$P(D \le Q^*) = \dfrac{c_u}{c_u + c_o} = \dfrac{0.46}{0.46 + 0.19} = 0.7077$

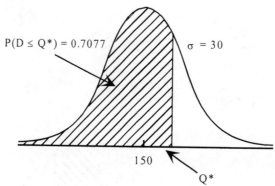

For a 0.7077 area below Q^*, $z = 0.55$

$Q^* = 150 + 0.55(30) = 166.5$

b. $P(\text{Stockout}) = P(D \ge Q^*) = 1 - 0.7077 = 0.2923$

c. $c_o = 1.19 - 0.25 = 0.94$

$P(D \le Q^*) = \dfrac{c_u}{c_u + c_o} = \dfrac{0.46}{0.46 + 0.94} = 0.3286$

For a 0.3286 area in the left tail, $z = -0.45$

$Q^* = 150 - 0.45(30) = 136.50$

The higher rebate increases the quantity that the supermarket should order.

28. a. $c_o = 8 - 5 = 3$

$c_u = 10 - 8 = 2$

$$P(D \le Q^*) = \frac{c_u}{c_u + c_o} = \frac{2}{2+3} = 0.40$$

Q^* is 40% of way between 700 and 800

$$Q^* = 200 + 0.40(600) = 440$$

b. $P(\text{stockout}) = P(D \ge Q^*) = 1 - 0.40 = 0.60$

c. $P(D \le Q^*) = 0.85$ $P(\text{Stockout}) = 0.15$

$$Q^* = 200 + 0.85(600) = 710$$

d.   Let g = goodwill cost

c_u = lost profit + goodwill cost = $(10 - 8) + g = 2 + g$

$$P(D \le Q^*) = \frac{c_u}{c_u + c_o} = 0.85$$

Solve for $c_u = 17$
$c_u = 2 + g = 17$
$g = 15$

29. a. $r = dm = (200/250)15 = 12$

b. $D / Q = 200 / 25 = 8$ orders / year

The limit of 1 stockout per year means that

$P(\text{Stockout/cycle}) = 1/8 = 0.125$

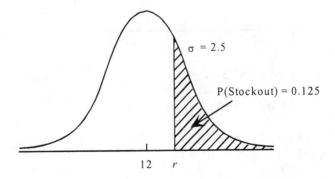

For area in tail = 0.125, $z = 1.15$

$$z = \frac{r - 12}{2.5} = 0.15$$

or

$r = 12 + 1.15(2.5) = 14.875$ Use 15

c.   Safety Stock = 3 units

Added Cost = 3($5) = $15/year

30. a.   *P*(Stockout/cycle) = 2/8 = 0.25

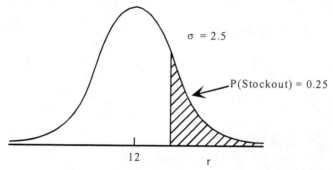

For area = 0.25, *z* = 0.67

$$z = \frac{r-12}{2.5} = 0.67$$

or

r = 12 + 0.67(2.5) = 13.675   Use 14

b.

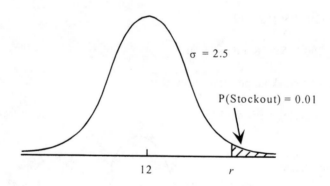

For an area in tail = 0.01, *z* = 2.33

r = 12 + 2.33(2.5) = 17.825   Use 18

c.   Safety Stock (a) = 14 - 12 = 2   Cost = 2($5) = $10
       Safety Stock (b) = 18 - 12 = 6   Cost = 6($5) = $30

31. a. $Q^* = \sqrt{\dfrac{2DC_o}{C_h}} = \sqrt{\dfrac{2(1000)(25.5)}{8}} = 79.84$

b.

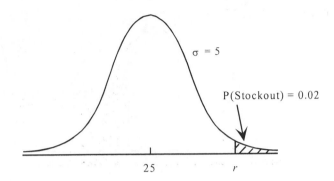

For area in tail = 0.02, z = 2.05

r = 25 + 2.05(5) = 35.3   Use 35

Safety Stock = 35 - 25 = 10

Safety Stock Cost = (10)($8) = $80/year

c.

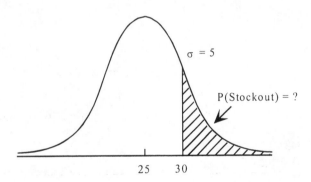

$z = \dfrac{r - 25}{5} = \dfrac{30 - 25}{5} = 1$

Area in tail at z = 1 is 0.5000 - 0.3413 = 0.1587

P(Stockout/cycle) = 0.1587

Number of Stockouts/year = 0.1587 (Number of Orders) = 0.1587 D/Q = 2

32. a. $Q^* = \sqrt{\dfrac{2DC_o}{C_h}} = \sqrt{\dfrac{2(300)(5)}{(0.15)(20)}} = 31.62$

b. $D/Q^* = 9.49$ orders per year

$$P(\text{Stockout}) = \frac{2}{D/Q^*} = 0.2108$$

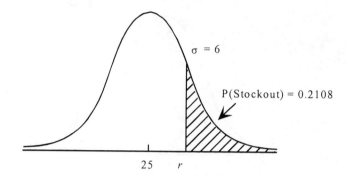

For area in tail $= 0.2108$, $z = 0.81$

$r = 15 + 0.81(6) = 19.86$ Use 20

c. Safety Stock $= 20 - 15 = 5$

Safety Stock Cost $= 5(0.15)(20) = \$15$

33. a. $1/52 = 0.0192$

b. $M = \mu + z\sigma = 60 + 2.07(12) = 85$

c. $M = 35 + (0.9808)(85\text{-}35) = 84$

34. a. $P(\text{Stockout}) = 0.01$ $z = 2.33$

$r = \mu + z\sigma = 150 + 2.33(40) = 243$

b. Safety Stock $= 243 - 150 = 93$ units
Annual Cost $= 93(0.20)(2.95) = \$54.87$

c. $M = \mu + z\sigma = 450 + 2.33(70) = 613$ units

d. Safety Stock $= 613 - 450 = 163$ units
Annual Cost $= 163(0.20)(2.95) = \$96.17$

e. The periodic review model is more expensive ($96.17 - $54.87) = $41.30 per year. However, this added cost may be worth the advantage of coordinating orders for multi products. Go with the periodic review system.

f. Unit Cost $= \$295$ Annual Difference $= \$4,130$
Use continuous review for the more expensive items.

35. a. $z = \dfrac{24 - 18}{6} = 1.0$

From z table, $P(\text{Stockout}) = 0.5000 - 0.3413 = 0.1587$

b.   For 2.5%, $z = 1.96$
$M = \mu + z\sigma = 18 + 1.96(6) = 29.76$
Use $M = 30$.
The manager should have ordered $Q = 30 - 8 = 22$ units.

36. a. μ = Week 1 demand + Week 2 demand + Lead Time demand
$= 16 + 16 + 8 = 40$

b. σ^2 = Var (Week 1) + Var (Week 2) + Var (Lead Time)
$= 25 + 25 + 12.25 = 62.25$
$\sigma = \sqrt{62.25} = 7.9$

c.   26 orders per year
$P(\text{Stockout}) = 1/26 = 0.0385$ per replenishment
$z = 1.77$
$M = \mu + z\sigma = 40 + 1.77(7.9) = 54$

d. $54 - 18 = 36$

Chapter 12
Waiting Line Models

Learning Objectives

1. Be able to identify where waiting line problems occur and realize why it is important to study these problems.

2. Know the difference between single-channel and multiple-channel waiting lines.

3. Understand how the Poisson distribution is used to describe arrivals and how the exponential distribution is used to describe services times.

4. Learn how to use formulas to identify operating characteristics of the following waiting line models:

   a. Single-channel model with Poisson arrivals and exponential service times
   b. Multiple-channel model with Poisson arrivals and exponential service times
   c. Single-channel model with Poisson arrivals and arbitrary service times
   d. Multiple-channel model with Poisson arrivals, arbitrary service times, and no waiting
   e. Single-channel model with Poisson arrivals, exponential service times, and a finite calling population

5. Know how to incorporate economic considerations to arrive at decisions concerning the operation of a waiting line.

6. Understand the following terms:

queuing theory	steady state
queue	utilization factor
single-channel	operating characteristics
multiple-channel	blocking
mean arrival rate	infinite calling population
mean service rate	finite calling population
queue discipline	

Solutions:

1. a. $\lambda = 5(0.4) = 2$ per five minute period

    b. $P(x) = \dfrac{\lambda^x e^{-\lambda}}{x!} = \dfrac{2^x e^{-2}}{x!}$

x	$P(x)$
0	0.1353
1	0.2707
2	0.2707
3	0.1804

    c. $P(\text{Delay Problems}) = P(x > 3) = 1 - P(x \leq 3) = 1 - 0.8571 = 0.1429$

2. a. $\mu = 0.6$ customers per minute

    $P(\text{service time} \leq 1) = 1 - e^{-(0.6)1} = 0.4512$

    b. $P(\text{service time} \leq 2) = 1 - e^{-(0.6)2} = 0.6988$

    c. $P(\text{service time} > 2) = 1 - 0.6988 = 0.3012$

3. a. $P_0 = 1 - \dfrac{\lambda}{\mu} = 1 - \dfrac{0.4}{0.6} = 0.3333$

    b. $L_q = \dfrac{\lambda^2}{\mu(\mu - \lambda)} = \dfrac{(0.4)^2}{0.6(0.6 - 0.4)} = 1.3333$

    c. $L = L_q + \dfrac{\lambda}{\mu} = 1.3333 + \dfrac{0.4}{0.6} = 2$

    d. $W_q = \dfrac{L_q}{\lambda} = \dfrac{1.3333}{0.4} = 3.3333$ min.

    e. $W = W_q + \dfrac{1}{\mu} = 3.3333 + \dfrac{1}{0.6} = 5$ min.

    f. $P_w = \dfrac{\lambda}{\mu} = \dfrac{0.4}{0.6} = 0.6667$

4. $P_n = \left(\dfrac{\lambda}{\mu}\right)^n P_0 = \left(\dfrac{0.4}{0.6}\right)^n (0.3333)$

n	P_n
0	0.3333
1	0.2222
2	0.1481
3	0.0988

    $P(n > 3) = 1 - P(n \leq 3) = 1 - 0.8024 = 0.1976$

5. a. $P_0 = 1 - \dfrac{\lambda}{\mu} = 1 - \dfrac{10}{12} = 0.1667$

    b. $L_q = \dfrac{\lambda^2}{\mu(\mu - \lambda)} = \dfrac{10^2}{12(12 - 10)} = 4.1667$

c. $W_q = \dfrac{L_q}{\lambda} = 0.4167$ hours (25 minutes)

d. $W = W_q + \dfrac{1}{\mu} = .5$ hours (30 minutes)

e. $P_w = \dfrac{\lambda}{\mu} = \dfrac{10}{12} = 0.8333$

6. a. $P_0 = 1 - \dfrac{\lambda}{\mu} = 1 - \dfrac{1.25}{2} = 0.375$

b. $L_q = \dfrac{\lambda^2}{\mu(\mu - \lambda)} = \dfrac{1.25^2}{2(2 - 1.25)} = 1.0417$

c. $W_q = \dfrac{L_q}{\lambda} = \dfrac{1.0417}{1.25} = 0.8333$ minutes (50 seconds)

d. $P_w = \dfrac{\lambda}{\mu} = \dfrac{1.25}{2} = 0.625$

e. Average one customer in line with a 50 second average wait appears reasonable.

7. a. $L_q = \dfrac{\lambda^2}{\mu(\mu - \lambda)} = \dfrac{(2.5)^2}{5(5 - 2.5)} = 0.5000$

$L = L_q + \dfrac{\lambda}{\mu} = 0.5000 + \dfrac{2.5}{5} = 1$

b. $W_q = \dfrac{L_q}{\lambda} = \dfrac{0.5000}{2.5} = 0.20$ hours (12 minutes)

c. $W = W_q + \dfrac{1}{\mu} = 0.20 + \dfrac{1}{5} = 0.40$ hours (24 minutes)

d. $P_w = \dfrac{\lambda}{\mu} = \dfrac{2.5}{5} = 0.50$

8. $\lambda = 1$ and $\mu = 1.25$

$$P_0 = 1 - \frac{\lambda}{\mu} = 1 - \frac{1}{1.25} = 0.20$$

$$L_q = \frac{\lambda^2}{\mu(\mu - \lambda)} = \frac{1}{1.25(0.25)} = 3.2$$

$$L = L_q + \frac{\lambda}{\mu} = 3.2 + \frac{1}{1.25} = 4$$

$$W_q = \frac{L_q}{\lambda} = \frac{3.2}{1} = 3.2 \text{ minutes}$$

$$W = W_q + \frac{1}{\mu} = 3.2 + \frac{1}{1.25} = 4 \text{ minutes}$$

$$P_w = \frac{\lambda}{\mu} = \frac{1}{1.25} = 0.80$$

Even though the services rate is increased to $\mu = 1.25$, this system provides slightly poorer service due to the fact that arrivals are occurring at a higher rate. The average waiting times are identical, but there is a higher probability of waiting and the number waiting increases with the new system.

9. a. $P_0 = 1 - \frac{\lambda}{\mu} = 1 - \frac{2.2}{5} = 0.56$

   b. $P_1 = \left(\frac{\lambda}{\mu}\right) P_0 = \frac{2.2}{5}(0.56) = 0.2464$

   c. $P_2 = \left(\frac{\lambda}{\mu}\right)^2 P_0 = \left(\frac{2.2}{5}\right)^2 (0.56) = 0.1084$

   d. $P_3 = \left(\frac{\lambda}{\mu}\right)^3 P_0 = \left(\frac{2.2}{5}\right)^3 (0.56) = 0.0477$

   e. P(More than 2 waiting) = P(More than 3 are in system)
$$= 1 - (P_0 + P_1 + P_2 + P_3) = 1 - 0.9625 = 0.0375$$

   f. $L_q = \frac{\lambda^2}{\mu(\mu - \lambda)} = \frac{2.2^2}{5(5 - 2.2)} = 0.3457$

$$W_q = \frac{L_q}{\lambda} = 0.157 \text{ hours} \quad (9.43 \text{ minutes})$$

10. a.

	$\lambda = 2$	$\mu = 3$	$\mu = 4$
Average number waiting (L_q)		1.3333	0.5000
Average number in system (L)		2.0000	1.0000
Average time waiting (W_q)		0.6667	0.2500
Average time in system (W)		1.0000	0.5000
Probability of waiting (P_w)		0.6667	0.5000

b. New mechanic $\quad = \$30(L) + \$14$

$\qquad\qquad\qquad\quad = 30(2) + 14 = \$74$ per hour

Experienced mechanic $= \$30(L) + \$20$

$\qquad\qquad\qquad\quad = 30(1) + 20 = \$50$ per hour

$\therefore$ Hire the experienced mechanic

11. a. $\lambda = 2.5 \quad \mu = 60/10 = 6$ customers per hour

$$L_q = \frac{\lambda^2}{\mu(\mu - \lambda)} = \frac{(2.5)^2}{6(6 - 2.5)} = 0.2976$$

$$L = L_q + \frac{\lambda}{\mu} = 0.7143$$

$$W_q = \frac{L_q}{\lambda} = 0.1190 \text{ hours} \quad (7.14 \text{ minutes})$$

$$W = W_q + \frac{1}{\mu} = 0.2857 \text{ hours}$$

$$P_w = \frac{\lambda}{\mu} = \frac{2.5}{6} = 0.4167$$

b. No; $W_q = 7.14$ minutes. Firm should increase the mean service rate (μ) for the consultant or hire a second consultant.

c. $\mu = 60/8 = 7.5$ customers per hour

$$L_q = \frac{\lambda^2}{\mu(\mu - \lambda)} = \frac{(2.5)^2}{7.5(7.5 - 2.5)} = 0.1667$$

$$W_q = \frac{L_q}{\lambda} = 0.0667 \text{ hours} \quad (4 \text{ minutes})$$

The service goal is being met.

12.

$$P_0 = 1 - \frac{\lambda}{\mu} = 1 - \frac{15}{20} = 0.25$$

$$L_q = \frac{\lambda^2}{\mu(\mu - \lambda)} = \frac{15^2}{20(20 - 15)} = 2.25$$

$$L = L + \frac{\lambda}{\mu} = 3$$

$$W_q = \frac{L_q}{\lambda} = 0.15 \text{ hours} \quad (9 \text{ minutes})$$

$$W = W_q + \frac{1}{\mu} = 0.20 \text{ hours} \quad (12 \text{ minutes})$$

$$P_w = \frac{\lambda}{\mu} = \frac{15}{20} = 0.75$$

With $W_q = 9$ minutes, the checkout service needs improvements.

13.   Average waiting time goal: 5 minutes or less.

a.   One checkout counter with 2 employees

$\lambda = 15 \quad \mu = 30$ per hour

$$L_q = \frac{\lambda^2}{\mu(\mu - \lambda)} = \frac{15^2}{30(30 - 15)} = 0.50$$

$$W_q = \frac{L_q}{\lambda} = 0.0333 \text{ hours} \quad (2 \text{ minutes})$$

b.   Two channel-two counter system

$\lambda = 15 \quad \mu = 20$ per hour for each

From Table, $P_0 = 0.4545$

$$L_q = \frac{(\lambda / \mu)^2 \lambda \mu}{1! \, (2(20) - 15)^2} P_0 = \frac{(15 / 20)^2 (15)(20)}{(40 - 15)^2} (0.4545) = 0.1227$$

$$W_q = \frac{L_q}{\lambda} = 0.0082 \text{ hours} \quad (0.492 \text{ minutes})$$

Recommend one checkout counter with two people. This meets the service goal with $W_q = 2$ minutes. The two counter system has better service, but has the added cost of installing a new counter.

14. a. $\mu = \dfrac{60}{7.5} = 8$ customers per hour

b. $P_0 = 1 - \dfrac{\lambda}{\mu} = 1 - \dfrac{5}{8} = 0.3750$

c. $L_q = \dfrac{\lambda^2}{\mu(\mu - \lambda)} = \dfrac{5^2}{8(8-5)} = 1.0417$

d. $W_q = \dfrac{L_q}{\lambda} = \dfrac{1.0417}{5} = 0.2083$ hours (12.5 minutes)

e. $P_w = \dfrac{\lambda}{\mu} = \dfrac{5}{8} = 0.6250$

f. 62.5% of customers have to wait and the average waiting time is 12.5 minutes. Ocala needs to add more consultants to meet its service guidelines.

15. $k = 2,\ \lambda = 5,\ \mu = 8$

Using the equation for P_0, $P_0 = 0.5238$

$L_q = \dfrac{(\lambda/\mu)^2\, \lambda\mu}{1!(k\mu - \lambda)^2} P_0 = 0.0676$

$W_q = \dfrac{L_q}{\lambda} = \dfrac{0.0676}{5} = 0.0135$ hours (0.81 minutes)

$P_0 = 0.5238 \qquad P_1 = \dfrac{(\lambda/\mu)^1}{1!} P_0 = \dfrac{5}{8}(0.5238) = 0.3274$

$\begin{aligned} P_w = P(n \geq 2) &= 1 - P(n \leq 1) \\ &= 1 - 0.5238 - 0.3274 = 0.1488 \end{aligned}$

Two consultants meet service goals with only 14.88% of customers waiting with an average waiting time of 0.81 minutes (49 seconds).

16. a. $P_0 = 1 - \dfrac{\lambda}{\mu} = 1 - \dfrac{5}{10} = 0.50$

b. $L_q = \dfrac{\lambda^2}{\mu(\mu - \lambda)} = \dfrac{5^2}{10(10-5)} = 0.50$

c. $W_q = \dfrac{L_q}{\lambda} = 0.1$ hours (6 minutes)

d. $W = W_q + \dfrac{1}{\mu} = 0.2$ hours (12 minutes)

e. Yes, unless $W_q = 6$ minutes is considered too long.

17. a. From Table, $P_0 = 0.60$

b. $L_q = \dfrac{(\lambda/\mu)^2\, \lambda\,\mu}{1!\,(k\,\mu - \lambda)^2} P_0 = 0.0333$

c. $W_q = \dfrac{L_q}{\lambda} = 0.0067$ hours (24.12 seconds)

d. $W = W_q + \dfrac{1}{\mu} = 0.1067$ (6.4 minutes)

e. This service is probably much better than necessary with average waiting time only 24 seconds. Both channels will be idle 60% of the time.

18. a. $k = 2$ $\lambda/\mu = 14/10 = 1.4$

From Table, $P_0 = 0.1765$

b. $L_q = \dfrac{(\lambda/\mu)^2 \lambda\mu}{1!(2\mu - \lambda)^2} P_0 = \dfrac{(1.4)^2(14)(10)}{(20-14)^2}(0.1765) = 1.3451$

$L = L_q + \dfrac{\lambda}{\mu} = 1.3451 + \dfrac{14}{10} = 2.7451$

c. $W_q = \dfrac{L_q}{\lambda} = \dfrac{1.3453}{14} = 0.0961$ hours (5.77 minutes)

d. $W = W_q + \dfrac{1}{\mu} = 0.0961 + \dfrac{1}{10} = 0.196$ hours (11.77 minutes)

e. $P_0 = 0.1765$

$P_1 = 1 - \dfrac{(\lambda/\mu)^1}{1!} P_0 = \dfrac{14}{10}(0.1765) = 0.2470$

$P(\text{wait}) = P(n \geq 2) = 1 - P(n \leq 1)$
$= 1 - 0.4235 = 0.5765$

19. a. From Table, $P_0 = 0.2360$

$L_q = \dfrac{(\lambda/\mu)^2 \lambda\mu}{2!(3\mu - \lambda)^2} P_0 = \dfrac{(1.4)^2(14)(10)}{2(30-14)^2}(0.2360) = 0.1771$

$L = L_q + \dfrac{\lambda}{\mu} = 1.5771$

$W_q = \dfrac{L_q}{\lambda} = \dfrac{0.1771}{14} = 0.0126$ hours (0.76 minutes)

$W = W_q + \dfrac{1}{\mu} = 0.126 + \dfrac{1}{10} = 0.1126$ hours (6.76 minutes)

b. $k = 2$ $P(\text{wait}) = 0.5765$

   $k = 3$ $P_0 = 0.2360$

$$P_1 = 1 - \frac{(\lambda/\mu)^2}{1!} P_0 = (1.4)(0.2360) = 0.3304$$

$$P_2 = 1 - \frac{(\lambda/\mu)^2}{2!} P_0 = \frac{(1.4)^2}{2}(0.2360) = 0.2312$$

$P(\text{wait}) = P(n \geq 3)$ $= 1 - P(n \leq 2)$
                            $= 1 - 0.7976 = 0.2024$

$\therefore$ Prefer the three-channel system.

20. a. Note $\dfrac{\lambda}{\mu} = \dfrac{1.2}{0.75} = 1.60 > 1.$ Thus, one postal clerk cannot handle the arrival rate.

   Try $k = 2$ postal clerks

   From Table with $\dfrac{\lambda}{\mu} = 1.60$ and $k = 2$, $P_0 = 0.1111$

$$L_q = \frac{(\lambda/\mu)^2 \lambda\mu}{1!(2\mu - \lambda)^2} P_0 = 2.8444$$

$$L = L_q + \frac{\lambda}{\mu} = 4.4444$$

$$W_q = \frac{L_q}{\lambda} = 2.3704 \text{ minutes}$$

$$W = W_q + \frac{1}{\mu} = 3.7037 \text{ minutes}$$

$$P_w = 0.7111$$

   Use 2 postal clerks with average time in system 3.7037 minutes. No need to consider $k = 3$.

b. Try $k = 3$ postal clerks.

   From Table with $\dfrac{\lambda}{\mu} = \dfrac{2.1}{.75} = 2.80$ and $k = 3$, $P_0 = 0.0160$

$$L_q = \frac{(\lambda/\mu)^3 \lambda\mu}{2(3\mu - \lambda)^2} P_0 = 12.2735$$

$$L = L_q + \frac{\lambda}{\mu} = 15.0735$$

$$W_q = \frac{L_q}{\lambda} = 5.8445 \text{ minutes}$$

$$W = W_q + \frac{1}{\mu} = 7.1778 \text{ minutes}$$

$$P_w = 0.8767$$

Three postal clerks will not be enough in two years. Average time in system of 7.1778 minutes and an average of 15.0735 customers in the system are unacceptable levels of service. Post office expansion to allow at least four postal clerks should be considered.

21.   From question 11, a service time of 8 minutes has $\mu = 60/8 = 7.5$

$$L_q = \frac{\lambda^2}{\mu(\mu - \lambda)} = \frac{(2.5)^2}{7.5(7.5 - 2.5)} = 0.1667$$

$$L = L_q + \frac{\lambda}{\mu} = 0.50$$

Total Cost $= \$25L + \$16$
$= 25(0.50) + 16 = \$28.50$

Two channels: $\lambda = 2.5$ $\mu = 60/10 = 6$

Using equation, $P_0 = 0.6552$

$$L_q = \frac{(\lambda/\mu)^2 \lambda \mu}{1!(2\mu - \lambda)^2} P_0 = 0.0189$$

$$L = L_q + \frac{\lambda}{\mu} = 0.4356$$

Total Cost $= 25(0.4356) + 2(16) = \$42.89$

Use the one consultant with an 8 minute service time.

22. $\lambda = 24$

Characteristic		System A $(k = 1, \mu = 30)$	System B $(k = 1, \mu = 48)$	System C $(k = 2, \mu = 30)$
a.	P_0	0.2000	0.5000	0.4286
b.	L_q	3.2000	0.5000	0.1524
c.	W_q	0.1333	0.0200	0.0063
d.	W	0.1667	0.0417	0.0397
e.	L	4.0000	1.0000	0.9524
f.	P_w	0.8000	0.5000	0.2286

System C provides the best service.

23. Service Cost per Channel

System A:	6.50	+	20.00	=	$26.50/hour
System B:	2(6.50)	+	20.00	=	$33.00/hour
System C:	6.50	+	20.00	=	$26.50/hour

Total Cost $= c_w L + c_s k$

System A:	25(4)	+	26.50(1)	=	$126.50
System B:	25(1)	+	33.00(1)	=	$ 58.00
System C:	25(0.9524)	+	26.50(2)	=	$ 76.81

System B is the most economical.

24. $\lambda = 2.8$, $\mu = 3.0$, $W_q = 30$ minutes

a. $\lambda = 2.8/60 = 0.0466$

$\mu = 3/60 = 0.0500$

b. $L_q = \lambda W_q = (0.0466)(30) = 1.4$

c. $W = W_q + 1/\mu = 30 + 1/0.05 = 50$ minutes

$\therefore$ 11:00 a.m.

25. $\lambda = 4$, $W = 10$ minutes

a. $\mu = 1/2 = 0.5$

b. $W_q = W - 1/\mu = 10 - 1/0.5 = 8$ minutes

c. $L = \lambda W = 4(10) = 40$

26. a. Express λ and μ in mechanics per minute

$\lambda = 4/60 = 0.0667$ mechanics per minute

$\mu = 1/6 = 0.1667$ mechanics per minute

$L_q = \lambda W_q = 0.0667(4) = 0.2668$

$W = W_q + 1/\mu = 4 + 1/0.1667 = 10$ minutes

$L = \lambda W = (0.0667)(10) = 0.6667$

b. $L_q = 0.0667(1) = 0.0667$

$W = 1 + 1/0.1667 = 7$ minutes

$L = \lambda W = (0.0667)(7) = 0.4669$

c. One-Channel

   Total Cost = 20(0.6667) + 12(1) = $25.33

   Two-Channel

   Total Cost = 20(0.4669) + 12(2) = $33.34

   One-Channel is more economical.

27. a. 2/8 hours = 0.25 per hour

   b. 1/3.2 hours = 0.3125 per hour

   c. $L_q = \dfrac{\lambda^2 \sigma^2 + (\lambda / \mu)^2}{2 (1 - \lambda / \mu)} = \dfrac{(0.25)^2 (2)^2 + (0.25 / 0.3125)^2}{2 (1 - 0.25 / 0.3125)} = 2.225$

   d. $W_q = \dfrac{L_q}{\lambda} = \dfrac{2.225}{0.25} = 8.9$ hours

   e. $W = W_q + \dfrac{1}{\mu} = 8.9 + \dfrac{1}{1.3125} = 12.1$ hours

   f. Same at $P_w = \dfrac{\lambda}{\mu} = \dfrac{0.25}{0.3125} = 0.80$

   80% of the time the welder is busy.

28. $\lambda = 5$

   a.

Design	μ
A	60/6 = 10
B	60/6.25 = 9.6

   b. Design A with $\mu = 10$ jobs per hour.

   c. 3/60 = 0.05 for A   0.6/60 = 0.01 for B

   d.

Characteristic	Design A	Design B
P_0	0.5000	0.4792
L_q	0.3125	0.2857
L	0.8125	0.8065
W_q	0.0625	0.0571
W	0.1625	0.1613
P_w	0.5000	0.5208

   e. Design B is slightly better due to the lower variability of service times.

System A:	$W = 0.1625$ hrs	(9.75 minutes)
System B:	$W = 0.1613$ hrs	(9.68 minutes)

29. a. $\lambda = 3/8 = .375$

   $\mu = 1/2 = .5$

   b. $L_q = \dfrac{\lambda^2 \sigma^2 + (\lambda/\mu)^2}{2(1 - \lambda/\mu)} = \dfrac{(.375)^2 (1.5)^2 + (.375/.5)^2}{2(1 - .375/.5)} = 1.7578$

   $L = L_q + \lambda/\mu = 1.7578 + .375/.5 = 2.5078$

   $TC = c_w L + c_s k = 35(2.5078) + 28(1) = \$115.71$

   c.

	Current System ($\sigma = 1.5$)	New System ($\sigma = 0$)
	$L_q = 1.7578$	$L_q = 1.125$
	$L = 2.5078$	$L = 1.875$
	$W_q = 4.6875$	$W_q = 3.00$
	$W = 6.6875$	$W = 5.00$
	$TC = \$115.77$	

   $TC = c_w L + c_s k = 35(1.875) + 32(1) = \$97.63$

   d. Yes; Savings $= 40(\$115.77 - \$97.63) = \$725.60$

   Note: Even with the advantages of the new system, $W_q = 3$ shows an average waiting time of 3 hours. The company should consider a second channel or other ways of improving the emergency repair service.

30. a. $\lambda = 42 \quad \mu = 20$

i	$(\lambda/\mu)^i / i!$
0	1.0000
1	2.1000
2	2.2050
3	1.5435
	6.8485

j	P_j		
0	1/6.8485	=	0.1460
1	2.1/6.8485	=	0.3066
2	2.2050/6.8485	=	0.3220
3	1.5435/6.8485	=	0.2254
			1.0000

   b. 0.2254

   c. $L = \lambda/\mu(1 - P_k) = 42/20(1 - 0.2254) = 1.6267$

   d. Four lines will be necessary. The probability of denied access is 0.1499.

31. a. $\lambda = 20$ $\mu = 12$

i	$(\lambda/\mu)^i / i\,!$
0	1.0000
1	1.6667
2	<u>1.3889</u>
	4.0556

j	P_j		
0	1/4.0556	=	0.2466
1	1.6667/4.0556	=	0.4110
2	1.3889/4.0556	=	0.3425

$P_2 = 0.3425$ 34.25%

   b. $k = 3$ $P_3 = 0.1598$

        $k = 4$ $P_4 = 0.0624$ Must go to $k = 4$.

   c. $L = \lambda/\mu(1 - P_4) = 20/12(1 - 0.0624) = 1.5626$

32. a. $\lambda = 40$ $\mu = 30$

i	$(\lambda/\mu)^i / i\,!$
0	1.0000
1	1.3333
2	<u>0.8888</u>
	3.2221

$P_0 = 1.0000/3.2221 = 0.3104$ 31.04%

   b. $P_2 = 0.8888/3.2221 = 0.2758$ 27.58%

   c.

i	$(\lambda/\mu)^i / i\,!$
3	0.3951
4	0.1317

$P_2 = 0.2758$

$P_3 = 0.3951/(3.2221 + 0.3951) = 0.1092$

$P_4 = 0.1317/(3.2221 + 0.3951 + 0.1317) = 0.0351$

   d. $k = 3$ with 10.92% of calls receiving a busy signal.

33. a. $\lambda = 0.05$ $\mu = 0.50$ $\lambda/\mu = 0.10$ $N = 8$

n	$\dfrac{N!}{(N-n)!}\left(\dfrac{\lambda}{\mu}\right)^n$
0	1.0000
1	0.8000
2	0.5600
3	0.3360
4	0.1680
5	0.0672
6	0.0202
7	0.0040
8	0.0004
	2.9558

$P_0 = 1/2.9558 = 0.3383$

$$L_q = N - \left(\frac{\lambda + \mu}{\lambda}\right)(1 - P_0) = 8 - \left(\frac{0.55}{0.05}\right)(1 - 0.3383) = 0.7215$$

$$L = L_q + (1 - P_0) = 0.7213 + (1 - 0.3383) = 1.3832$$

$$W_q = \frac{L_q}{(N-L)\lambda} = \frac{0.7215}{(8 - 1.3832)(0.05)} = 2.1808 \text{ hours}$$

$$W = W_q + \frac{1}{\mu} = 2.1808 + \frac{1}{0.50} = 4.1808 \text{ hours}$$

b. $P_0 = 0.4566$

$L_q = 0.0646$

$L = 0.7860$

$W_q = 0.1791$ hours

$W = 2.1791$ hours

c. One Employee

Cost $= 80L + 20$
$= 80(1.3832) + 20 = \$130.65$

Two Employees

Cost $= 80L + 20(2)$
$= 80(0.7860) + 40 = \$102.88$

Use two employees.

34. $N = 5$ $\lambda = 0.025$ $\mu = 0.20$ $\lambda/\mu = 0.125$

a.

n	$\dfrac{N!}{(N-n)!}\left(\dfrac{\lambda}{\mu}\right)^{n}$
0	1.0000
1	0.6250
2	0.3125
3	0.1172
4	0.0293
5	0.0037
	2.0877

$P_0 = 1/2.0877 = 0.4790$

b. $L_q = N - \left(\dfrac{\lambda + \mu}{\lambda}\right)(1 - P_0) = 5 - \left(\dfrac{0.225}{0.025}\right)(1 - 0.4790) = 0.3110$

c. $L = L_q + (1 - P_0) = 0.3110 + (1 - 0.4790) = 0.8321$

d. $W_q = \dfrac{L_q}{(N - L)\lambda} = \dfrac{0.3110}{(5 - 0.8321)(0.025)} = 2.9854$ min

e. $W = W_q + \dfrac{1}{\mu} = 2.9854 + \dfrac{1}{0.20} = 7.9854$ min

f.   Trips/Days   = (8 hours)(60 min/hour) (λ)
                   = (8)(60)(0.025) = 12 trips

Time at Copier: 12 x 7.9854 = 95.8 minutes/day
Wait Time at Copier: 12 x 2.9854 = 35.8 minutes/day

g.   Yes. Five administrative assistants x 35.8 = 179 min. (3 hours/day)
     3 hours per day are lost to waiting.

     (35.8/480)(100) = 7.5% of each administrative assistant's day is spent waiting for the copier.

35. $N = 10$ $\lambda = 0.25$ $\mu = 4$ $\lambda/\mu = 0.0625$

a.

n	$\dfrac{N!}{(N-n)!}\left(\dfrac{\lambda}{\mu}\right)^{n}$
0	1.0000
1	0.6250
2	0.3516
3	0.1758
4	0.0769
5	0.0288
6	0.0090
7	0.0023
8	0.0004
9	0.0001
10	0.0000
	2.2698

$P_0 = 1/2.2698 = 0.4406$

b. $L_q = N - \left(\dfrac{\lambda + \mu}{\lambda}\right)(1 - P_0) = 10 - \left(\dfrac{4.25}{0.25}\right)(1 - 0.4406) = 0.4895$

c. $L = L_q + (1 - P_0) = 0.4895 + (1 - 0.4406) = 1.0490$

d. $W_q = \dfrac{L_q}{(N - L)\lambda} = \dfrac{0.4895}{(10 - 1.0490)(0.25)} = 0.2188$

e. $W = W_q + \dfrac{1}{\mu} = 0.2188 + \dfrac{1}{4} = 0.4688$

f. $\begin{aligned} TC &= c_w L + c_s k \\ &= 50(1.0490) + 30(1) = \$82.45 \end{aligned}$

g. $k = 2$

$\begin{aligned} TC &= c_w L + c_s k \\ &= 50L + 30(2) = \$82.45 \\ 50L &= 22.45 \\ L &= 0.4490 \text{ or less.} \end{aligned}$

h.   Using *The Management Scientist* with $k = 2$,

$L \quad = \quad 0.6237$

$\begin{aligned} TC &= c_w L + c_s k \\ &= 50(1.6237) + 30(2) = \$91.18 \end{aligned}$

The company should not expand to the two-channel truck dock.

Chapter 13
Simulation

Learning Objectives

1. Understand what simulation is and how it aids in the analysis of a problem.

2. Learn why simulation is a significant problem-solving tool.

3. Understand the difference between static and dynamic simulation.

4. Identify the important role probability distributions, random numbers, and the computer play in implementing simulation models.

5. Realize the relative advantages and disadvantages of simulation models.

6. Understand the following terms:

   simulation   Monte Carlo simulation
   simulation model   discrete-event simulation

Solutions:

1. a. Profit $= (249 - c_1 - c_2)x - 1{,}000{,}000$
       $= (249 - 45 - 90)(20{,}000) - 1{,}000{,}000$
       $= \$1{,}280{,}000$ (Engineer's)

    b. Profit $= (249 - 45 - 100)(10{,}000) - 1{,}000{,}000$
       $= \$40{,}000$ (Financial Analyst)

    c. Simulation will provide probability information about the various profit levels possible. What if scenarios show possible profit outcomes but do not provide probability information.

2. a. Let c = variable cost per unit
           x = demand

       Profit $= 50x - cx - 30{,}000$
            $= (50 - c)x - 30{,}000$

    b. Base case: Profit $= (50 - 20)\,1200 - 30{,}000 = 6{,}000$
       Worst case: Profit $= (50 - 24)\,300 - 30{,}000 = -22{,}200$
       Best case: Profit $= (50 - 16)\,2100 - 30{,}000 = 41{,}400$

    c. The possibility of a $41,400 profit is interesting, but the worst case loss of $22,200 is risky. Risk analysis would be helpful in evaluating the probability of a loss.

3.

Random Number	Direct Labor Cost
0.3753	$45
0.9218	$47
0.0336	$43
0.5145	$45
0.7000	$46

4. a.

Sales	Interval
0	.00 but less than .08
1	.08 but less than .20
2	.20 but less than .48
3	.48 but less than .72
4	.72 but less than .86
5	.86 but less than .96
6	.96 but less than 1.00

    b. 2, 5, 2, 3, 2, 4, 2, 1, 1, 2

    c. Total Sales = 24 units

5. a.

Stock Price Change	Probability	Interval
-2	.05	.00 but less than .05
-1	.10	.05 but less than .15
0	.25	.15 but less than .40
+1	.20	.40 but less than .60
+2	.20	.60 but less than .80
+3	.10	.80 but less than .90
+4	.10	.90 but less than 1.00

b.

Random Number	Price Change	Ending Price Per Share
0.1091	-1	$38
0.9407	+4	$42
0.1941	0	$42
0.8083	+3	$45

Ending price per share = $45

6. a.

Payment	Interval
$0	.00 but less than .83
500	.83 but less than .89
1,000	.89 but less than .94
2,000	.94 but less than .96
5,000	.96 but less than .98
8,000	.98 but less than .99
10,000	.99 but less than 1.00

b.

Payments to Policy Holders	Payment
1	8,000
12	2,000
14	10,000
16	2,000
	$22,000

No payments were made to the other 16 policy holders.

7.

$$\text{Time} = a + r(b - a)$$
$$= 10 + r(18 - 10)$$
$$= 10 + 8r$$

r	Time
0.1567	11.25 minutes
0.9823	17.86 minutes
0.3419	12.74 minutes
0.5572	14.46 minutes
0.7758	16.21 minutes

8. a. The following table can be used to simulate a win for Atlanta

Game	Interval for Atlanta Win
1	.00 but less than .60
2	.00 but less than .55
3	.00 but less than .48
4	.00 but less than .45
5	.00 but less than .48
6	.00 but less than .55
7	.00 but less than .50

b. Using the random numbers in column 6 beginning with 0.3813, 0.2159 and so on, Atlanta wins games 1 and 2, loses game 3, wins game 4, loses game 5 and wins game 6. Thus, Atlanta wins the 6-game World Series 4 games to 2 games.

c. Repeat the simulation many times. In each case, record who wins the series and the number of games played, 4, 5, 6 or 7. Count the number of times Atlanta wins. Divide this number by the total number of simulation runs to estimate the probability that Atlanta will win the World Series. Count the number of times the series ends in 4 games and divide this number by the total number of simulation runs to estimate the probability of the World Series ending in 4 games. This can be repeated for 5-game, 6-game and 7-game series.

9. a. Base case using most likely completion times.

A	6
B	5
C	14
D	8
	33 weeks

Worst case: $8 + 7 + 18 + 10 = 43$ weeks
Best case: $5 + 3 + 10 + 8 = 26$ weeks

b.

Activity	Random Number	Completion Time
A	0.1778	5
B	0.9617	7
C	0.6849	14
D	0.4503	8
Total:		34 Weeks

c. Simulation will provide a distribution of project completion time values. Calculating the percentage of simulation trials with completion times of 35 weeks or less can be used to estimate the probability of meeting the completion time target of 35 weeks.

10. a. $P(\text{Win}) = 18/38 = 0.4737$

    b. Win if RAND < 0.4737

    c. Using random numbers in column 3, payoffs are in terms of money taken off the table.

| | Payoff | | | | Payoff | |
Win/Lose	a	b	Win/Loss	a	b
Win	25	0	Win	25	0
Lose	-25	-50	Lose	-25	-50
Win	25	0	Win	25	0
Win	25	75	Lose	-25	-50
Lose	-25	-25	Win	25	0
Win	25	0	Lose	-25	-50
Lose	-25	-50	Win	25	0
Lose	-25	-25	Lose	-25	-50
Win	25	0	Win	25	0
Lose	-25	-50	Win	25	75

Strategy a $ 50
Strategy b -$250

Strategy a is the best and shows a winning of $50 for the twenty bets.

    d. Note that the twenty simulations show 11 wins. This is a probability of winning of $11/20 = .55$, which is more winning than can be expected in the long run. Longer simulation runs are needed to evaluate the two betting strategies.

11. a. Let r = random number
          a = smallest value = -8
          b = largest value = 12

    Return % = $a + r(b - a)$

$$= -8 + r(12-(-8)) = -8 + r20$$

1st Quarter $r = .52$

$$\text{Return \%} = -8 + .52(20) = 2.4\%$$

For all quarters:

Quarter	r	Return %
1	0.52	2.4%
2	0.99	11.8%
3	0.12	-5.6%
4	0.15	-5.0%
5	0.50	2.0%
6	0.77	7.4%
7	0.40	0.0%
8	0.52	2.4%

b.   For each quarter,

Ending price = Beginning price + Change

For Quarter 1: Ending price = $80.00 + .024($80.00)
                                              = $80.00 + $1.92 = $81.92

For Quarter 2: Ending price = $81.92 + .118($81.92)
                                              = $81.92 + $9.67 = $91.59

Quarter	Starting Price/Share	Return %	Change $	Ending Price/Share
1	$80.00	2.4%	$1.92	$81.92
2	$81.92	11.8%	$9.67	$91.59
3	$91.59	-5.6%	-$5.13	$86.46
4	$86.46	-5.0%	-$4.32	$82.13
5	$82.13	2.0%	$1.64	$83.78
6	$83.78	7.4%	$6.20	$89.98
7	$89.98	0.0%	$0.00	$89.98
8	$89.98	2.4%	$2.16	$92.14

Price per share at the end of two years = $92.14

c.   Conducting a risk analysis would require multiple simulations of the eight-quarter, two-year period. For each simulation, the price per share at the end of two years would be recorded. The distribution of the ending price per share values would provide an indication of the maximum possible gain, the maximum possible loss and other possibilities in between.

12. a.   Profit = Selling Price - Purchase Cost - Labor Cost - Transportation Cost

Base Case using most likely costs
                     Profit =   45 - 11 - 24 - 3 = $7/unit
Worst Case
                     Profit =   45 - 12 - 25 - 5 = $3/unit
Best Case
                     Profit =   45 - 10 - 20 - 3 = $12/unit

b.

Purchase Cost	Interval	Labor Cost	Interval	Transportation Cost	Interval
$10	.00 but less than .25	$20	.00 but less than .10	$3	.00 but less than .75
11	.25 but less than .70	22	.10 but less than .35	5	.75 but less than 1.00
12	.70 but less than 1.00	24	.35 but less than .70		
		25	.70 but less than 1.00		

c.   Profit = 45 - 11 - 24 - 5 = $5/unit

d.   Profit = 45 - 10 - 25 - 3 = $7/unit

e.   Simulation will provide a distribution of the profit per unit values. Calculating the percentage of simulation trials providing a profit less than $5 per unit would provide an estimate of the probability the profit per unit will be unacceptably low.

13. Use the PortaCom spreadsheet. Simulation results will vary, but a mean profit of approximately $710,000 with a probability of a loss in the 0.07 to 0.10 range can be anticipated.

14. The spreadsheet for this problem is as follows:

	A	B	C	D	E	F	G
1	**Madeira Manufacturing Company**						
2							
3	Selling Price per Unit		$50				
4	Fixed Cost		$30,000				
5							
6	**Variable Cost (Uniform Distribution)**				**Demand (Normal distribution)**		
7	Smallest Value		$16		Mean		1200
8	Largest Value		$24		Standard Deviation		300
9							
10	**Simulation Trials**						
11		Variable					
12	Trial	Cost per Unit	Demand	Profit			
13	1	$23.41	1179	$1,338			
14	2	$19.95	1022	$722			
15							
16	**Note: To reconstruct the complete speadsheet:**						
17	1. **Block** rows 21 to 509						
18	2. On the **Insert** menu, click**Rows**						
19	3. **Copy** row 14 (Trial 2) to fill rows 15 to 510.						
20	Trial 500 will appear in row 512 of the spreadsheet.						
21							
22	499	$16.36	1044	$5,117			
23	500	$19.93	924	($2,209)			
24							
25		**Summary Statistics**					
26		Mean Profit		$5,891			
27		Standard Deviation		$9,439			
28		Minimum Profit		-$24,013			
29		Maximum Profit		$34,554			
30		Number of Losses		129			
31		Probability of Loss		0.2580			

Selected cell formulas are as follows:

Cell	Formula
B13	=$C$7+RAND()*($C$8-$C$7)
C13	=NORMINV(RAND(),$G$7,$G$8)
D13	=($C$3-B13)*C13-$C$4

a. The mean profit should be approximately $6,000. Simulation results will vary with most simulations having a mean profit between $5,500 and $6,500.

b. 120 to 150 of the 500 simulation trails should show a loss. Thus, the probability of a loss should be between 0.24 and 0.30.

c. This project appears too risky. The relatively high probability of a loss and only roughly $6,000 as a mean profit indicate that the potential gain is not worth the risk of a loss. More precise estimates of the variable cost per unit and the demand could help determine a more precise profit estimate.

15.   The spreadsheet for this problem is as follows:

	A	B	C	D	E	F	G	H
1	**Dice Experiment**							
2								
3	**Die Outcome**							
4	Lower	Upper						
5	Random No.	Random No.	Outcome					
6	0	1/6	1					
7	1/6	1/3	2					
8	1/3	1/2	3					
9	1/2	2/3	4					
10	2/3	5/6	5					
11	5/6	1	6					
12								
13	**Simulation Trials**					**Results**		
14	Trial	Die 1	Die 2	Total				
15	1	6	3	9		Number of 7's		155
16	2	6	3	9		Probability of a 7		0.1550
17	3	1	6	7				
18								
19	**Note: To reconstruct the complete speadsheet:**							
20	1. **Block** rows 24 to 1011							
21	2. On the **Insert** menu, click **Rows**							
22	3. **Copy** row 17 (Trial 3) to fill rows 18 to 1012.							
23	Trial 1000 will appear in row 1014 of the spreadsheet.							
24								
25	999	3	2	5				
26	1000	1	2	3				

Selected cell formulas are as follows:

Cell	Formula
B15	=VLOOKUP(RAND(),$A$6:$C$11,3)
C15	=VLOOKUP(RAND(),$A$6:$C$11,3)
D15	=B15+C15
H15	=COUNTIF(D15:D1014,7)
H16	=H15/COUNT(D15:D1014)

Simulation results will vary with most simulations showing between 155 and 180 7's. The probability of a 7 should be approximately 0.1667.

16. Target Answers:

a. Simulation runs will vary. Generally, 340 to 380, or roughly 36% of the simulation runs will show $130,000 to be the highest and winning bid.

b. $150,000. Profit = $160,000 = $150,000 = $10,000

c. Again, simulation results will vary. Simulation results should be consistent with the following:

Amount Bid	Win the Bid	Profit per Win	Average Profit
$130,000	340 to 380 times	$30,000	Approx. $10,800
$140,000	620 to 660 times	$20,000	Approx. $12,800
$150,000	1000 times	$10,000	$10,000

Using an average profit criterion, both the $130,000 and $140,000 bids are preferred to the $150,000 bid. Of the three alternatives, $140,000 is the recommended bid.

17. The spreadsheet for this problem is as follows:

	A	B	C	D	E	F	G
1	Grear Tire Company						
2							
3	Tire Mileage						
4	Mean		36500				
5	Standard Deviation		5000				
6							
7	Simulation			Results			
8	Tire	Mileage					
9	1	38,379		Mileage		Number	Percent
10	2	36,597		Exceed 40,000		118	23.6%
11	3	28,820		Less Than 32,000		88	17.6%
12	4	38,387		Less Than 30,000		48	9.6%
13	5	39,638		Less Than 28,000		25	5.0%
14	6	34,548					
15							
16	Note: To reconstruct the complete speadsheet:						
17	1. Block rows 21 to 505						
18	2. On the Insert menu, click Rows						
19	3. Copy row 14 (Tire 6) to fill rows 15 to 506.						
20	Trial 500 will appear in row 508 of the spreadsheet.						
21							
22	499	34,613					
23	500	38,730					

Selected cell formulas are as follows:

Cell	Formula
B9	=NORMINV(RAND(),$C$4,$C$5)
F10	=COUNTIF(B9:B508,">40000")

a. Most simulations will provide between 105 and 130 tires exceeding 40,000 miles. The percentage should be roughly 24%.

b.

Mileage	In Most Simulations Number of Tires	Approximate Percentage
32,000	80 to 100	18%
30,000	42 to 55	10%
28,000	18 to 30	4%

c. Of mileages considered, 30,000 miles should come closest to meeting the tire guarantee mileage guideline.

18. The spreadsheet with data in thousands of dollars is as follows:

	A	B	C	D	E	F	G	H
1	Contractor Bidding							
2								
3	Contractor A (Uniform Distribution)					Contractor B (Normal Distribution)		
4	Smallest Value		$600			Mean		$700
5	Largest Value		$800			Standard Deviation		$50
6								
7								
8	Simulation					Results		
9		Contractor	Contractor	Highest		Contractor's	Number	Probability
10	Trial	A's Bid	B's Bid	Bid		Bid	of Wins	of Winning
11	1	$739.2	$628.2	$739.2		750	629	0.629
12	2	$705.9	$729.6	$729.6		775	824	0.824
13	3	$795.2	$771.1	$795.2		785	887	0.887
14	4	$630.4	$690.8	$690.8				
15								
16	Note: To reconstruct the complete speadsheet:							
17	1. Block rows 21 to 1007							
18	2. On the Insert menu, click Rows							
19	3. Copy row 14 (Trial 4) to fill rows 15 to 1008.							
20	Trial 1000 will appear in row 1010 of the spreadsheet.							
21								
22	999	$660.0	$709.2	$709.2				
23	1000	$751.7	$586.4	$751.7				

Selected cell formulas are as follows:

Cell	Formula
B11	=$C$4+RAND()*($C$5-$C$4)
C11	=NORMINV(RAND(),$H$4,$H$5)
D11	=MAX(B11:C11)
G11	=COUNTIF(D11:D1010,"<750")
H11	=G11/COUNT(D11:D1010)

a. Cell G11 provides the number of times the contractor's bid of $750,000 will beat the highest competitive bid shown in column D. Simulation results will vary but the bid of $750,000 should win roughly 600 to 650 of the 1000 times. The probability of winning the bid should be between 0.60 and 0.65.

b. Cells G12 and G13 provide the number of times the bids of $775,000 and $785,000 win. Again, simulation results vary but the probability of $750,000 winning should be roughly 0.82 and the probability of $785,000 winning should be roughly 0.88. Given these results, a contractor's bid of $775,000 is recommended.

19. Butler Inventory simulation spreadsheet. The shortage cost has been eliminated so $0 can be entered in cell C5. Trial replenishment levels of 110, 115, 120 and 125 can be entered in cell C7.

Since the shortage cost has been eliminated, Butler can be expected to reduce the replenishment level. This will allow more shortages. However, since the cost of a stockout is only the lost profit and not the lost profit plus a goodwill shortage cost, Butler can permit more shortages and still show an improvement in profit.

A replenishment level of 115 should provide a mean profit of approximately $4600. The replenishment levels of 110, 115 and 120 all provide near optimal results.

20. The spreadsheet for this problem is as follows:

	A	B	C	D	E	F	G	H
1	Mandrell Toy Company							
2								
3	Fixed Production Cost			$100,000		Demand (Normal Distribution)		
4	Variable Cost per Unit			$34		Mean		60000
5	Selling Price per Unit			$42		Standard Deviation		15000
6	Surplus Price per Unit			$10				
7								
8	Production Quantity			60000				
9								
10								
11	Simulation							
12				Sales		Surplus		
13	Trial	Demand	Sales	Revenue	Surplus	Revenue	Total Cost	Net Profit
14	1	79778	60000	$2,520,000	0	$0	$2,140,000	$380,000
15	2	53392	53392	$2,242,485	6608	$66,075	$2,140,000	$168,560
16								
17	Note: To reconstruct the complete spreadsheet:							
18	1. Block rows 22 to 510							
19	2. On the Insert menu, click Rows							
20	3. Copy row 15 (Trial 2) to fill rows 16 to 511.							
21	Trial 500 will appear in row 513 of the spreadsheet.							
22								
23	499	35958	35958	$1,510,223	24042	$240,423	$2,140,000	($389,354)
24	500	53384	53384	$2,242,133	6616	$66,159	$2,140,000	$168,291
25								
26						Summary Statistics		
27						Mean Profit		$192,667
28						Standard Deviation		$284,079
29						Minimum Profit		($900,021)
30						Maximum Profit		$380,000
31						Number of Stockouts		257
32						Probability of a Stockout		0.514

Selected cell formulas are as follows:

Cell	Formula
B14	=NORMINV(RAND(),$H$4,$H$5)
C14	=IF(B14<$D$8,B14,$D$8)
D14	=$D$5*C14
E14	=IF(C14<$D$8,($D$8-C14),0)
F14	=$D$6*E14
G14	=$D$3+$D$4*$D$8
H14	=D14+F14-G14

The number of stockouts can be computed by using the cell formula

=COUNTIF(E14:E513,"=0")

a. The simulated mean profit with a production quantity of 60,000 units should be in the $170,000 to $210,000 range. The probability of a stockout is about 0.50.

b. The conservative 50,000 unit production quantity is recommended with a simulated mean profit of approximately $230,000. The more aggressive 70,000 unit production quantity should show a simulated mean profit less than $100,000.

c. When a 50,000 unit production quantity is used, the probability of a stockout should be approximately 0.75. This is a relative high probability indicating that Mandrell has a good chance of being able to sell all the dolls it produces for the holiday season. As a result, a shortage of dolls is likely to occur. However, this production strategy will enable the company to avoid the high cost associated with selling excess dolls for a loss after the first of the year.

21.   The spreadsheet for this problem is as follows:

	A	B	C	D	E	F	G
1	**South Central Airlines**						
2							
3	**Passenger Demand - 32 Reservations**				**Profit/Cost Data Per Passenger**		
4	Lower	Upper	Number of		Profit		$100
5	Random No.	Random No.	Passengers		Overbooking Cost		$150
6	0.00	0.05	28				
7	0.05	0.30	29		Airplane Capacity		30
8	0.30	0.80	30				
9	0.80	0.95	31				
10	0.95	1.00	32				
11							
12							
13	**Simulation**						
14		Passenger	Passengers	Profit from	Overbooked	Overbooking	
15	Trial	Demand	on the Flight	the Flight	Passengers	Cost	Net Profit
16	1	29	29	$2,900	0	$0	$2,900
17	2	31	30	$3,000	1	$150	$2,850
18							
19	**Note: To reconstruct the complete speadsheet:**						
20	1. **Block** rows 24 to 512						
21	2. On the **Insert** menu, click**Rows**						
22	3. **Copy** row 17 (Trial 2) to fill rows 18 to 513.						
23	Trial 500 will appear in row 515 of the spreadsheet.						
24							
25	499	30	30	$3,000	0	$0	$3,000
26	500	30	30	$3,000	0	$0	$3,000
27							
28	Total	119	118		**Summary Statistics**		
29					Mean Profit		$2,930
30					Standard Deviation		$82
31					Minimum Profit		$2,700
32					Maximum Profit		$3,000
33					Service Level		99.2%

Selected cell formulas are as follows:

Cell	Formula
B16	=VLOOKUP(RAND(),$A$6:$C$10,3)
C16	=IF(B16>$G$7,$G$7,B16)
D16	=$G$4*C16
E16	=B16-C16
F16	=$G$5*E16
G16	=D16-F16

a. Without overbooking, the problem states that South Central has a mean profit of $2,800 per flight. The overbooking simulation model with a total of 32 reservations (2 overbookings) projects a mean profit of approximately $2925. This is an increase in profit of $125 per flight (4.5%). The overbooking strategy appears worthwhile. The simulation spreadsheet indicates a service level of approximately 99.2% for all passenger demand. This indicates that only 0.8% of the passengers would encounter an overbooking problem. The overbooking strategy up to a total of 32 reservations is recommended.

b. The same spreadsheet design can be used to simulate other overbooking strategies including accepting 31, 33 and 34 passenger reservations. In each case, South Central would need to obtain data on the passenger demand probabilities. Changing the passenger demand table and rerunning the simulation model would enable South Central to evaluate the other overbooking alternatives and arrive at the most beneficial overbooking policy.

22.   Use the Hammondsport Savings Bank spreadsheet. Changing the interarrival times to a uniform distribution between 0 and 4 is the only change needed for each spreadsheet.

The mean time between arrivals is 2 minutes and the mean service time is 2 minutes. On the surface it appears that there is an even balance between the arrivals and the services. However, since both arrivals and services have variability, simulated system performance with 1 ATM will probably be surprisingly poor. Simulation results can be expected to show some waiting times of 30 minutes or more near the end of the simulation period. One ATM is clearly not acceptable.

23.   Use the Hammondsport Savings Bank spreadsheet.

a. The interarrival times and service times section of the spreadsheet will need to be modified. Assume that the mean interarrival time of 0.75 is placed in cell B4 and that the mean service time of 1 is placed in cell B8. The following cell formulas would be required.

Cell	Formula
B16	=(1/$B$4)*LN(RAND())
F16	=(1/$B$8)*LN(RAND())

The simulation results will vary but most should show an average waiting time in a 2 to 4 minute range.

b. The service time mean and standard deviation would be entered in cells B8 and B9 as in the original Hammondsport 1 ATM spreadsheet. Cell F16 would have its original cell formula =NORMINV(RAND(),$B$8,$B$9).

Again simulation results will vary. The lower variability of the normal probability distribution should improve the performance of the waiting line by reducing the average waiting time. An average waiting time in the range 1.4 to 2 minutes should be observed for most simulation runs.

24.   Use the Hammondsport 2 ATMs spreadsheet on the CD that accompanies the text. The interarrival times section of the spreadsheet will need to be modified. Assume that the mean interarrival time of 4 is placed in cell B4. The following cell formula would be placed in cell B16: =(1/$B$4)*LN(RAND())

a. Both the mean interarrival time and the mean service time should be approximately 4 minutes.

b. Simulation results should provide a mean waiting time of approximately .8 minutes (48 seconds).

c. Simulation results should predict approximately 150 to 170 customers had to wait. Generally, the percentage should be 30 to 35%.

Chapter 14
Decision Analysis

Learning Objectives

1. Learn how to describe a problem situation in terms of decisions to be made, chance events and consequences.

2. Be able to analyze a simple decision analysis problem from both a payoff table and decision tree point of view.

3. Be able to develop a risk profile and interpret its meaning.

4. Be able to use sensitivity analysis to study how changes in problem inputs affect or alter the recommended decision.

5. Be able to determine the potential value of additional information.

6. Learn how new information and revised probability values can be used in the decision analysis approach to problem solving.

7. Understand what a decision strategy is.

8. Learn how to evaluate the contribution and efficiency of additional decision making information.

9. Be able to use a Bayesian approach to computing revised probabilities.

10. Know what is meant by utility.

11. Understand why utility could be preferred to monetary value in some situations.

12. Be able to use expected utility to select a decision alternative.

13. Be able to use TreePlan software for decision analysis problems.

14. Understand the following terms:

decision alternatives	decision strategy
chance events	risk profile
states of nature	sensitivity analysis
influence diagram	prior probabilities
payoff table	posterior probabilities
decision tree	expected value of sample information (EVSI)
optimistic approach	efficiency of sample information
conservative approach	Bayesian revision
minimax regret approach	utility
opportunity loss or regret	lottery
expected value approach	expected utility
expected value of perfect information (EVPI)	

Chapter 14

Solutions:

1. a.

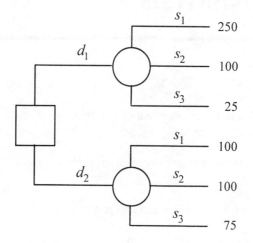

    b.

Decision	Maximum Profit	Minimum Profit
d_1	250	25
d_2	100	75

Optimistic approach: select d_1

Conservative approach: select d_2

Regret or opportunity loss table:

	s_1	s_2	s_3
d_1	0	0	50
d_2	150	0	0

Maximum Regret: 50 for d_1 and 150 for d_2; select d_1

2. a.

Decision	Maximum Profit	Minimum Profit
d_1	14	5
d_2	11	7
d_3	11	9
d_4	13	8

Optimistic approach: select d_1

Conservative approach: select d_3

Regret or Opportunity Loss Table with the Maximum Regret

	s_1	s_2	s_3	s_4	Maximum Regret
d_1	0	1	1	8	8
d_2	3	0	3	6	6
d_3	5	0	1	2	5
d_4	6	0	0	0	6

Minimax regret approach: select d_3

b. The choice of which approach to use is up to the decision maker. Since different approaches can result in different recommendations, the most appropriate approach should be selected before analyzing the problem.

c.

Decision	Minimum Cost	Maximum Cost
d_1	5	14
d_2	7	11
d_3	9	11
d_4	8	13

Optimistic approach: select d_1

Conservative approach: select d_2 or d_3

Regret or Opportunity Loss Table

	s_1	s_2	s_3	s_4	Maximum Regret
d_1	6	0	2	0	6
d_2	3	1	0	2	3
d_3	1	1	2	6	6
d_4	0	1	3	8	8

Minimax regret approach: select d_2

3. a. The decision to be made is to choose the best plant size. There are 2 alternatives to choose from: a small plant or a large plant.

The chance event is the market demand for the new product line. It is viewed as having 3 possible outcomes (states of nature): low, medium and high.

b. Influence Diagram:

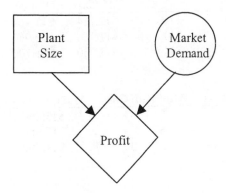

c.

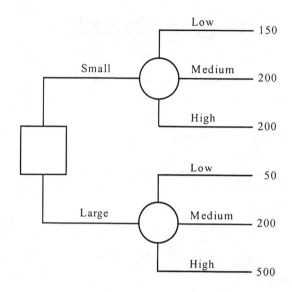

d.

Decision	Maximum Profit	Minimum Profit	Maximum Regret
Small	200	150	300
Large	500	50	100

Optimistic approach: select Large plant

Conservative approach: select Small plant

Minimax regret approach: select Large plant

4. a. The decision is to choose the best lease option; there are three alternatives. The chance event is the number of miles Amy will drive per year. There are three possible outcomes.

b. The payoff table for Amy's problem is shown below. To illustrate how the payoffs were computed, we show how to compute the total cost of the Forno Saab lease assuming Amy drives 15,000 miles per year.

Total Cost = (Total Monthly Charges) + (Total Additional Mileage Cost)
= 36($299) + $0.15(45,000 - 36,000)
= $10,764 + $1350
= $12,114

	Annual Miles Driven		
Dealer	12,000	15,000	18,000
Forno Saab	$10,764	$12,114	$13,464
Midtown Motors	$11,160	$11,160	$12,960
Hopkins Automotive	$11,700	$11,700	$11,700

c.

Decision Alternative	**Minimum Cost**	**Maximum Cost**
Forno Saab	$10,764	$13,464
Midtown Motors	$11,160	$12,960
Hopkins Automotive	$11,700	$11,700

Optimistic Approach: Forno Saab ($10,764)

Conservative Approach: Hopkins Automotive ($11,160)

Opportunity Loss or Regret Table

	Actual Miles Driven			
Decision Alternative	36,000	45,000	54,000	Maximum Regret
Forno Saab	0	$954	$1,764	$1764
Midtown Motors	$396	0	$1,260	$1260
Hopkins Automotive	$936	$540	0	$936

Minimax Regret Approach: Hopkins Automotive

d. EV (Forno Saab)   = 0.5($10,764) + 0.4($12,114) + 0.1($13,464) = $11,574
    EV (Midtown Motors)   = 0.5($11,160) + 0.4($11,160) + 0.1($12,960) = $11,340
    EV (Hopkins Automotive) = 0.5($11,700) + 0.4($11,700) + 0.1($11,700) = $11,700

Best Decision: Midtown Motors

e.

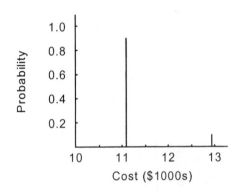

The most likely cost is $11,160 with a probability of 0.9. There is a probability of 0.1 of incurring a cost of $12,960.

f. EV (Forno Saab)   = 0.3($10,764) + 0.4($12,114) + 0.3($13,464) = $12,114
    EV (Midtown Motors)   = 0.3($11,160) + 0.4($11,160) + 0.3($12,960) = $11,700
    EV (Hopkins Automotive) = 0.3($11,700) + 0.4($11,700) + 0.3($11,700) = $11,700

Best Decision: Midtown Motors or Hopkins Automotive

With these probabilities, Amy would be indifferent between the Midtown Motors and Hopkins Automotive leases. However, if the probability of driving 18,000 miles per year goes up any further, the Hopkins Automotive lease will be the best.

5. $EV(d_1) = .65(250) + .15(100) + .20(25) = 182.5$
    $EV(d_2) = .65(100) + .15(100) + .20(75) = 95$

The optimal decision is d_1

6. a. $EV(d_1) = 0.5(14) + 0.2(9) + 0.2(10) + 0.1(5) = 11.3$
   $EV(d_2) = 0.5(11) + 0.2(10) + 0.2(8) + 0.1(7) = 9.8$
   $EV(d_3) = 0.5(9) + 0.2(10) + 0.2(10) + 0.1(11) = 9.6$
   $EV(d_4) = 0.5(8) + 0.2(10) + 0.2(11) + 0.1(13) = 9.5$

   Recommended decision: d_1

   b. The best decision in this case is the one with the smallest expected value; thus, d_4, with an expected cost of 9.5, is the recommended decision.

7. a. EV(own staff) $= 0.2(650) + 0.5(650) + 0.3(600) = 635$
   EV(outside vendor) $= 0.2(900) + 0.5(600) + 0.3(300) = 570$
   EV(combination) $= 0.2(800) + 0.5(650) + 0.3(500) = 635$

   The optimal decision is to hire an outside vendor with an expected annual cost of $570,000.

   b. The risk profile in tabular form is shown.

Cost	Probability
300	0.3
600	0.5
900	0.2
	1.0

   A graphical representation of the risk profile is also shown:

   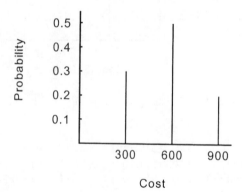

8. a. $EV(d_1) = p(10) + (1 - p)(1) = 9p + 1$
   $EV(d_2) = p(4) + (1 - p)(3) = 1p + 3$

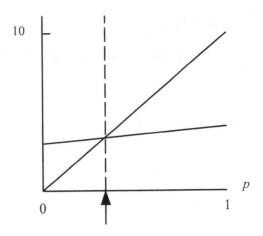

Value of p for
which EVs are equal

$9p + 1 = 1p + 3$ and hence $p = .25$

d_2 is optimal for $p \leq 0.25$; d_1 is optimal for $p \geq 0.25$.

b. The best decision is d_2 since $p = 0.20 < 0.25$.

EV$(d_1) = 0.2(10) + 0.8(1) = 2.8$
EV$(d_2) = 0.2(4) + 0.8(3) = 3.2$

c. The best decision in part (b) is d_2 with EV$(d_2) = 3.2$. Decision d_2 will remain optimal as long as its expected value is higher than that for d_1 (EV$(d_1) = 2.8$).

Let s = payoff for d_2 under state of nature s_1. Decision d_2 will remain optimal provided that

EV $(d_2) = 0.2(s) + 0.8(3) \geq 2.8$
$0.2s \geq 2.8 - 2.4$
$0.2s \geq 0.4$
$s \geq 2$

As long as the payoff for s_1 is ≥ 2, then d_2 will be optimal.

9. a. The decision to be made is to choose the type of service to provide. The chance event is the level of demand for the Myrtle Air service. The consequence is the amount of quarterly profit. There are two decision alternatives (full price and discount service). There are two outcomes for the chance event (strong demand and weak demand).

b.

Type of Service	Maximum Profit	Minimum Profit
Full Price	$960	-$490
Discount	$670	$320

Optimistic Approach: Full price service
Conservative Approach: Discount service

Opportunity Loss or Regret Table

	High Demand	Low Demand	Maximum Regret
Full Service	0	810	810
Discount Service	290	0	290

Minimax Regret Approach: Discount service

c.   EV(Full) = 0.7(960) + 0.3(-490) = 525
     EV (Discount) = 0.7(670) + 0.3(320) = 565

Optimal Decision: Discount service

d.   EV(Full) = 0.8(960) + 0.2(-490) = 670
     EV (Discount) = 0.8(670) + 0.2(320) = 600

Optimal Decision: Full price service

e.   Let p = probability of strong demand

EV(Full) = p(960) + (1- p)(-490) = 1450p - 490
EV (Discount) = p(670) + (1- p)(320) = 350p + 320

EV (Full) = EV(Discount)
1450p - 490 = 350p + 320
1100p = 810
p = 810/1100 = 0.7364

If p = 0.7364, the two decision alternatives provide the same expected value.

For values of p below 0.7364, the discount service is the best choice. For values of p greater than 0.7364, the full price service is the best choice.

10. a.

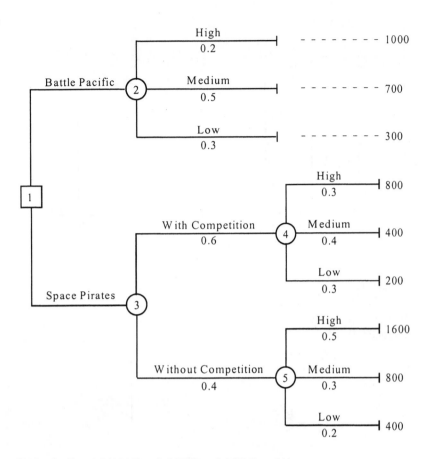

b. EV(node 2) = 0.2(1000) + 0.5(700) + 0.3(300) = 640

EV(node 4) = 0.3(800) + 0.4(400) + 0.3(200) = 460

EV(node 5) = 0.5(1600) + 0.3(800) + 0.2(400) = 1120

EV(node 3) = 0.6EV(node 4) + 0.4EV(node 5) = 0.6(460) + 0.4(1120) = 724

Space Pirates is recommended. Expected value of $724,000 is $84,000 better than Battle Pacific.

c. Risk Profile for Space Pirates

Outcome:

1600	(0.4)(0.5)	= 0.20
800	(0.6)(0.3) + (0.4)(0.3)	= 0.30
400	(0.6)(0.4) + (0.4)(0.2)	= 0.32
200	(0.6)(0.3)	= 0.18

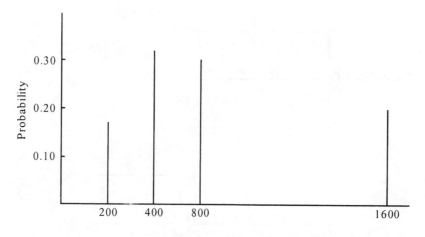

Profit ($ thousands)

d. Let p = probability of competition

$p = 0$ EV(node 5) = 1120
$p = 1$ EV(node 4) = 460

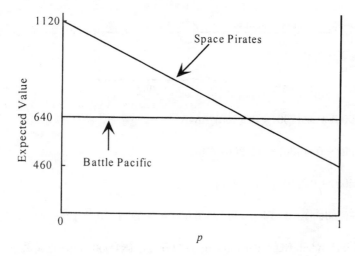

$$1120 - p(1120 - 460) = 640$$
$$660p = 480$$
$$p = 480/660 = 0.7273$$

The probability of competition would have to be greater than 0.7273 before we would change to the Battle Pacific video game.

11. a. Currently, the large complex decision is optimal with EV(d_3) = 0.8(20) + 0.2(-9) = 14.2. In order for d_3 to remain optimal, the expected value of d_2 must be less than or equal to 14.2.

Let s = payoff under strong demand

$EV(d_2) = 0.8(s) + 0.2(5) \leq 14.2$

$0.8\,s + 1 \leq 14.2$

$0.8\,s \leq 13.2$

$s \leq 16.5$

Thus, if the payoff for the medium complex under strong demand remains less than or equal to $16.5 million, the large complex remains the best decision.

b. A similar analysis is applicable for d_1

$EV(d_1) = 0.8(s) + 0.2(7) \leq 14.2$

$0.8\,s + 1.4 \leq 14.2$

$0.8\,s \leq 12.8$

$s \leq 16$

If the payoff for the small complex under strong demand remains less than or equal to $16 million, the large complex remains the best decision.

12. a. There is only one decision to be made: whether or not to lengthen the runway. There are only two decision alternatives. The chance event represents the choices made by Air Express and DRI concerning whether they locate in Potsdam. Even though these are decisions for Air Express and DRI, they are chance events for Potsdam.

The payoffs and probabilities for the chance event depend on the decision alternative chosen. If Potsdam lengthens the runway, there are four outcomes (both, Air Express only, DRI only, neither). The probabilities and payoffs corresponding to these outcomes are given in the tables of the problem statement. If Potsdam does not lengthen the runway, Air Express will not locate in Potsdam so we only need to consider two outcomes: DRI and no DRI. The approximate probabilities and payoffs for this case are given in the last paragraph of the problem statements.

The consequence is the estimated annual revenue.

b. Runway is Lengthened

New Air Express Center	New DRI Plant	Probability	Annual Revenue
Yes	Yes	0.3	$600,000
Yes	No	0.1	$150,000
No	Yes	0.4	$250,000
No	No	0.2	-$200,000

EV (Runway is Lengthened) $= 0.3(\$600,000) + 0.1(\$150,000) + 0.4(\$250,000) - 0.2(\$200,000)$
$= \$255,000$

c. EV (Runway is Not Lengthened) $= 0.6(\$450,000) + 0.4(\$0) = \$270,000$

d. The town should not lengthen the runway.

e. EV (Runway is Lengthened) $= 0.4(600,000) + 0.1(\$150,000) + 0.3(\$250,000) - 0.2(200,000)$
$= \$290,000$

The revised probabilities would lead to the decision to lengthen the runway.

13. a. The decision is to choose what type of grapes to plant, the chance event is demand for the wine and the consequence is the expected annual profit contribution. There are three decision alternatives (Chardonnay, Riesling and both). There are four chance outcomes: (W,W); (W,S); (S,W); and (S,S). For instance, (W,S) denotes the outcomes corresponding to weak demand for Chardonnay and strong demand for Riesling.

b. In constructing a decision tree, it is only necessary to show two branches when only a single grape is planted. But, the branch probabilities in these cases are the sum of two probabilities. For example, the probability that demand for Chardonnay is strong is given by:

$$\begin{aligned} \text{P (Strong demand for Chardonnay)} &= \text{P(S,W)} + \text{P(S,S)} \\ &= 0.25 + 0.20 \\ &= 0.45 \end{aligned}$$

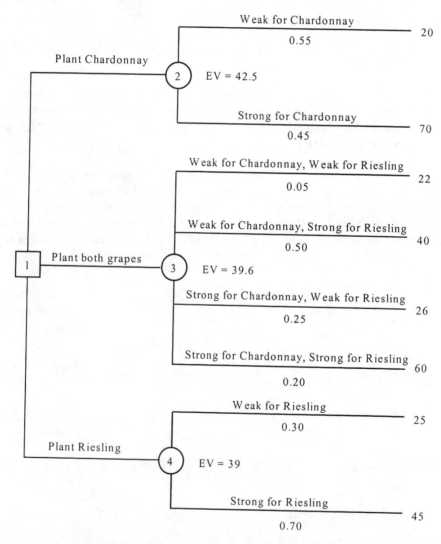

c. EV (Plant Chardonnay) = 0.55(20) +0.45(70) = 42.5
EV (Plant both grapes) = 0.05(22) + 0.50(40) + 0.25(26) + 0.20(60) = 39.6
EV (Plant Riesling)   = 0.30(25) + 0.70(45) = 39.0

Optimal decision: Plant Chardonnay grapes only.

d. This changes the expected value in the case where both grapes are planted and when Riesling only is planted.

EV (Plant both grapes) = 0.05(22) + 0.50(40) +0.05(26) + 0.40(60) = 46.4

EV (Plant Riedling) = 0.10(25) + 0.90(45) = 43.0

We see that the optimal decision is now to plant both grapes. The optimal decision is sensitive to this change in probabilities.

e. Only the expected value for node 2 in the decision tree needs to be recomputed.

EV (Plant Chardonnay) = 0.55(20) + 0.45(50) = 33.5
This change in the payoffs makes planting Chardonnay only less attractive. It is now best to plant both types of grapes. The optimal decision is sensitive to a change in the payoff of this magnitude.

14. a. If s_1 then d_1 ; if s_2 then d_1 or d_2; if s_3 then d_2

 b. EVwPI = .65(250) + .15(100) + .20(75) = 192.5

 c. From the solution to Problem 5 we know that $EV(d_1) = 182.5$ and $EV(d_2) = 95$; thus, the recommended decision is d_1. Hence, EVwoPI = 182.5.

 d. EVPI = EVwPI - EVwoPI = 192.5 - 182.5 = 10

15. a. EV (Small)   = 0.1(400) + 0.6(500) + 0.3(660) = 538
  EV (Medium) = 0.1(-250) + 0.6(650) + 0.3(800) = 605
  EV (Large)   = 0.1(-400) + 0.6(580) + 0.3(990) = 605

  Best decision: Build a medium or large-size community center.

  Note that using the expected value approach, the Town Council would be indifferent between building a medium-size community center and a large-size center.

 b. Risk profile for medium-size community center:

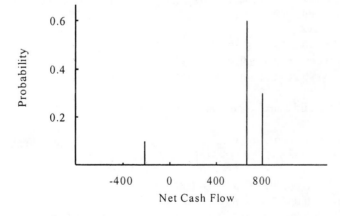

Risk profile for large-size community center:

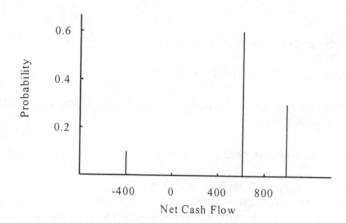

Given the mayor's concern about the large loss that would be incurred if demand is not large enough to support a large-size center, we would recommend the medium-size center. The large-size center has a probability of 0.1 of losing $400,000. With the medium-size center, the most the town can loose is $250,000.

c. The Town's optimal decision strategy based on perfect information is as follows:

If the worst-case scenario, build a small-size center
If the base-case scenario, build a medium-size center
If the best-case scenario, build a large-size center

Using the consultant's original probability assessments for each scenario, 0.10, 0.60 and 0.30, the expected value of a decision strategy that uses perfect information is:

EVwPI = 0.1(400) + 0.5(650) + 0.4(990) = 761

In part (a), the expected value approach showed that EV(Medium) = EV(Large) = 605. Therefore, EVwoPI = 605 and EVPI = 761 - 605 = 156

The town should seriously consider additional information about the likelihood of the three scenarios. Since perfect information would be worth $156,000, a good market research study could possibly make a significant contribution.

d. EV (Small)   = 0.2(400) + 0.5(500) + 0.3(660) = 528
    EV (Medium) = 0.2(-250) + 0.5(650) + 0.3(800) = 515
    EV (Small)   = 0.2(-400) + 0.5(580) + 0.3(990) = 507

Best decision: Build a small-size community center.

e. If the promotional campaign is conducted, the probabilities will change to 0.0, 0.6 and 0.4 for the worst case, base case and best case scenarios respectively.

EV (Small)   = 0.0(400) + 0.6(500) + 0.4(660) = 564
EV (Medium) = 0.0(-250) + 0.6(650) + 0.4(800) = 710
EV (Small)   = 0.0(-400) + 0.6(580) + 0.4(990) = 744

In this case, the recommended decision is to build a large-size community center. Compared to the analysis in Part (a), the promotional campaign has increased the best expected value by $744,000 - 605,000 = $139,000. Compared to the analysis in part (d), the promotional campaign has increased the best expected value by $744,000 - 528,000 = $216,000.

Even though the promotional campaign does not increase the expected value by more than its cost ($150,000) when compared to the analysis in part (a), it appears to be a good investment. That is, it eliminates the risk of a loss, which appears to be a significant factor in the mayor's decision-making process.

16. a.

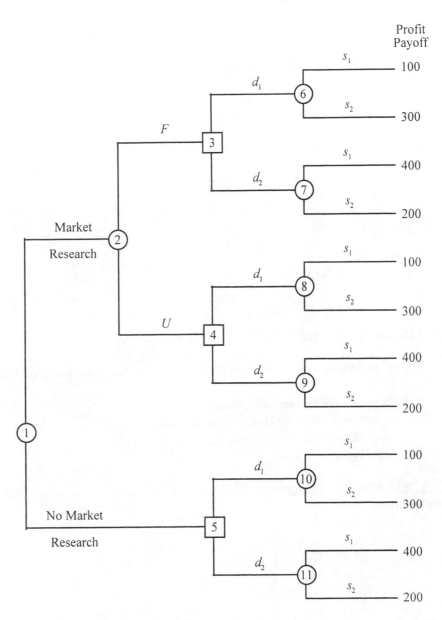

b. EV (node 6) = 0.57(100) + 0.43(300) =   186
    EV (node 7) = 0.57(400) + 0.43(200) =   314
    EV (node 8) = 0.18(100) + 0.82(300) =   264
    EV (node 9) = 0.18(400) + 0.82(200) =   236

$$EV \text{ (node 10)} = 0.40(100) + 0.60(300) = 220$$
$$EV \text{ (node 11)} = 0.40(400) + 0.60(200) = 280$$

$$EV \text{ (node 3)} = Max(186,314) = 314 \quad d_2$$
$$EV \text{ (node 4)} = Max(264,236) = 264 \quad d_1$$
$$EV \text{ (node 5)} = Max(220,280) = 280 \quad d_2$$

$$EV \text{ (node 2)} = 0.56(314) + 0.44(264) = 292$$
$$EV \text{ (node 1)} = Max(292,280) = 292$$

$\therefore$ Market Research

      If Favorable, decision d_2

      If Unfavorable, decision d_1

17.   The decision tree is as shown in the answer to problem 16a. The calculations using the decision tree in problem 16a with the probabilities and payoffs here are as follows:

a,b. $EV \text{ (node 6)} = 0.18(600) + 0.82(-200) = -56$
$$EV \text{ (node 7)} = 0$$
$$EV \text{ (node 8)} = 0.89(600) + 0.11(-200) = 512$$
$$EV \text{ (node 9)} = 0$$
$$EV \text{ (node 10)} = 0.50(600) + 0.50(-200) = 200$$
$$EV \text{ (node 11)} = 0$$

$$EV \text{ (node 3)} = Max(-56,0) = 0 \quad d_2$$
$$EV \text{ (node 4)} = Max(512,0) = 512 \quad d_1$$
$$EV \text{ (node 5)} = Max(200,0) = 200 \quad d_1$$

$$EV \text{ (node 2)} = 0.55(0) + 0.45(512) = 230.4$$

Without the option, the recommended decision is d_1 purchase with an expected value of $200,000.

With the option, the best decision strategy is

      If high resistance H, d_2 do not purchase

      If low resistance L, d_1 purchase

Expected Value = $230,400

c.   EVSI = $230,400 - $200,000 = $30,400. Since the cost is only $10,000, the investor should purchase the option.

18. a.   Outcome 1 ($ in 000s)

Bid	-$200
Contract	-2000
Market Research	-150
High Demand	+5000
	$2650

Outcome 2 ($ in 000s)

Bid	-$200
Contract	-2000
Market Research	-150
Moderate Demand	+3000
	$650

b.   EV (node 8) = 0.85(2650) + 0.15(650) = 2350
 EV (node 5) = Max(2350, 1150) = 2350   Decision: Build
 EV (node 9) = 0.225(2650) + 0.775(650) = 1100
 EV (node 6) = Max(1100, 1150) = 1150   Decision: Sell
 EV (node 10) = 0.6(2800) + 0.4(800)= 2000
 EV (node 7) = Max(2000, 1300) = 2000   Decision: Build

 EV (node 4) = 0.6 EV(node 5) + 0.4 EV(node 6) = 0.6(2350) + 0.4(1150) = 1870

 EV (node 3) = MAX (EV(node 4), EV (node 7)) = Max (1870, 2000) = 2000
                 Decision: No Market Research

 EV (node 2) = 0.8 EV(node 3) + 0.2 (-200) = 0.8(2000) + 0.2(-200) = 1560

 EV (node 1) = MAX (EV(node 2), 0) = Max (1560, 0) = 1560
                 Decision: Bid on Contract

Decision Strategy:

         Bid on the Contract
         Do not do the Market Research
         Build the Complex
                          Expected Value is $1,560,000

c.   Compare Expected Values at nodes 4 and 7.

     EV(node 4) = 1870   Includes $150 cost for research
     EV (node 7) = 2000

     Difference is 2000 - 1870 = $130

     Market research cost would have to be lowered $130,000 to $20,000 or less to make undertaking the research desirable.

d. Shown below is the reduced decision tree showing only the sequence of decisions and chance events for Dante's optimal decision strategy. If Dante follows this strategy, only 3 outcomes are possible with payoffs of -200, 800, and 2800. The probabilities for these payoffs are found by multiplying the probabilities on the branches leading to the payoffs. A tabular presentation of the risk profile is:

Payoff ($million)	Probability
-200	.20
800	(.8)(.4) = .32
2800	(.8)(.6) = .48

Reduced Decision Tree Showing Only Branches for Optimal Strategy

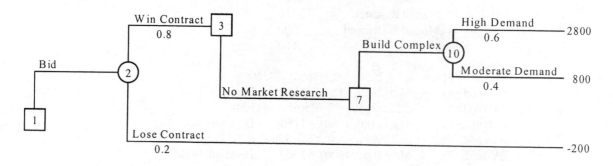

19. a.

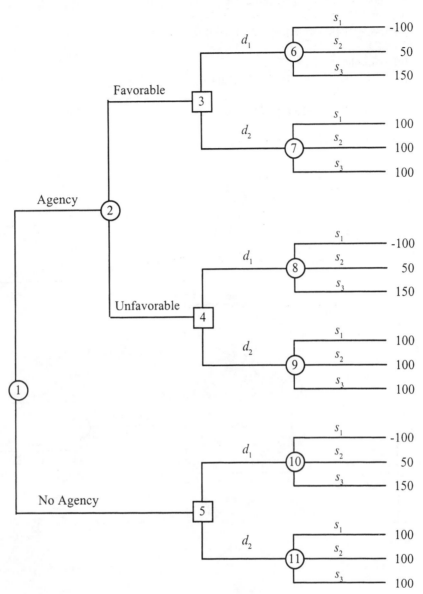

b. Using node 5,

EV (node 10) = 0.20(-100) + 0.30(50) + 0.50(150) = 70
EV (node 11) = 100

Decision Sell Expected Value = $100

c. EVwPI = 0.20(100) + 0.30(100) + 0.50(150) = $125

EVPI = $125 - $100 = $25

d. EV (node 6) = 0.09(-100) + 0.26(50) + 0.65(150) = 101.5
EV (node 7) = 100
EV (node 8) = 0.45(-100) + 0.39(50) + 0.16(150) = -1.5
EV (node 9) = 100

EV (node 3) = Max(101.5,100)   =   101.5   Produce
EV (node 4) = Max(-1.5,100)   =   100   Sell

EV (node 2) = 0.69(101.5) + 0.31(100) = 101.04

If Favorable, Produce
If Unfavorable, Sell   EV = $101.04

  e. EVSI = $101.04 - 100 = $1.04 or $1,040.

  f. No, maximum Hale should pay is $1,040.

  g. No agency; sell the pilot.

20. a.

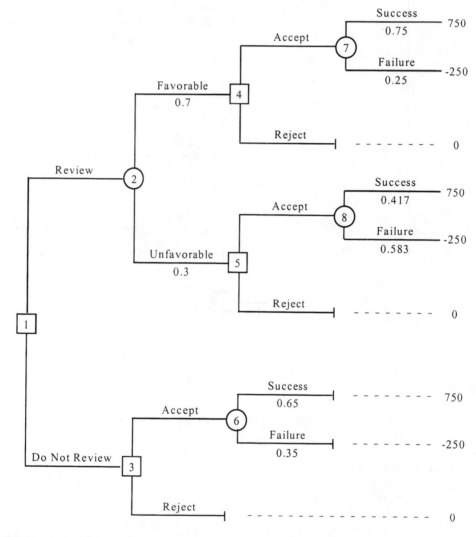

  b. EV (node 7) = 0.75(750) + 0.25(-250) = 500
       EV (node 8) = 0.417(750) + 0.583(-250) = 167

       Decision (node 4) → Accept EV = 500
       Decision (node 5) → Accept EV = 167

EV(node 2) = 0.7(500) + 0.3(167) = $400

Note: Regardless of the review outcome F or U, the recommended decision alternative is to accept the manuscript.

EV(node 3) = .65(750) + .35(-250) = $400

The expected value is $400,000 regardless of review process. The company should accept the manuscript.

c. The manuscript review cannot alter the decision to accept the manuscript. Do not do the manuscript review.

d. Perfect Information.

If s_1, accept manuscript $750
If s_2, reject manuscript -$250

EVwPI = 0.65(750) + 0.35(0) = 487.5

EVwoPI = 400

EVPI = 487.5 - 400 = 87.5 or $87,500.

A better procedure for assessing the market potential for the textbook may be worthwhile.

21. a. EV (1 lot) = 0.3(60) + 0.3(60) + 0.4(50) = 56
        EV (2 lots) = 0.3(80) + 0.3(80) + 0.4(30) = 60
        EV (3 lots) = 0.3 (100) + 0.3(70) + 0.4(10) = 55

Decision: Order 2 lots   Expected Value $60,000

b. The following decision tree applies.

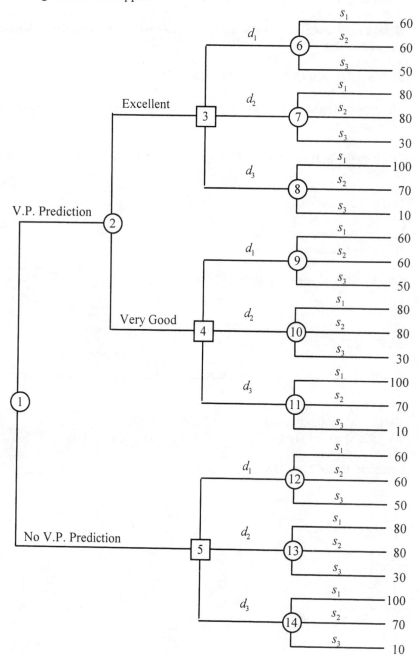

Calculations

$$EV \text{ (node 6)} = 0.34(60) + 0.32(60) + 0.34(50) = 56.6$$
$$EV \text{ (node 7)} = 0.34(80) + 0.32(80) + 0.34(30) = 63.0$$
$$EV \text{ (node 8)} = 0.34(100) + 0.32(70) + 0.34(10) = 59.8$$
$$EV \text{ (node 9)} = 0.20(60) + 0.26(60) + 0.54(50) = 54.6$$
$$EV \text{ (node 10)} = 0.20(80) + 0.26(80) + 0.54(30) = 53.0$$
$$EV \text{ (node 11)} = 0.20(100) + 0.26(70) + 0.54(10) = 43.6$$
$$EV \text{ (node 12)} = 0.30(60) + 0.30(60) + 0.40(50) = 56.0$$
$$EV \text{ (node 13)} = 0.30(80) + 0.30(80) + 0.40(30) = 60.0$$
$$EV \text{ (node 14)} = 0.30(100) + 0.30(70) + 0.40(10) = 55.0$$

EV (node 3) = Max(56.6,63.0,59.8) = 63.0 2 lots
EV (node 4) = Max(54.6,53.0,43.6) = 54.6 1 lot
EV (node 5) = Max(56.0,60.0,55.0) = 60.0 2 lots

EV (node 2) = 0.70(63.0) + 0.30(54.6) = 60.5
EV (node 1) = Max(60.5,60.0) = 60.5 Prediction

Optimal Strategy:
If prediction is excellent, 2 lots
If prediction is very good, 1 lot

c. EVwPI = 0.3(100) + 0.3(80) + 0.4(50) = 74
    EVPI = 74 - 60 = 14
    EVSI = 60.5 - 60 = 0.5

$$\text{Efficiency} = \frac{\text{EVSI}}{\text{EVPI}}(100) = \frac{0.5}{14}(100) = 3.6\%$$

The V.P.'s recommendation is only valued at EVSI = \$500. The low efficiency of 3.6% indicates other information is probably worthwhile. The ability of the consultant to forecast market conditions should be considered.

22.

State of Nature	$P(s_j)$	$P(I \mid s_j)$	$P(I \cap s_j)$	$P(s_j \mid I)$
s_1	0.2	0.10	0.020	0.1905
s_2	0.5	0.05	0.025	0.2381
s_3	0.3	0.20	0.060	0.5714
	1.0	$P(I) =$	0.105	1.0000

23. a. EV (d_1) = 0.8(15) + 0.2(10) = 14.0
    EV (d_2) = 0.8(10) + 0.2(12) = 10.4
    EV (d_3) = 0.8(8) + 0.2(20) = 10.4

    Decision d_1 Expected Value 14

b. EVwPI = 0.8(15) + 0.2(20) = 16
    EVPI = 16 - 14 = 2

c. Indicator I

State of Nature	Prior Probabilities	Conditional Probabilities	Joint Probabilities	Posterior Probabilities
State s1	0.8	0.20	0.16	0.52
State s2	0.2	0.75	0.15	0.48
		$P(I) =$	0.31	1.00

EV (d_1) = 0.5161(15) + 0.4839(10) = 12.6
EV (d_2) = 0.5161(10) + 0.4839(12) = 11.0
EV (d_3) = 0.5161(8) + 0.4839(20) = 13.8

If indicator I occurs, decision d_3 is recommended.

24.   The revised probabilities are shown on the branches of the decision tree.

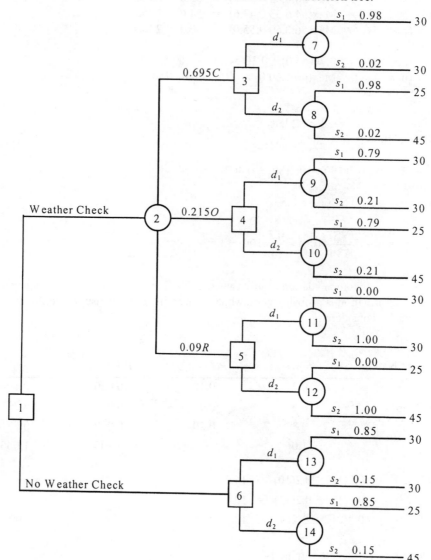

EV (node 7)   =   30
EV (node 8)   =   0.98(25) + 0.02(45)   =   25.4
EV (node 9)   =   30
EV (node 10) =   0.79(25) + 0.21(45)   =   29.2
EV (node 11) =   30
EV (node 12) =   0.00(25) + 1.00(45)   =   45.0
EV (node 13) =   30
EV (node 14) =   0.85(25) + 0.15(45)   =   28.0

EV (node 3)   =   Min(30,25.4)   =   25.4   Expressway
EV (node 4)   =   Min(30,29.2)   =   29.2   Expressway
EV (node 5)   =   Min(30,45)   =   30.0   Queen City
EV (node 6)   =   Min(30,28)   =   28.0   Expressway

EV (node 2)   =   0.695(25.4) + 0.215(29.2) + 0.09(30.0)   =   26.6
EV (node 1)   =   Min(26.6,28)   =   26.6   Weather

Strategy:

Check the weather, take the expressway unless there is rain. If rain, take Queen City Avenue.

Expected time: 26.6 minutes.

25. a. d_1 = Manufacture component s_1 = Low demand
         d_2 = Purchase component s_2 = Medium demand
                                               s_3 = High demand

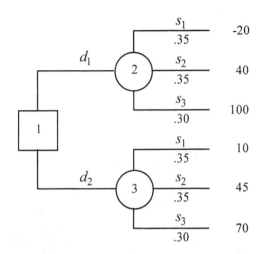

EV(node 2) = (0.35)(-20) + (0.35)(40) + (0.30)(100) = 37

EV(node 3) = (0.35)(10) + (0.35)(45) + (0.30)(70) = 40.25

Recommended decision: d_2 (purchase component)

b. Optimal decision strategy with perfect information:

   If s_1 then d_2

   If s_2 then d_2

   If s_3 then d_1

   Expected value of this strategy is 0.35(10) + 0.35(45) + 0.30(100) = 49.25
   EVPI = 49.25 - 40.25 = 9 or $9,000

c. If F - Favorable

State of Nature	$P(s_j)$	$P(F \mid s_j)$	$P(F \cap s_j)$	$P(s_j \mid F)$
s_1	0.35	0.10	0.035	0.0986
s_2	0.35	0.40	0.140	0.3944
s_3	0.30	0.60	0.180	0.5070
		$P(F) =$	0.355	

If U - Unfavorable

State of Nature	$P(s_j)$	$P(U \mid s_j)$	$P(U \cap s_j)$	$P(s_j \mid U)$
s_1	0.35	0.90	0.315	0.4884
s_2	0.35	0.60	0.210	0.3256
s_3	0.30	0.40	0.120	0.1860
		$P(U) =$	0.645	

The probability the report will be favorable is $P(F) = 0.355$

d. Assuming the test market study is used, a portion of the decision tree is shown below.

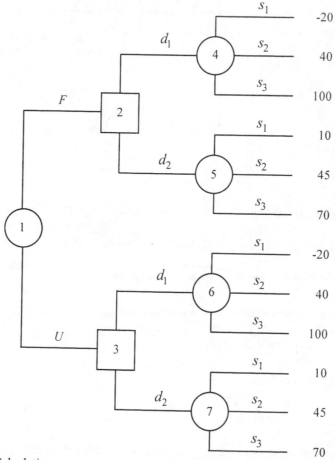

Summary of Calculations

Node	Expected Value
4	64.51
5	54.23
6	21.86
7	32.56

Decision strategy:

If F then d_1 since EV(node 4) > EV(node 5)

If U then d_2 since EV(node 7) > EV(node 6)

EV(node 1) = 0.355(64.51) + 0.645(32.56) = 43.90

e. With no information:

EV(d_1) = 0.35(-20) + 0.35(40) + 0.30(100) = 37

EV(d_2) = 0.35(10) + 0.35(45) + 0.30(70) = 40.25

Recommended decision: d_2

f. Optimal decision strategy with perfect information:

If s_1 then d_2
If s_2 then d_2
If s_3 then d_1

Expected value of this strategy is 0.35(10) + 0.35(45) + 0.30(100) = 49.25
EVPI = 49.25 - 40.25 = 9 or \$9,000
Efficiency = (3650 / 9000)100 = 40.6%

26. Risk avoider, at \$20 payoff $p = 0.70$

$\therefore$ EV(Lottery) = 0.70(100) + 0.30(-100) = \$40

$\therefore$ Will Pay 40 - 20 = \$20

Risk taker B, at \$20 payoff $p = 0.45$

$\therefore$ EV(Lottery) = 0.45(100) + 0.55(-100) = -\$10

$\therefore$ Will Pay 20 - (-10) = \$30

27. Risk Avoider

$$\left.\begin{array}{l} EU(d_1) = 0.25(7.0) + 0.50(9.0) + 0.25(5.0) = 7.5 \\ EU(d_2) = 0.25(9.5) + 0.50(10.0) + 0.25(0.0) = 7.375 \end{array}\right\} d_1$$

Risk Taker

$$\left.\begin{array}{l} EU(d_1) = 0.25(4.5) + 0.50(6.0) + 0.25(2.5) = 4.75 \\ EU(d_2) = 0.25(7.0) + 0.50(10.0) + 0.25(0.0) = 6.75 \end{array}\right\} d_2$$

Risk Neutral

$$EU(d_1) = 0.25(6.0) + 0.50(7.5) + 0.25(4.0) = 6.175$$
$$EU(d_2) = 0.25(9.0) + 0.50(10.0) + 0.25(0.0) = 7.25 \Big\} \ d_2$$

28. a.

$$EV(d_1) = 0.40(100) + 0.30(25) + 0.30(0) = 47.5$$
$$EV(d_2) = 0.40(75) + 0.30(50) + 0.30(25) = 52.5 \Big\} \ d_2$$
$$EV(d_3) = 0.40(50) + 0.30(50) + 0.30(50) = 50.0$$

   b.   Using Utilities

Decision Maker A		Decision Maker B	
$EU(d_1) = 4.9$		$EU(d_1) = 4.45$	
$EU(d_2) = 5.9$	d_3	$EU(d_2) = 3.75$	d_1
$EU(d_3) = 6.0$		$EU(d_3) = 3.00$	

   c.   Difference in attitude toward risk. Decision maker A tends to avoid risk, while decision maker B tends to take a risk for the opportunity of a large payoff.

29. a. $P(\text{Win}) = 1/250,000$ \qquad $P(\text{Lose}) = 249,999/250,000$

   $EV(d_1) = 1/250,000(300,000) + 249,999/250,000(-2) = -0.80$

   $EV(d_2) = 0$

   $\therefore \ d_2$ - Do not purchase lottery ticket.

   b.

		s_1 Win	s_2 Lose
Purchase	d_1	10	0
Do Not Purchase	d_2	0.00001	0.00001

   $EU(d_1) = 1/250,000(10) + 249,999/250,000(0) = 0.00004$

   $EU(d_2) = 0.00001$

   $\therefore \ d_1$ - purchase lottery ticket.

30. a. $EV(d_1) = 10,000$

   $EV(d_2) = 0.96(0) + 0.03(100,000) + 0.01(200,000) = 5,000$

   Using EV approach $\rightarrow$ No Insurance (d_2)

   b.   Lottery:

$$p \quad = \text{probability of a \$0 Cost}$$
$$1 - p \quad = \text{probability of a \$200,000 Cost}$$

c.

		s_1 None	s_2 Minor	s_3 Major
Insurance	d_1	9.9	9.9	9.9
No Insurance	d_2	10.0	6.0	0.0

$EU(d_1) = 9.9$

$EU(d_2) = 0.96(10.0) + 0.03(6.0) + 0.01(0.0) = 9.78$

∴ Using EU approach → Insurance (d_1)

d. Use expected utility approach.

31. a. $EV(d_1) = 0.60(1000) + 0.40(-1000) = \$200$

$EV(d_2) = \$0$

∴ $d_1 \rightarrow$ Bet

b.

$$\left.\begin{array}{l}\text{Lottery: p of winning \$1,000} \\ \text{(1 - p) of losing \$1,000}\end{array}\right\} \text{ vs. } \left\{\begin{array}{l}\$0\end{array}\right.$$

Most students, if realistic, should require a high value for p. While students will differ, let us use $p = 0.90$ as an example.

c. $EU(d_1) = 0.60(10.0) + 0.40(0.0) = 6.0$
$EU(d_2) = 0.60(9.0) + 0.40(9.0) = 9.0$

∴ $d_2 \rightarrow$ Do Not Bet (Risk Avoider)

d. No, different decision makers have different attitudes toward risk, therefore different utilities.

32. a.

$$\left.\begin{array}{l}EV(A) = 0.80(60) + 0.20(70) = 62 \\ EV(B) = 0.70(45) + 0.30(90) = 58.5\end{array}\right\} \text{ Route B}$$

b. Lottery:

p = probability of a 45 minute travel time
$(1 - p)$ = probability of a 90 minute travel time

c.

		Route Open	Route Delays
Route A	d_1	8.0	6.0
Route B	d_2	10.0	0.0

$$EU(A) = 0.80(8.0) + 0.20(6.0) = 7.6$$
$$EU(B) = 0.70(10.0) + 0.30(0.00) = 7.0$$
Route A

Risk avoider strategy.

33. a.   EV $= 0.10(150,000) + 0.25(100,000) + 0.20(50,000) + 0.15(0) + 0.20(-50,000) + 0.10(-100,000)$
          $= \$30,000$

Market the new product.

b.   Lottery

$$p = \text{probability of } \$150,000$$
$$(1 - p) = \text{probability of } -\$100,000$$

c.   Risk Avoider.

d. $EU(\text{market}) = 0.10(10.0) + 0.25(9.5) + 0.20(7.0) + 0.15(5.0) + 0.20(2.5) + 0.10(0.0) = 6.025$
     $EU(\text{don't market}) = EU(\$0) = 5.0$

Market the new product.

e.   Yes - Both EV and EU recommend marketing the product.

34. a.

		s_1 Win	s_2 Lose
Bet	d_1	350	-10
Do Not Bet	d_2	0	0

b. $EV(d_1) = 1/38(350) + 37/38(-10) = -\$0.53$
     $EV(d_2) = 0$

     $\therefore\ d_2 \rightarrow$ Do Not Bet

c.   Risk takers, because risk neutral and risk avoiders would not bet.

d. $EU(d_1) \geq EU(d_2)$ for decision maker to prefer Bet decision.

     $1/38(10.0) + 37/38(0.0) \geq EU(d_2)$
     $0.26 \geq EU(d_2)$

     $\therefore$ Utility of $0 payoff must be between 0 and 0.26.

Chapter 15
Multicriteria Decision Problems

Learning Objectives

1. Understand the concept of multicriteria decision making and how it differs from situations and procedures involving a single criterion.

2. Be able to develop a goal programming model of a multiple criteria problem.

3. Know how to use the goal programming graphical solution procedure to solve goal programming problems involving two decision variables.

4. Understand how the relative importance of the goals can be reflected by altering the weights or coefficients for the decision variables in the objective function.

5. Know how to develop a solution to a goal programming model by solving a sequence of linear programming models using a general purpose linear programming package.

6. Know what a scoring model is and how to use it to solve a multicriteria decision problem.

7. Understand how a scoring model uses weights to identify the relative importance of each criterion.

8. Know how to apply the analytic hierarchy process (AHP) to solve a problem involving multiple criteria.

9. Understand how AHP utilizes pairwise comparisons to establish priority measures for both the criteria and decision alternatives.

10. Understand the following terms:

multicriteria decision problem	analytic hierarchy process (AHP)
goal programming	hierarchy
deviation variables	pairwise comparison matrix
priority levels	synthesization
goal equation	consistency
preemptive priorities	consistency ratio
scoring model	

Solutions:

1. a.

	Amount Needed to
Raw Material	Achieve Both P_1 Goals
1	$^2/_5\,(30) + {}^1/_2\,(15) = 12 + 7.5 = 19.5$
2	$^1/_5\,(15) = 3$
3	$^3/_5\,(30) + {}^3/_{10}\,(15) = 18 + 4.5 = 22.5$

Since there are only 21 tons of Material 3 available, it is not possible to achieve both goals.

b. Let
x_1 = the number of tons of fuel additive produced
x_2 = the number of tons of solvent base produced
d_1^+ = the amount by which the number of tons of fuel additive produced exceeds the target value of 30 tons
d_1^- = the amount by which the number of tons of fuel additive produced is less than the target of 30 tons
d_2^+ = the amount by which the number of tons of solvent base produced exceeds the target value of 15 tons
d_2^- = the amount by which the number of tons of solvent base is less than the target value of 15 tons

$$\text{Min} \quad d_1^- + d_2^-$$

s.t.

$$
\begin{array}{rcrcccccccrl}
^2/_5\,x_1 & + & {}^1/_2\,x_2 & & & & & & & \leq & 20 & \text{Material 1} \\
& & {}^1/_5\,x_2 & & & & & & & \leq & 5 & \text{Material 2} \\
^3/_5\,x_1 & + & {}^3/_{10}\,x_2 & & & & & & & \leq & 21 & \text{Material 3} \\
x_1 & & & - & d_1^+ & + & d_1^- & & & = & 30 & \text{Goal 1} \\
& & x_2 & - & d_2^+ & + & d_2^- & & & = & 15 & \text{Goal 2} \\
\end{array}
$$

$$x_1,\ x_2,\ d_1^+,\ d_1^-,\ d_2^+,\ d_2^- \geq 0$$

c. In the graphical solution, point A minimizes the sum of the deviations from the goals and thus provides the optimal product mix.

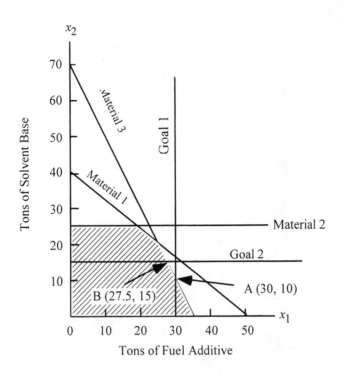

d. In the graphical solution shown above, point B minimizes $2d_1^- + d_2^-$ and thus provides the optimal product mix.

2. a. Let

x_1 = number of shares of AGA Products purchased

x_2 = number of shares of Key Oil purchased

To obtain an annual return of exactly 9%

$$0.06(50)x_1 + 0.10(100)x_2 = 0.09(50,000)$$
$$3x_1 + 10x_2 = 4500$$

To have exactly 60% of the total investment in Key Oil

$$100x_2 = 0.60(50,000)$$
$$x_2 = 300$$

Therefore, we can write the goal programming model as follows:

Min $P_1(d_1^-)$ + $P_2(d_2^+)$

s.t.

$50x_1$	+	$100x_2$				$\leq$	50,000	Funds Available
$3x_1$	+	$10x_2$	$- d_1^+$	$+ d_1^-$	$=$	4,500	P_1 Goal
		x_2	$- d_2^+$	$+ d_2^-$	$=$	300	P_2 Goal

$$x_1, x_2, d_1^+, d_1^-, d_2^+, d_2^- \geq 0$$

b. In the graphical solution shown below, $x_1 = 250$ and $x_2 = 375$.

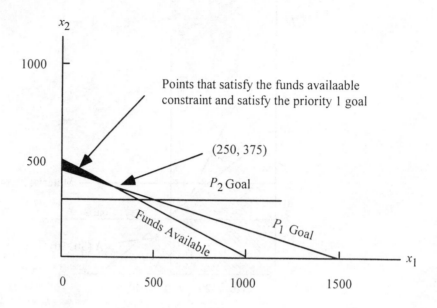

3. a. Let

x_1 = number of units of product 1 produced

x_2 = number of units of product 2 produced

Min $P_1(d_1^+) + P_1(d_1^-) + P_1(d_2^+) + P_1(d_2^-) + P_2(d_3^-)$

s.t.

$1x_1$	+	$1x_2$	-	d_1^+	+	d_1^-	=	350	Goal 1
$2x_1$	+	$5x_2$	-	d_2^+	+	d_2^-	=	1000	Goal 2
$4x_1$	+	$2x_2$	-	d_3^+	+	d_3^-	=	1300	Goal 3

$$x_1, x_2, d_1^+, d_1^-, d_2^+, d_2^-, d_3^-, d_3^+ \geq 0$$

b. In the graphical solution, point A provides the optimal solution. Note that with $x_1 = 250$ and $x_2 = 100$, this solution achieves goals 1 and 2, but underachieves goal 3 (profit) by $100 since $4(250) + 2(100) = \$1200$.

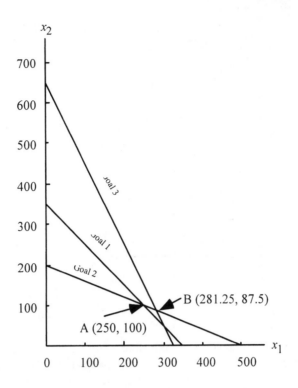

c.

$$\text{Max} \quad 4x_1 \quad + \quad 2x_2$$

s.t.

$1x_1$	+	$1x_2$	$\leq$	350	Dept. A
$2x_1$	+	$5x_2$	$\leq$	1000	Dept. B
$x_1,$		x_2	$\geq$	0	

The graphical solution indicates that there are four extreme points. The profit corresponding to each extreme point is as follows:

Extreme Point	Profit
1	4(0) + 2(0) = 0
2	4(350) + 2(0) = 1400
3	4(250) + 2(100) = 1200
4	4(0) + 2(200) = 400

Thus, the optimal product mix is $x_1 = 350$ and $x_2 = 0$ with a profit of $1400.

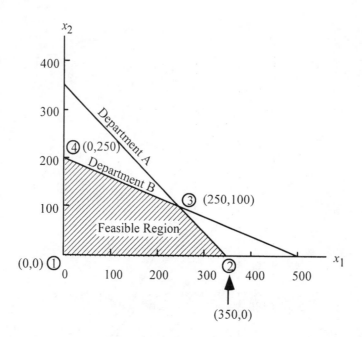

d. The solution to part (a) achieves both labor goals, whereas the solution to part (b) results in using only $2(350) + 5(0) = 700$ hours of labor in department B. Although (c) results in a \$100 increase in profit, the problems associated with underachieving the original department labor goal by 300 hours may be more significant in terms of long-term considerations.

e. Refer to the graphical solution in part (b). The solution to the revised problem is point B, with $x_1 = 281.25$ and $x_2 = 87.5$. Although this solution achieves the original department B labor goal and the profit goal, this solution uses $1(281.25) + 1(87.5) = 368.75$ hours of labor in department A, which is 18.75 hours more than the original goal.

4. a. Let

x_1 = number of gallons of IC-100 produced
x_2 = number of gallons of IC-200 produced

$$\text{Min} \quad P_1(d_1^-) \;+\; P_1(d_2^+) \;+\; P_2(d_3^-) \;+\; P_2(d_4^-) \;+\; P_3(d_5^-)$$

s.t.

$20x_1$	+	$30x_2$	−	d_1^+	+	d_1^-	=	4800	Goal 1
$20x_1$	+	$30x_2$	−	d_2^+	+	d_2^-	=	6000	Goal 2
x_1			−	d_3^+	+	d_3^-	=	100	Goal 3
		x_2	−	d_4^+	+	d_4^-	=	120	Goal 4
x_1	+	x_2	−	d_5^+	+	d_5^-	=	300	Goal 5

x_1, x_2, all deviation variables ≥ 0

b. In the graphical solution, the point $x_1 = 120$ and $x_2 = 120$ is optimal.

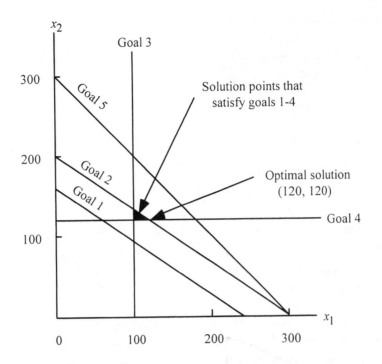

5. a.

May:	$x_1 - s_1$	$= 200$
June:	$s_1 + x_2 - s_2$	$= 600$
July:	$s_2 + x_3 - s_3$	$= 600$
August:	$s_3 + x_4$	$= 600$ (no need for ending inventory)

b.

May to June:	$x_2 - x_1 - d_1^+ + d_1^- = 0$
June to July:	$x_3 - x_2 - d_2^+ + d_2^- = 0$
July to August:	$x_4 - x_3 - d_3^+ + d_3^- = 0$

c. No. For instance, there must be at least 200 pumps in inventory at the end of May to meet the June requirement of shipping 600 pumps.

The inventory variables are constrained to be nonnegative so we only need to be concerned with positive deviations.

June:	$s_1 - d_4^+ = 0$
July:	$s_2 - d_5^+ = 0$
August:	$s_3 - d_6^+ = 0$

d. Production capacity constraints are needed for each month.

May:	$x_1 \leq 500$
June:	$x_2 \leq 400$
July:	$x_3 \leq 800$
August:	$x_4 \leq 500$

e. Min $d_1^+ + d_1^- + d_2^+ + d_2^- + d_3^+ + d_3^- + d_4^+ + d_5^+ + d_6^+$

s.t.

      3 Goal equations in (b)
      3 Goal equations in (c)
      4 Demand constraints in (a)
      4 Capacity constraints in (d)

$x_1, x_2, x_3, x_4, s_1, s_2, s_3, d_1^+, d_1^-, d_2^+, d_2^-, d_3^+, d_3^-, d_4^+, d_5^+, d_6^+ \geq 0$

Optimal Solution: $x_1 = 400$, $x_2 = 400$, $x_3 = 700$, $x_4 = 500$, $s_1 = 200$, $s_2 = 0$, $s_3 = 100$,
$d_2^+ = 300$, $d_3^- = 200$, $d_4^+ = 200$, $d_6^+ = 100$

f. Yes. Note in part (c) that the inventory deviation variables are equal to the ending inventory variables. So, we could eliminate those goal equations and substitute s_1, s_2, and s_3 for d_4^+, d_5^+ and d_6^+ in the objective function. In this case the inventory variables themselves represent the deviations from the goal of zero.

6. a. Note that getting at least 10,000 customers from group 1 is equivalent to $x_1 = 40,000$ (25% of 40,000 = 10,000) and getting 5,000 customers is equivalent to $x_2 = 50,000$ (10% of 50,000 = 5,000). Thus, to satisfy both goals, 40,000 + 50,000 = 90,000 letters would have to be mailed at a cost of 90,000($1) = $90,000.

Let

    x_1 = number of letters mailed to group 1 customers
    x_2 = number of letters mailed to group 2 customers
    d_1^+ = number of letters mailed to group 1 customers over the desired 40,000
    d_1^- = number of letters mailed to group 1 customers under the desired 40,000
    d_2^+ = number of letters mailed to group 2 customers over the desired 50,000
    d_2^- = number of letters mailed to group 2 customers under the desired 50,000
    d_3^+ = the amount by which the expenses exceeds the target value of $70,000
    d_3^- = the amount by which the expenses falls short of the target value of $70,000

Min $P_1(d_1^-) + P_1(d_2^-) + P_2(d_3^+)$

s.t.

x_1			$- d_1^+$	$+ d_1^-$			= 40,000	Goal 1
	x_2				$- 1d_2^+$	$+ 1d_2^-$	= 50,000	Goal 2
$1x_1$	$+ 1x_2$	$-$	d_3^+	$+ d_3^-$			= 70,000	Goal 3

$x_1, x_2, d_1^+, d_1^-, d_2^+, d_2^-, d_3^+, d_3^- \geq 0$

b. Optimal Solution: $x_1 = 40,000$, $x_2 = 50,000$

c. Objective function becomes

        $\min P_1(d_1^-) + P_1(2d_2^-) + P_2(d_3^+)$

Optimal solution does not change since it is possible to achieve both goals 1 and 2 in the original problem.

7. a. Let

x_1 = number of TV advertisements

x_2 = number of radio advertisements

x_3 = number of newspaper advertisements

$$\text{Min} \quad P_1(d_1^-) \;+\; P_2(d_2^-) \;+\; P_3(d_3^+) \;+\; P_4(d_4^+)$$

s.t.

x_1								$\leq$	10	TV
		x_2						$\leq$	15	Radio
				x_3				$\leq$	20	Newspaper
$20x_1$	+	$5x_2$	+	$10x_3$	-	d_1^+	+	d_1^-	=	400	Goal 1
$0.7x_1$	-	$0.3x_2$	-	$0.3x_3$	-	d_2^+	+	d_2^-	=	0	Goal 2
$-0.2x_1$	+	$0.8x_2$	-	$0.2x_3$	-	d_3^+	+	d_3^-	=	0	Goal 3
$25x_1$	+	$4x_2$	+	$5x_3$	-	d_4^+	+	d_4^-	=	200	Goal 4

$$x_1, x_2, x_3, d_1^+, d_1^-, d_2^+, d_2^-, d_3^+, d_3^-, d_4^+, d_4^- \geq 0$$

b. Optimal Solution: $x_1 = 9.474$, $x_2 = 2.105$, $x_3 = 20$

Rounding down leads to a recommendation of 9 TV advertisements, 2 radio advertisements, and 20 newspaper advertisements. Note, however, that rounding down results in not achieving goals 1 and 2.

8. Let x_1 = first coordinate of the new machine location

x_2 = second coordinate of the new machine location

d_i^+ = amount by which x_1 coordinate of new machine exceeds x_1 coordinate of machine i

d_i^- = amount by which x_1 coordinate of machine i exceeds x_1 coordinate of new machine

e_i^+ = amount by which x_2 coordinate of new machine exceeds x_2 coordinate of machine i

e_i^- = amount by which x_2 coordinate of machine i exceeds x_2 coordinate of new machine

The goal programming model is given below.

$$\text{Min} \quad d_1^- + d_1^+ + e_1^- + e_1^+ + d_2^- + d_2^+ + e_2^- + e_2^+ + d_3^- + d_3^+ + e_3^- + e_3^+$$

s.t.

$$
\begin{aligned}
x_1 \quad &+ d_1^- - d_1^+ &&= 1 \\
x_2 \quad &+ e_1^- - e_1^+ &&= 7 \\
x_1 \quad &+ d_2^- - d_2^+ &&= 5 \\
x_2 \quad &+ e_2^- - e_2^+ &&= 9 \\
x_1 \quad &+ d_3^- - d_3^+ &&= 6 \\
x_2 \quad &+ e_3^- - e_3^+ &&= 2
\end{aligned}
$$

$$x_1, x_2, d_1^-, d_1^+, e_1^-, e_1^+, d_2^-, d_2^+, e_2^-, e_2^+, d_3^-, d_3^+, e_3^-, e_3^+ \geq 0$$

b. The optimal solution is given by

$$
\begin{aligned}
x_1 &= 5 \\
x_2 &= 7 \\
d_i^+ &= 4 \\
e_2^- &= 2 \\
d_3^- &= 1 \\
e_3^+ &= 5
\end{aligned}
$$

The value of the solution is 12.

9.

Scoring Calculations

Criteria		Analyst Chicago	Accountant Denver	Auditor Houston
Career Advancement		35	20	20
Location		10	12	8
Management		30	25	35
Salary		28	32	16
Prestige		32	20	24
Job Security		8	10	16
Enjoy the Work		28	20	20
Score		171	139	139

The analyst position in Chicago is recommended. The overall scores for the accountant position in Denver and the auditor position in Houston are the same. There is no clear second choice between the two positions.

10.

Kenyon Manufacturing Plant Location

Criteria	Weight	Georgetown Kentucky	Ratings Marysville Ohio	Clarksville Tennessee
Land Cost	4	7	4	5
Labor Cost	3	6	5	8
Labor Availability	5	7	8	6
Construction Cost	4	6	7	5
Transportation	3	5	7	4
Access to Customers	5	6	8	5
Long Range Goals	4	7	6	5

Scoring Calculations				
Criteria		Georgetown Kentucky	Marysville Ohio	Clarksville Tennessee
Land Cost		28	16	20
Labor Cost		18	15	24
Labor Availability		35	40	30
Construction Cost		24	28	20
Transportation		15	21	12
Access to Customers		30	40	25
Long Range Goals		28	24	20
Score		178	184	151

Marysville, Ohio (184) is the leading candidate. However, Georgetown, Kentucky is a close second choice (178). Kenyon Management may want to review the relative advantages and disadvantages of these two locations one more time before making a final decision.

11.

Criteria		Myrtle Beach South Carolina	Smokey Mountains	Branson Missouri
Travel Distance		10	14	6
Vacation Cost		25	30	20
Entertainment Available		21	12	24
Outdoor Activities		18	12	10
Unique Experience		24	28	32
Family Fun		40	35	35
Score		138	131	127

Myrtle Beach is the recommended choice.

12.

Criteria		Midwestern University	State College at Newport	Handover College	Techmseh State
School Prestige		24	18	21	15
Number of Students		12	20	32	28
Average Class Size		20	25	40	35
Cost		25	40	15	30
Distance From Home		14	16	14	12
Sports Program		36	20	16	24
Housing Desirability		24	20	28	24
Beauty of Campus		15	9	24	15
Score		170	168	190	183

Handover College is recommended. However Tecumseh State is the second choice and is less expensive than Handover. If cost becomes a constraint, Tecumseh State may be the most viable alternative.

13.

Criteria		Park Shore	The Terrace	Gulf View
Cost		25	30	25
Location		28	16	36
Appearance		35	20	35
Parking		10	16	10
Floor Plan		32	28	20
Swimming Pool		7	2	3
View		15	12	27
Kitchen		32	28	24
Closet Space		18	24	12
Score		202	176	192

Park Shore is the preferred condominium.

14. a.

Criteria		220 Bowrider	230 Overnighter	240 Sundancer
Cost		40	25	15
Overnight Capability		6	18	27
Kitchen/Bath Facilities		2	8	14
Appearance		35	35	30
Engine/Speed		30	40	20
Towing/Handling		32	20	8
Maintenance		28	20	12
Resale Value		21	15	18
Score		194	181	144

Clark Anderson prefers the 220 Bowrider.

b.

Criteria		220 Bowrider	230 Overnighter	240 Sundancer
Cost		21	18	15
Overnight Capability		5	30	40
Kitchen/Bath Facilities		5	15	35
Appearance		20	28	28
Engine/Speed		8	10	6
Towing/Handling		16	12	4
Maintenance		6	5	4
Resale Value		10	12	12
Score		91	130	144

Julie Anderson prefers the 240 Sundancer.

15. Synthesization

Step 1: Column totals are 8, 10/3, and 7/4

Step 2:

Price	Accord	Saturn	Cavalier
Accord	1/8	1/10	1/7
Saturn	3/8	3/10	2/7
Cavalier	4/8	6/10	4/7

Step 3:

Price	Accord	Saturn	Cavalier	Row Average
Accord	0.125	0.100	0.143	0.123
Saturn	0.375	0.300	0.286	0.320
Cavalier	0.500	0.600	0.571	0.557

Consistency Ratio

Step 1:

$$0.123\begin{bmatrix}1\\3\\4\end{bmatrix}+0.320\begin{bmatrix}1/3\\1\\2\end{bmatrix}+0.557\begin{bmatrix}1/4\\1/2\\1\end{bmatrix}$$

$$\begin{bmatrix}0.123\\0.369\\0.492\end{bmatrix}+\begin{bmatrix}0.107\\0.320\\0.640\end{bmatrix}+\begin{bmatrix}0.139\\0.279\\0.557\end{bmatrix}=\begin{bmatrix}0.369\\0.967\\1.688\end{bmatrix}$$

Step 2:
$0.369/0.123 = 3.006$
$0.967/0.320 = 3.019$
$1.688/0.557 = 3.030$

Step 3: $\lambda_{max} = (3.006 + 3.019 + 3.030)/3 = 3.02$

Step 4: $CI = (3.02 - 3)/2 = 0.010$

Step 5: $CR = 0.010/0.58 = 0.016$

Since $CR = 0.016$ is less than 0.10, the degree of consistency exhibited in the pairwise comparison matrix for price is acceptable.

16. Synthesization

Step 1: Column totals are 17/4, 31/21, and 12

Step 2:

Style	Accord	Saturn	Cavalier
Accord	4/17	7/31	4/12
Saturn	12/17	21/31	7/12
Cavalier	1/17	3/31	1/12

Step 3:

Style	Accord	Saturn	Cavalier	Row Average
Accord	0.235	0.226	0.333	0.265
Saturn	0.706	0.677	0.583	0.656
Cavalier	0.059	0.097	0.083	0.080

Consistency Ratio

Step 1:

$$0.265\begin{bmatrix} 1 \\ 3 \\ 1/4 \end{bmatrix} + 0.656\begin{bmatrix} 1/3 \\ 1 \\ 1/7 \end{bmatrix} + 0.080\begin{bmatrix} 4 \\ 7 \\ 1 \end{bmatrix}$$

$$\begin{bmatrix} 0.265 \\ 0.795 \\ 0.066 \end{bmatrix} + \begin{bmatrix} 0.219 \\ 0.656 \\ 0.094 \end{bmatrix} + \begin{bmatrix} 0.320 \\ 0.560 \\ 0.080 \end{bmatrix} = \begin{bmatrix} 0.802 \\ 2.007 \\ 0.239 \end{bmatrix}$$

Step 2:
$0.802/0.265 = 3.028$
$2.007/0.656 = 3.062$
$0.239/0.080 = 3.007$

Step 3:
$\lambda_{max} = (3.028 + 3.062 + 3.007)/3 = 3.032$

Step 4:
$CI = (3.032 - 3)/2 = 0.016$

Step 5:
$CR = 0.016/0.58 = 0.028$

Since $CR = 0.028$ is less than 0.10, the degree of consistency exhibited in the pairwise comparison matrix for style is acceptable.

17. a.

Reputation	School A	School B
School A	1	6
School B	1/6	1

b. Step 1: Column totals are 7/6 and 7

Step 2:

Reputation	School A	School B
School A	6/7	6/7
School B	1/7	1/7

Step 3:

Reputation	School A	School B	Row Average
School A	0.857	0.857	0.857
School B	0.143	0.143	0.143

18. a. Step 1: Column totals are 47/35, 19/3, 11

Step 2:

Desirability	City 1	City 2	City 3
City 1	35/47	15/19	7/11
City 2	7/47	3/19	3/11
City 3	5/47	1/19	1/11

Step 3:

Desirability	City 1	City 2	City 3	Row Average
City 1	0.745	0.789	0.636	0.724
City 2	0.149	0.158	0.273	0.193
City 3	0.106	0.053	0.091	0.083

b. Step 1:

$$0.724 \begin{bmatrix} 1 \\ 1/5 \\ 1/7 \end{bmatrix} + 0.193 \begin{bmatrix} 5 \\ 1 \\ 1/3 \end{bmatrix} + 0.083 \begin{bmatrix} 7 \\ 3 \\ 1 \end{bmatrix}$$

$$\begin{bmatrix} 0.723 \\ 0.145 \\ 0.103 \end{bmatrix} + \begin{bmatrix} 0.965 \\ 0.193 \\ 0.064 \end{bmatrix} + \begin{bmatrix} 0.581 \\ 0.249 \\ 0.083 \end{bmatrix} = \begin{bmatrix} 2.273 \\ 0.588 \\ 0.251 \end{bmatrix}$$

Step 2: $2.273/0.724 = 3.141$
$0.588/0.193 = 3.043$
$0.251/0.083 = 3.014$

Step 3: $\lambda_{max} = (3.141 + 3.043 + 3.014)/3 = 3.066$

Step 4: $CI = (3.066 - 3)/2 = 0.033$

Step 5: $CR = 0.033/0.58 = 0.057$

Since $CR = 0.057$ is less than 0.10, the degree of consistency exhibited in the pairwise comparison matrix is acceptable.

19. a. Step 1: Column totals are 4/3 and 4

Step 2:

	A	B
A	3/4	3/4
B	1/4	1/4

Step 3:

	A	B	Row Average
A	0.75	0.75	0.75
B	0.25	0.25	0.25

b. The individual's judgements could not be inconsistent since there are only two programs being compared.

20. a.

Flavor	A	B	C
A	1	3	2
B	1/3	1	5
C	1/2	1/5	1

b. Step 1: Column totals are 11/6, 21/5, and 8

Step 2:

Flavor	A	B	C
A	6/11	15/21	2/8
B	2/11	5/21	5/8
C	3/11	1/21	1/8

Step 3:

Flavor	A	B	C	Row Average
A	0.545	0.714	0.250	0.503
B	0.182	0.238	0.625	0.348
C	0.273	0.048	0.125	0.148

c. Step 1:

$$0.503 \begin{bmatrix} 1 \\ 1/3 \\ 1/2 \end{bmatrix} + 0.348 \begin{bmatrix} 3 \\ 1 \\ 1/5 \end{bmatrix} + 0.148 \begin{bmatrix} 2 \\ 5 \\ 1 \end{bmatrix}$$

Weighted Sum:

$$\begin{bmatrix} 0.503 \\ 0.168 \\ 0.252 \end{bmatrix} + \begin{bmatrix} 1.044 \\ 0.348 \\ 0.070 \end{bmatrix} + \begin{bmatrix} 0.296 \\ 0.740 \\ 0.148 \end{bmatrix} = \begin{bmatrix} 1.845 \\ 1.258 \\ 0.470 \end{bmatrix}$$

Step 2:
1.845/0.503 = 3.668
1.258/0.348 = 3.615
0.470/0.148 = 3.123

Step 3: $\lambda_{max} = (3.668 + 3.615 + 3.123)/3 = 3.469$

Step 4: CI = (3.469 - 3)/2 = 0.235

Step 5: CR = 0.235/0.58 = 0.415

Since CR = 0.415 is greater than 0.10, the individual's judgements are not consistent.

21. a.

Flavor	A	B	C
A	1	1/2	5
B	2	1	5
C	1/5	1/5	1

b. Step 1: Column totals are 16/5, 17/10, and 11

Step 2:

Flavor	A	B	C
A	5/16	5/17	5/11
B	10/16	10/17	5/11
C	1/16	2/17	1/11

Step 3:

Flavor	A	B	C	Row Average
A	0.313	0.294	0.455	0.354
B	0.625	0.588	0.455	0.556
C	0.063	0.118	0.091	0.090

c. Step 1:

$$0.354 \begin{bmatrix} 1 \\ 2 \\ 1/5 \end{bmatrix} + 0.556 \begin{bmatrix} 1/2 \\ 1 \\ 1/5 \end{bmatrix} + 0.090 \begin{bmatrix} 5 \\ 5 \\ 1 \end{bmatrix}$$

$$\begin{bmatrix} 0.354 \\ 0.708 \\ 0.071 \end{bmatrix} + \begin{bmatrix} 0.278 \\ 0.556 \\ 0.111 \end{bmatrix} + \begin{bmatrix} 0.450 \\ 0.450 \\ 0.090 \end{bmatrix} = \begin{bmatrix} 1.083 \\ 1.715 \\ 0.272 \end{bmatrix}$$

Step 2: $1.083/0.354 = 3.063$
$1.715/0.556 = 3.085$
$0.272/0.090 = 3.014$

Step 3: $\lambda_{max} = (3.063 + 3.085 + 3.014)/3 = 3.054$

Step 4: $CI = (3.054 - 3)/2 = 0.027$

Step 5: $CR = 0.027/0.58 = 0.046$

Since CR = 0.046 is less than 0.10, the individual's judgements are consistent.

22. a. Let

D = Dallas
S = San Francisco
N = New York

Location	D	S	N
D	1	1/4	1/7
S	4	1	1/3
N	7	3	1

b. Step 1: Column totals are 12, 17/4, and 31/21

Step 2:

Location	D	S	N
D	1/12	1/17	3/31
S	4/12	4/17	7/31
N	7/12	12/17	21/31

Step 3:

Location	D	S	N	Row Average
D	0.083	0.059	0.097	0.080
S	0.333	0.235	0.226	0.265
N	0.583	0.706	0.677	0.656

c. Step 1:

$$0.080 \begin{bmatrix} 1 \\ 4 \\ 7 \end{bmatrix} + 0.265 \begin{bmatrix} 1/4 \\ 1 \\ 3 \end{bmatrix} + 0.656 \begin{bmatrix} 1/7 \\ 1/3 \\ 1 \end{bmatrix}$$

$$\begin{bmatrix} 0.080 \\ 0.320 \\ 0.560 \end{bmatrix} + \begin{bmatrix} 0.066 \\ 0.265 \\ 0.795 \end{bmatrix} + \begin{bmatrix} 0.094 \\ 0.219 \\ 0.656 \end{bmatrix} = \begin{bmatrix} 0.239 \\ 0.802 \\ 2.007 \end{bmatrix}$$

Step 2: $0.239/0.080 = 3.007$
$0.802/0.265 = 3.028$
$2.007/0.656 = 3.062$

Step 3: $\lambda_{max} = (3.007 + 3.028 + 3.062)/3 = 3.035$

Step 4: $CI = (3.035 - 3)/2 = 0.017$

Step 5: $CR = 0.017/0.58 = 0.028$

Since $CR = 0.028$ is less than 0.10, the manager's judgements are consistent.

23. a. Step 1: Column totals are 94/21, 33/4, 18, and 21/12

Step 2:

Performance	1	2	3	4
1	21/94	12/33	7/18	4/21
2	7/94	4/33	4/18	3/21
3	3/94	1/33	1/18	2/21
4	63/94	16/33	6/18	12/21

Step 3:

Performance	1	2	3	4	Row Average
1	0.223	0.364	0.389	0.190	0.292
2	0.074	0.121	0.222	0.143	0.140
3	0.032	0.030	0.056	0.095	0.053
4	0.670	0.485	0.333	0.571	0.515

b. Step 1:

$$0.292 \begin{bmatrix} 1 \\ 1/3 \\ 1/7 \\ 3 \end{bmatrix} + 0.140 \begin{bmatrix} 3 \\ 1 \\ 1/4 \\ 4 \end{bmatrix} + 0.053 \begin{bmatrix} 7 \\ 4 \\ 1 \\ 6 \end{bmatrix} + 0.515 \begin{bmatrix} 1/3 \\ 1/4 \\ 1/6 \\ 1 \end{bmatrix}$$

$$\begin{bmatrix} 0.292 \\ 0.097 \\ 0.042 \\ 0.876 \end{bmatrix} + \begin{bmatrix} 0.420 \\ 0.140 \\ 0.035 \\ 0.560 \end{bmatrix} + \begin{bmatrix} 0.371 \\ 0.212 \\ 0.053 \\ 0.318 \end{bmatrix} + \begin{bmatrix} 0.172 \\ 0.129 \\ 0.086 \\ 0.515 \end{bmatrix} = \begin{bmatrix} 1.257 \\ 0.579 \\ 0.216 \\ 2.270 \end{bmatrix}$$

Step 2: $1.257/0.292 = 4.305$
            $0.579/0.140 = 4.136$
            $0.216/0.053 = 4.075$
            $2.270/0.515 = 4.408$

Step 3: $\lambda_{max} = (4.305 + 4.136 + 4.075 + 4.408)/4 = 4.231$

Step 4: $CI = (4.231 - 4)/3 = 0.077$

Step 5: $CR = 0.077/0.90 = 0.083$

Since $CR = 0.083$ is less than 0.10, the judgements are consistent.

24. a. Criteria: Yield and Risk

    Step 1:   Column totals are 1.5 and 3

    Step 2:

Criterion	Yield	Risk	Priority
Yield	0.667	0.667	0.667
Risk	0.333	0.333	0.333

With only two criteria, $CR = 0$ and no computation of CR is made.

The same calculations for the Yield and the Risk pairwise comparison matrices provide the following:

Stocks	Yield Priority	Risk Priority
CCC	0.750	0.333
SRI	0.250	0.667

b. Overall Priorities:

CCC $0.667(0.750) + 0.333(0.333) = 0.611$
SRI $0.667(0.250) + 0.333(0.667) = 0.389$

CCC is preferred.

25. a. Criteria: Leadership, Personal, Administrative

Step 1: Column Totals are 8, 11/6 and 13/4

Step 2:

Criterion	Leader	Personal	Administrative	Priority
Leadership	0.125	0.182	0.077	0.128
Personal	0.375	0.545	0.615	0.512
Administrative	0.500	0.273	0.308	0.360

CR = 0.094 if computed.

The same calculations for the leadership, personal and administrative pairwise comparison matrices provide the following.

Candidate	Leadership Priority	Personal Priority	Administrative Priority
Jacobs	0.800	0.250	0.667
Martin	0.200	0.750	0.333

b. Overall Priorities:

Jacobs 0.128(0.800) + 0.512(0.250) + 0.360(0.667) = 0.470
Martin 0.128(0.200) + 0.512(0.250) + 0.360(0.333) = 0.530

Martin is preferred.

26. a. Criteria: Price, Sound and Reception

Step 1:   Column totals are 19/12, 13/3 and 8

Step 2:

Criterion	Price	Sound	Reception	Priority
Price	0.632	0.692	0.500	0.608
Sound	0.211	0.231	0.375	0.272
Reception	0.158	0.077	0.125	0.120

CR = 0.064

The same calculations for the price, sound and reception pairwise comparison matrices provide the following:

System	Price Priority	Sound Priority	Reception Priority
System A	0.557	0.137	0.579
System B	0.123	0.239	0.187
System C	0.320	0.623	0.234
CR	0.016	0.016	0.046

b. Overall Priorities:

System A $0.608(0.557) + 0.272(0.137) + 0.120(0.579) = 0.446$
System B $0.608(0.123) + 0.272(0.239) + 0.120(0.187) = 0.162$
System C $0.608(0.320) + 0.272(0.623) + 0.120(0.046) = 0.392$

System A is preferred.

Chapter 16
Forecasting

Learning Objectives

1. Understand that the long-run success of an organization is often closely related to how well management is able to predict future aspects of the operation.

2. Know the various components of a time series.

3. Be able to use smoothing techniques such as moving averages and exponential smoothing.

4. Be able to use the least squares method to identify the trend component of a time series.

5. Understand how the classical time series model can be used to explain the pattern or behavior of the data in a time series and to develop a forecast for the time series.

6. Be able to determine and use seasonal indexes for a time series.

7. Know how regression models can be used in forecasting.

8. Know the definition of the following terms:

   time series   mean squared error
   forecast   moving averages
   trend component   weighted moving averages
   cyclical component   smoothing constant
   seasonal component   seasonal index
   irregular component

Solutions:

1. a.

Month	Time-Series Value	3-Month Moving Average Forecast	(Error)^2	4-Month Moving Average Forecast	(Error)^2
1	9.5				
2	9.3				
3	9.4				
4	9.6	9.40	0.04		
5	9.8	9.43	0.14	9.45	0.12
6	9.7	9.60	0.01	9.53	0.03
7	9.8	9.70	0.01	9.63	0.03
8	10.5	9.77	0.53	9.73	0.59
9	9.9	10.00	0.01	9.95	0.00
10	9.7	10.07	0.14	9.98	0.08
11	9.6	10.03	0.18	9.97	0.14
12	9.6	9.73	0.02	9.92	0.10
			1.08		1.09

   MSE(3-Month) = 1.08 / 9 = .12

   MSE(4-Month) = 1.09 / 8 = .14

   Use 3-Month moving averages.

   b.   forecast = (9.7 + 9.6 + 9.6) / 3 = 9.63

   c.   For the limited data provided, the 5-week moving average provides the smallest MSE.

2. a.

Week	Time-Series Value	4-Week Moving Average Forecast	(Error)^2	5-Week Moving Average Forecast	(Error)^2
1	17				
2	21				
3	19				
4	23				
5	18	20.00	4.00		
6	16	20.25	18.06	19.60	12.96
7	20	19.00	1.00	19.40	0.36
8	18	19.25	1.56	19.20	1.44
9	22	18.00	16.00	19.00	9.00
10	20	19.00	1.00	18.80	1.44
11	15	20.00	25.00	19.20	17.64
12	22	18.75	10.56	19.00	9.00
			77.18		51.84

   b.   MSE(4-Week) = 77.18 / 8 = 9.65

   MSE(5-Week) = 51.84 / 7 = 7.41

c. For the limited data provided, the 5-week moving average provides the smallest MSE.

3. a.

Week	Time-Series Value	Weighted Moving Average Forecast	Forecast Error	$(Error)^2$
1	17			
2	21			
3	19			
4	23	19.33	3.67	13.47
5	18	21.33	-3.33	11.09
6	16	19.83	-3.83	14.67
7	20	17.83	2.17	4.71
8	18	18.33	-0.33	0.11
9	22	18.33	3.67	13.47
10	20	20.33	-0.33	0.11
11	15	20.33	-5.33	28.41
12	22	17.83	4.17	17.39
				103.43

b. MSE = 103.43 / 9 = 11.49

Prefer the unweighted moving average here.

c. You could always find a weighted moving average at least as good as the unweighted one. Actually the unweighted moving average is a special case of the weighted ones where the weights are equal.

4.

Week	Time-Series Value	Forecast	Error	$(Error)^2$
1	17			
2	21	17.00	4.00	16.00
3	19	17.40	1.60	2.56
4	23	17.56	5.44	29.59
5	18	18.10	-0.10	0.01
6	16	18.09	-2.09	4.37
7	20	17.88	2.12	4.49
8	18	18.10	-0.10	0.01
9	22	18.09	3.91	15.29
10	20	18.48	1.52	2.31
11	15	18.63	-3.63	13.18
12	22	18.27	3.73	13.91
				101.72

MSE = 101.72 / 11 = 9.25

$\alpha = .2$ provided a lower MSE; therefore $\alpha = .2$ is better than $\alpha = .1$

5. a.

Month	Y_t	3-Month Moving Averages Forecast	(Error)^2	$\alpha = 2$ Forecast	(Error)^2
1	80				
2	82			80.00	4.00
3	84			80.40	12.96
4	83	82.00	1.00	81.12	3.53
5	83	83.00	0.00	81.50	2.25
6	84	83.33	0.45	81.80	4.84
7	85	83.33	2.79	82.24	7.62
8	84	84.00	0.00	82.79	1.46
9	82	84.33	5.43	83.03	1.06
10	83	83.67	0.45	82.83	0.03
11	84	83.00	1.00	82.86	1.30
12	83	83.00	0.00	83.09	0.01
			11.12		39.06

MSE(3-Month) = 11.12 / 9 = 1.24

MSE(α = .2) = 39.06 / 11 = 3.55

Use 3-month moving averages.

b. $(83 + 84 + 83) / 3 = 83.3$

6. a. $F_{13} = .2Y_{12} + .16Y_{11} + .64(.2Y_{10} + .8F_{10}) = .2Y_{12} + .16Y_{11} + .128Y_{10} + .512F_{10}$

$F_{13} = .2Y_{12} + .16Y_{11} + .128Y_{10} + .512(.2Y_9 + .8F_9) = .2Y_{12} + .16Y_{11} + .128Y_{10} + .1024Y_9 + .4096F_9$

$F_{13} = .2Y_{12} + .16Y_{11} + .128Y_{10} + .1024Y_9 + .4096(.2Y_8 + .8F_8) = .2Y_{12} + .16Y_{11} + .128Y_{10} + .1024Y_9$
$+ .08192Y_8 + .32768F_8$

b. The more recent data receives the greater weight or importance in determining the forecast. The moving averages method weights the last n data values equally in determining the forecast.

7. a.

Month	Time-Series Value	3-Month Moving Average Forecast	(Error)^2	$\alpha = .2$ Forecast	(Error)^2
1	240				
2	350			240.00	12100.00
3	230			262.00	1024.00
4	260	273.33	177.69	255.60	19.36
5	280	280.00	0.00	256.48	553.19
6	320	256.67	4010.69	261.18	3459.79
7	220	286.67	4444.89	272.95	2803.70
8	310	273.33	1344.69	262.36	2269.57
9	240	283.33	1877.49	271.89	1016.97
10	310	256.67	2844.09	265.51	1979.36
11	240	286.67	2178.09	274.41	1184.05
12	230	263.33	1110.89	267.53	1408.50
			17,988.52		27,818.49

MSE(3-Month) = 17,988.52 / 9 = 1998.72

MSE(α = .2) = 27,818.49 / 11 = 2528.95

Based on the above MSE values, the 3-month moving averages appears better. However, exponential smoothing was penalized by including month 2 which was difficult for any method to forecast. Using only the errors for months 4 to 12, the MSE for exponential smoothing is revised to

$$MSE(\alpha = .2) = 14,694.49 / 9 = 1632.72$$

Thus, exponential smoothing was better considering months 4 to 12.

b. Using exponential smoothing,

$$F_{13} = \alpha Y_{12} + (1 - \alpha)F_{12} = .20(230) + .80(267.53) = 260$$

8. a.

Day	Time-Series Value	5-Day Moving Average Forecast	Forecast Error	(Error)^2
1	14.45			
2	15.75			
3	16.45			
4	17.40			
5	17.32			
6	15.96	16.27	-0.31	0.10
7	16.45	16.58	-0.13	0.02
8	15.60	16.72	-1.12	1.25
9	15.09	16.55	-1.46	2.12
10	16.42	16.08	0.34	0.11
11	16.21	15.90	0.31	0.09
12	15.22	15.95	-0.73	0.54

Note: MSE = 4.23/7 = 0.60

Forecast for September 4 is (15.60 + 15.09 + 16.42 + 16.21 + 15.22)/5 = 15.71

b. The weighted moving average forecasts for days 5-12 are 16.49, 17.01, 16.71, 16.57, 16.10, 15.60, 15.09, 16.42, 16.21 and 15.22

Note: MSE = 5.21/8 = 0.65

Forecast for September 4 is 0.1(15.09) + 0.2(16.42) + 0.3(16.21) + 0.4(15.22) = 15.74

c. The exponential smoothing forecasts for days 2-12 are 14.45, 15.36, 16.12, 17.02, 17.23, 16.34, 16.42, 15.85, 15.32, 16.09 and 16.17

Note: MSE = 9.57/11 = 0.87

Forecast for September 4 is 0.7(15.22) + 0.3(16.17) = 15.51

d.

Method	MSE
Moving Averages	0.60
Weighted Moving Average	0.65
Exponential Smoothing	0.87

Moving Averages is the best of the three approaches because it has the smallest MSE.

9. Note: Results were obtained using the Forecasting module of The Management Scientist.

a.

Method	Forecast	MSE
3-Quarter	80.73	2.53
4-Quarter	80.55	2.81

The 3-quarter moving average forecast is better because it has the smallest MSE.

b.

Method	Forecast	MSE
$\alpha = .4$	80.40	2.40
$\alpha = .5$	80.57	2.01

The $\alpha = .5$ smoothing constant is better because it has the smallest MSE.

c. The $\alpha = .5$ is better because it has the smallest MSE.

10. a.

Season	Time-Series Value	$\alpha = 0.1$ Forecast	$\alpha = 0.1$ (Error)^2	$\alpha = 0.2$ Forecast	$\alpha = 0.2$ (Error)^2
1991-1992	30.1				
1992-1993	32.6	30.10	6.2500	30.10	6.2500
1993-1994	29.8	30.35	0.3025	30.60	0.6400
1994-1995	29.3	30.30	0.9900	30.44	1.2996
1995-1996	30.4	30.20	0.0418	30.21	0.0353
1996-1997	29.6	30.22	0.3794	30.25	0.4220
1997-1998	28.7	30.15	2.1151	30.12	2.0155
1998-1999	26.8	30.01	10.2972	29.84	9.2157
1999-2000	29.7	29.69	0.0001	29.23	0.2222
2000-2001	31.1	29.69	1.9903	29.32	3.1582
2001-2002	31.4	29.83	2.4640	29.68	2.9642
Totals:			24.8304		26.2228

Smoothing Constant	MSE
0.1	24.8304/10 = 2.48
0.2	26.2228/10 = 2.62

A smoothing constant of 0.1 is better.

b.   Using $\alpha = 0.1$

Forecast for 2002 - 2003 season $= 0.1(31.4) + 0.9(29.83) = 29.99$

11. a.

Period	Time Series Value	$\alpha = .2$ Forecasts	$\alpha = .3$ Forecasts	$\alpha = .4$ Forecasts
1	28.9			
2	31.0	29.80	29.80	29.80
3	29.9	30.04	30.16	30.28
4	30.1	30.01	30.08	30.13
5	32.2	30.03	30.09	30.12
6	31.5	30.46	30.72	30.95
7	32.0	30.67	30.95	31.17
8	31.9	30.94	31.27	31.50
9	30.0	31.13	31.46	31.66

MSE($\alpha = .2$) $=$ 1.40

MSE($\alpha = .3$) $=$ 1.27

MSE($\alpha = .4$) $=$ 1.23 $\alpha = .4$ provides the best forecast

b.   Using $\alpha = .4$, $F_{10} = .4(.30) + .6(31.66) = 31.00$

12.

t	Y_t	F_t	$Y_t - F_t$	$(Y_t - F_t)^2$
1	2,750			
2	3,100	2,750.00	350.00	122,500.00
3	3,250	2,890.00	360.00	129,600.00
4	2,800	3,034.00	-234.00	54,756.00
5	2,900	2,940.40	-40.40	1,632.16
6	3,050	2,924.24	125.76	15,815.58
7	3,300	2,974.54	325.46	105,924.21
8	3,100	3,104.73	-4.73	22.37
9	2,950	3,102.84	-152.84	23,260.07
10	3,000	3,041.70	-41.70	1,738.89
11	3,200	3,025.02	174.98	30,618.00
12	3,150	3,095.01	54.99	3,023.90
			Total	488,991.18

MSE = 488,991.18 / 11 = 44,453.74
Forecast for week 13:

$$F_{13} = 0.4(3,150) + 0.6(3,095.01) = 3,117.01$$

13. a & b.

Week	Time-Series Value	$\alpha = .2$ Forecast	$(Error)^2$	$\alpha = .3$ Forecast	$(Error)^2$
1	7.35				
2	7.40	7.35	.0025	7.35	.0025
3	7.55	7.36	.0361	7.36	.0361
4	7.56	7.40	.0256	7.42	.0196
5	7.60	7.43	.0289	7.46	.0196
6	7.52	7.46	.0036	7.50	.0004
7	7.52	7.48	.0016	7.51	.0001
8	7.70	7.48	.0484	7.51	.0361
9	7.62	7.53	.0081	7.57	.0025
10	7.55	7.55	.0000	7.58	.0009
			.1548		.1178

c. $MSE(\alpha = .2) = .1548 / 9 = .0172$

$MSE(\alpha = .3) = .1178 / 9 = .0131$

Use $\alpha = .3$.

$F_{11} = .3Y_{10} + .7F_{10} = .3(7.55) + .7(7.58) = 7.57$

14. The following values are needed to compute the slope and intercept:

$$\sum t = 21 \qquad \sum t^2 = 91 \qquad \sum Y_t = 117.1 \qquad \sum tY_t = 403.7$$

Computation of slope:

$$b_1 = \frac{\sum tY_t - \left(\sum t \sum Y_t\right)/n}{\sum t^2 - \left(\sum t\right)^2/n} = \frac{403.7 - (21)(117.1)/6}{91 - (21)^2/6} = -0.3514$$

Computation of intercept:

$$b_0 = \overline{Y} - b_1\overline{t} = 19.5167 - (-0.3514)(3.5) = 20.7466$$

Equation for linear trend: $T_t = 20.7466 - 0.3514t$

Conclusion: enrollment appears to be decreasing by an average of approximately 351 students per year.

15. A linear trend model is not appropriate. A nonlinear model would provide a better approximation.

16. a.   A linear trend appears to be reasonable.

b.   The following values are needed to compute the slope and intercept:

$$\sum t = 36 \qquad \sum t^2 = 204 \qquad \sum Y_t = 223.8 \qquad \sum tY_t = 1081.6$$

Computation of slope:

$$b_1 = \frac{\sum tY_t - \left(\sum t \sum Y_t\right)/n}{\sum t^2 - \left(\sum t\right)^2/n} = \frac{1081.6 - (36)(223.8)/8}{204 - (36)^2/8} = 1.7738$$

Computation of intercept:

$$b_0 = \overline{Y} - b_1 \overline{t} = 27.975 - 1.7738(4.5) = 19.993$$

Equation for linear trend: $T_t = 19.993 + 1.774\,t$

Conclusion: The firm has been realizing an average cost increase of \$1.77 per unit per year.

17. a.

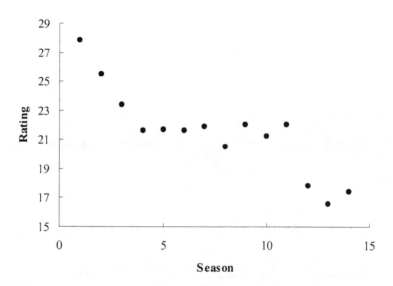

The graph shows a linear trend.

b. The following values are needed to compute the slope and intercept:

$$\sum t = 105 \qquad \sum t^2 = 1015 \qquad \sum Y_t = 301 \qquad \sum tY_t = 2115.8$$

Computation of slope:

$$b_1 = \frac{\sum tY_t - \left(\sum t \sum Y_t\right)/n}{\sum t^2 - \left(\sum t\right)^2/n} = \frac{2115.8 - (105)(301)/14}{1015 - (105)^2/14} = -0.62286$$

Computation of intercept:

$$b_0 = \overline{Y} - b_1\overline{t} = 21.5(-0.62286)(7.5) = 26.1714$$

Equation for linear trend: $T_t = 26.171 - 0.623t$

c. 2001 - 2002: $T_t = 26.171 - 0.623(15) = 16.83$

18. a.

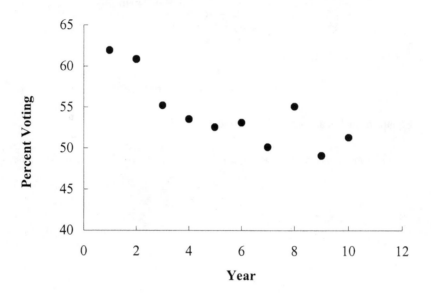

The graph shows a linear trend.

b. The following values are needed to compute the slope and intercept:

$$\sum t = 55 \qquad \sum t^2 = 385 \qquad \sum Y_t = 542.77 \qquad \sum tY_t = 2891.1$$

Computation of slope:

$$b_1 = \frac{\sum tY_t - \left(\sum t \sum Y_t\right)/n}{\sum t^2 - \left(\sum t\right)^2/n} = \frac{2891.1 - (55)(542.77)/10}{385 - (55)^2/10} = -1.141$$

Computation of intercept:

$$b_0 = \overline{Y} - b_1\overline{t} = (542.77/10) - (-1.141)(55/10) = 60.553$$

Equation for linear trend: $T_t = 60.553 - 1.141t$

The average decrease per presidential election is approximately 1.14%

c. 2004 forecast: $T_8 = 60.553 - 1.141(11) = 48.0\%$

19. a. The following values are needed to compute the slope and intercept:

$$\sum t = 78 \qquad \sum t^2 = 650 \qquad \sum Y_t = 343 \qquad \sum t Y_t = 2441$$

Computation of slope:

$$b_1 = \frac{\sum tY_t - \left(\sum t \sum Y_t\right)/n}{\sum t^2 - \left(\sum t\right)^2/n} = \frac{2441 - (78)(343)/12}{650 - (78)^2/12} = 1.479$$

Computation of intercept:

$$b_0 = \overline{Y} - b_1 \overline{t} = (343/12) - 1.479(78/12) = 18.97$$

Equation for linear trend: $T_t = 18.97 + 1.479\, t$

b.

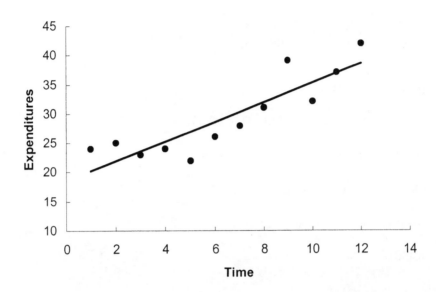

c. Capital expenditures are increasing by 1.479 billions of dollars per quarter.
$$T_{16} = 18.97 + 1.479(16) = 42.6340$$

20. a. A graph of these data shows a linear trend.

b. The following values are needed to compute the slope and intercept:

$$\sum t = 15 \quad \sum t^2 = 55 \quad \sum Y_t = 200 \quad \sum t\, Y_t = 750$$

Computation of slope:

$$b_1 = \frac{\sum tY_t - \left(\sum t \sum Y_t\right)/n}{\sum t^2 - \left(\sum t\right)^2 / n} = \frac{750 - (15)(200)/5}{55 - (15)^2/5} = 15$$

Computation of intercept:

$$b_0 = \overline{Y} - b_1 \overline{t} = 40 - 15(3) = -5$$

Equation for linear trend: $T_t = -5 + 15t$

Conclusion: average increase in sales is 15 units per year

21. a. Yes, a linear trend appears to exist.

    b. The following values are needed to compute the slope and intercept:

    $$\sum t = 28 \quad \sum t^2 = 140 \quad \sum Y_t = 595 \quad \sum t\,Y_t = 2815$$

    Computation of slope:

    $$b_1 = \frac{\sum tY_t - \left(\sum t \sum Y_t\right)/n}{\sum t^2 - \left(\sum t\right)^2/n} = \frac{2815 - (28)(595)/7}{140 - (28)^2/7} = 15.5357$$

    Computation of intercept:

    $$b_0 = \overline{Y} - b_1 \overline{t} = 85 - 15.5357(4) = 22.857$$

    Equation for linear trend: $T_t = 22.857 + 15.536t$

    c. Forecast: $T_8 = 22.857 + 15.536(8) = 147.15$

22. a. A linear trend appears to be appropriate.

    b. $T_2 = 6.4564 + 0.5345t$

    c. 5.345 million

    d. 2001 - 2002 season: $T_{13} = 6.4564 + 0.5345(12) = 12.87$ million

23. Note: Results were obtained using the Forecasting module of *The Management Scientist*.

    a.

Smoothing Constant	MSE
$\alpha = .3$	4,492.37
$\alpha = .4$	2,964.67
$\alpha = .5$	2,160.31

    The $\alpha = .5$ smoothing constant is better because it has the smallest MSE.

    b. $T_t = 244.778 + 22.088t$

    MSE = 357.81

    c. Trend projection provides much better forecasts because it has the smallest MSE. The reason MSE is smaller for trend projection is that sales are increasing over time; as a result, exponential smoothing continuously underestimates the value of sales. If you look at the forecast errors for exponential smoothing you will see that the forecast errors are positive for periods 2 through 18.

24.   Note: Results were obtained using the forecasting module of The Management Scientist.

   a. Forecast for July is 236.97

   Forecast for August, using forecast for July as the actual sales in July, is 236.97.

   Exponential smoothing provides the same forecast for every period in the future. This is why it is not usually recommended for long-term forecasting.

   b. $T_t = 149.719 + 18.451t$

   Forecast for July is 278.88

   Forecast for August is 297.33

   c. The proposed settlement is not fair since it does not account for the upward trend in sales. Based upon trend projection, the settlement should be based on forecasted lost sales of $278,880 in July and $297,330 in August.

25. a. Four quarter moving averages beginning with

   $(1690 + 940 + 2625 + 2500) / 4 = 1938.75$

   Other moving averages are

1966.25	2002.50
1956.25	2052.50
2025.00	2060.00
1990.00	2123.75

   b.

Quarter	Seasonal-Irregular Component Values		Seasonal Index	Adjusted Seasonal Index
1	0.904	0.900	0.9020	0.900
2	0.448	0.526	0.4970	0.486
3	1.344	1.453	1.3985	1.396
4	1.275	1.164	1.2195	1.217
			4.0070	

   Note: Adjustment for seasonal index = 4.000 / 4.007 = 0.9983

   c. The largest seasonal effect is in the third quarter which corresponds to the back-to-school demand during July, August, and September of each year.

26.

Month	Seasonal-Irregular Component Values		Seasonal Index	Adjusted Seasonal Index
1	0.72	0.70	0.71	0.707
2	0.80	0.75	0.78	0.777
3	0.83	0.82	0.83	0.827
4	0.94	0.99	0.97	0.966
5	1.01	1.02	1.02	1.016
6	1.25	1.36	1.31	1.305
7	1.49	1.51	1.50	1.494
8	1.19	1.26	1.23	1.225
9	0.98	0.97	0.98	0.976
10	0.98	1.00	0.99	0.986
11	0.93	0.94	0.94	0.936
12	0.78	0.80	0.79	0.787
			12.05	

Notes: 1. Adjustment for seasonal index = 12 / 12.05 = 0.996

2. The adjustment is really not necessary in this problem since it implies more accuracy than is warranted. That is, the seasonal component values and the seasonal index were rounded to two decimal places.

27. a. Use a twelve period moving averages. After centering the moving averages, you should obtain the following seasonal indexes:

Hour	Seasonal Index	Hour	Seasonal Index
1	0.771	7	1.207
2	0.864	8	0.994
3	0.954	9	0.850
4	1.392	10	0.647
5	1.571	11	0.579
6	1.667	12	0.504

b. The hours of July 18 are number 37 to 48 in the time series. Thus the trend component for 7:00 a.m. on July 18 (period 37) would be

$$T_{37} = 32.983 + .3922(37) = 47.49$$

A summary of the trend components for the twelve hours on July 18 is as follows:

Hour	Trend Component	Hour	Trend Component
1	47.49	7	49.85
2	47.89	8	50.24
3	48.28	9	50.63
4	48.67	10	51.02
5	49.06	11	51.42
6	49.46	12	51.81

c. Multiply the trend component in part b by the seasonal indexes in part a to obtain the twelve hourly forecasts for July 18. For example, 47.49 x (.771) = 36.6 or rounded to 37, would be the forecast for 7:00 a.m. on July 18th.

The seasonally adjusted hourly forecasts for July 18 are as follows:

Hour	Forecast	Hour	Forecast
1	37	7	60
2	41	8	50
3	46	9	43
4	68	10	33
5	77	11	30
6	82	12	26

28. a.

t	Sales	Centered Moving Average	Seasonal-Irregular Component
1	6		
2	15		
3	10	9.250	1.081
4	4	10.125	0.395
5	10	11.125	0.899
6	18	12.125	1.485
7	15	13.000	1.154
8	7	14.500	0.483
9	14	16.500	0.848
10	26	18.125	1.434
11	23	19.375	1.187
12	12	20.250	0.593
13	19	20.750	0.916
14	28	21.750	1.287
15	25	22.875	1.093
16	18	24.000	0.750
17	22	25.125	0.876
18	34	25.875	1.314
19	28	26.500	1.057
20	21	27.000	0.778
21	24	27.500	0.873
22	36	27.625	1.303
23	30	28.000	1.071
24	20	29.000	0.690
25	28	30.125	0.929
26	40	31.625	1.265
27	35		
28	27		

b.

Quarter	Seasonal-Irregular Component Values	Seasonal Index
1	0.899, 0.848, 0.916, 0.876, 0.873, 0.929	0.890
2	1.485, 1.434, 1.287, 1.314, 1.303, 1.265	1.348
3	1.081, 1.154, 1.187, 1.093, 1.057, 1.071	1.107
4	0.395, 0.483, 0.593, 0.750, 0.778, 0.690	0.615
	Total	3.960

Quarter	Adjusted Seasonal Index
1	0.899
2	1.362
3	1.118
4	0.621

Note: Adjustment for seasonal index = 4.00 / 3.96 = 1.0101

   c. Hudson Marine experiences the largest seasonal increase in quarter 2. Since this quarter occurs prior to the peak summer boating season, this result seems reasonable.

29. a.

t	Sales	Centered Moving Average	Seasonal-Irregular Component
1	4		
2	2		
3	1	3.250	0.308
4	5	3.750	1.333
5	6	4.375	1.371
6	4	5.875	0.681
7	4	7.500	0.533
8	14	7.875	1.778
9	10	7.875	1.270
10	3	8.250	0.364
11	5	8.750	0.571
12	16	9.750	1.641
13	12	10.750	1.116
14	9	11.750	0.766
15	7	13.250	0.528
16	22	14.125	1.558
17	18	15.000	1.200
18	10	17.375	0.576
19	13		
20	35		

Quarter	Seasonal-Irregular Component Values	Seasonal Index
1	1.371, 1.270, 1.116, 1.200	1.239
2	0.681, 0.364, 0.776, 0.576	0.597
3	0.308, 0.533, 0.571, 0.528	0.485
4	1.333, 1.778, 1.641, 1.558	1.578
	Total	3.899

Quarter	Adjusted Seasonal Index
1	1.271
2	0.613
3	0.498
4	1.619

Note: Adjustment for seasonal index = 4 / 3.899 = 1.026

b. The largest effect is in quarter 4; this seems reasonable since retail sales are generally higher during October, November, and December.

30. a. Note: To simplify the calculations the seasonal indexes calculated in problem 28 have been rounded to two decimal places.

Year	Quarter	Sales Y_t	Seasonal Factor S_t	Deseasonalized Sales $Y_t / S_t = T_t I_t$
1	1	6	0.90	6.67
	2	15	1.36	11.03
	3	10	1.12	8.93
	4	4	0.62	6.45
2	1	10	0.90	11.11
	2	18	1.36	13.24
	3	15	1.12	13.39
	4	7	0.62	11.29
3	1	14	0.90	15.56
	2	26	1.36	19.12
	3	23	1.12	20.54
	4	12	0.62	19.35
4	1	19	0.90	21.11
	2	28	1.36	20.59
	3	25	1.12	22.32
	4	18	0.62	29.03
5	1	22	0.90	24.44
	2	34	1.36	25.00
	3	28	1.12	25.00
	4	21	0.62	33.87
6	1	24	0.90	26.67
	2	36	1.36	26.47
	3	30	1.12	26.79
	4	20	0.62	32.26
7	1	28	0.90	31.11
	2	40	1.36	29.41
	3	35	1.12	31.25
	4	27	0.62	43.55

t	Y_t (deseasonalized)	tY_t	t^2
1	6.67	6.67	1
2	11.03	22.06	4
3	8.93	26.79	9
4	6.45	25.80	16
5	11.11	55.55	25
6	13.24	79.44	36
7	13.39	93.73	49
8	11.29	90.32	64
9	15.56	140.04	81
10	19.12	191.20	100
11	20.54	225.94	121
12	19.35	232.20	144
13	21.11	274.43	169
14	20.59	288.26	196
15	22.32	334.80	225
16	29.03	464.48	256
17	24.44	415.48	289
18	25.00	450.00	324
19	25.00	475.00	361
20	33.87	677.40	400
21	26.67	560.07	441
22	26.47	582.34	484
23	26.79	616.17	529
24	32.26	774.24	576
25	31.11	777.75	625
26	29.41	764.66	676
27	31.25	843.75	729
$\underline{28}$	$\underline{43.55}$	$\underline{1,219.40}$	$\underline{784}$
406	605.55	10,707.34	7,714

$\bar{t} = 14.5$ $\bar{Y} = 21.627$ $b_1 = 1.055$ $b_0 = 6.329$ $T_t = 6.329 + 1.055t$

b.

t	Trend Forecast
29	36.92
30	37.98
31	39.03
32	40.09

c.

Year	Quarter	Trend Forecast	Seasonal Index	Quarterly Forecast
8	1	36.92	0.90	33.23
	2	37.98	1.36	51.65
	3	29.03	1.12	43.71
	4	40.09	0.62	24.86

31. a. Note: To simplify the calculations the seasonal indexes in problem 29 have been round to two decimal places.

Year	Quarter	Sales Y_t	Seasonal Factor S_t	Deseasonalized Sales $Y_t / S_t = T_t I_t$
1	1	4	1.27	3.15
	2	2	0.61	3.28
	3	1	0.50	2.00
	4	5	1.62	3.09
2	1	6	1.27	4.72
	2	4	0.61	6.56
	3	4	0.50	8.00
	4	14	1.62	8.64
3	1	10	1.27	7.87
	2	3	0.61	4.92
	3	5	0.50	10.00
	4	16	1.62	9.88
4	1	12	1.27	9.45
	2	9	0.61	14.75
	3	7	0.50	14.00
	4	22	1.62	13.58
5	1	18	1.27	14.17
	2	10	0.61	16.39
	3	13	0.50	26.00
	4	35	1.62	21.60

t	Y_t (deseasonalized)	tY_t	t^2
1	3.15	3.15	1
2	3.28	6.56	4
3	2.00	6.00	9
4	3.09	12.36	16
5	4.72	23.60	25
6	6.56	39.36	36
7	8.00	56.00	49
8	8.64	69.12	64
9	7.87	70.83	81
10	4.92	49.20	100
11	10.00	110.00	121
12	9.88	118.56	144
13	9.45	122.85	169
14	14.75	206.50	196
15	14.00	210.00	225
16	13.58	217.28	256
17	14.17	240.89	289
18	16.39	295.02	324
19	26.00	494.00	361
20	21.60	432.00	400
210	202.05	2783.28	2870

$$\overline{t} = 10.5 \quad \overline{Y} = 10.1025 \quad b_1 = .995 \quad b_0 = -.345 \quad T_t = -.345 + .995\,t$$

b.

y	Trend Forecast
21	20.55
22	21.55
23	22.54
24	23.54

c.

Year	Quarter	Trend Forecast	Seasonal Index	Quarterly Forecast
6	1	20.55	1.27	26.10
	2	21.55	0.61	13.15
	3	22.54	0.50	11.27
	4	23.54	1.62	38.13

32.   Note: Results were obtained using the Forecasting module of The Management Scientist.

a.   Yes, there is a seasonal effect over the 24 hour period.

Time Period	Seasonal Index
12 - 4 a.m.	1.696
4 - 8 a.m.	1.458
8 - 12	0.711
12 - 4 p.m.	0.326
4 - 8 p.m.	0.448
8 - 12	1.362

b.

Time Period	Forecast
12 - 4 p.m.	166,761.13
4 - 8 p.m.	146,052.99

33.

Restaurant (i)	x_i	y_i	$x_i y_i$	x_i^2
1	1	19	19	1
2	4	44	176	16
3	6	40	240	36
4	10	52	520	100
5	14	53	742	196
Totals	35	208	1,697	349

$$\overline{x} = 7 \quad \overline{y} = 41.6 \quad b_1 = 2.317 \quad b_0 = 25.381 \quad \hat{y} = 25.381 + 2.317x$$

b. $\hat{y} = 25.381 + 2.317(8) = 43.917$ or $43,917

34.   Note: To simplify the calculations let y = sales ($100s)

x_i	y_i	$x_i y_i$	x_i^2
1	36	36	1
1	33	33	1
2	31	62	4
3	29	87	9
3	27	81	9
4	25	100	16
5	23	115	25
5	20	100	25
24	224	614	90

$\bar{x} = 3$ $\bar{y} = 28$ $b_1 = -3.222$ $b_0 = 37.666$ $\hat{y} = 37.666 - 3.222x$

b. $\hat{y} = 37.666 - 3.222\,(1) = 34.44$ or $3444

35.

x_i	y_i	$x_i y_i$	x_i^2
20	21	420	400
20	19	380	400
40	15	600	1600
30	16	480	900
60	14	840	3600
40	17	680	1600
210	102	3400	8500

$\bar{x} = 35$ $\bar{y} = 17$ $b_1 = -0.1478$ $b_0 = 22.713$ $\hat{y} = 22.713 - 0.1478x$

b. $\hat{y} = 22.173 - 0.1478(50) = 14.783$ or approximately 15 defective parts

Chapter 17
Markov Processes

Learning Objectives

1. Learn about the types of problems that can be modeled as Markov processes.

2. Understand the Markov process approach to the market share or brand loyalty problem.

3. Be able to set up and use the transition probabilities for specific problems.

4. Know what is meant by the steady-state probabilities.

5. Know how to solve Markov processes models having absorbing states.

6. Understand the following terms:

   state of the system
   transition probability
   state probability
   steady-state probability
   absorbing state
   fundamental matrix

Solutions:

1.

State Probability	0	1	2	3	4	5	6	7	8	9	10	Large $\rightarrow n$
$\pi_1 (n)$	0.5	0.55	0.585	0.610	0.627	0.639	0.647	0.653	0.657	0.660	0.662	$\rightarrow 2/3$
$\pi_2 (n)$	0.5	0.45	0.415	0.390	0.373	0.361	0.353	0.347	0.343	0.340	0.338	$\rightarrow 1/3$

Probabilities are approaching $\pi_1 = 2/3$ and $\pi_2 = 1/3$.

2.   a.

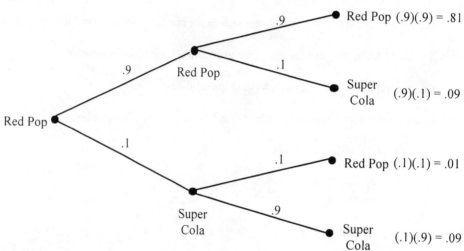

b. $\pi_1 = 0.5$, $\pi_2 = 0.5$

c. $P = \begin{bmatrix} 0.90 & 0.10 \\ 0.10 & 0.85 \end{bmatrix}$ $\pi_1 = .6$, $\pi_2 = .4$

3.   a.   0.10

b. $\pi_1 = 0.75$, $\pi_2 = 0.25$

4.   a. $\pi_1 = 0.92$, $\pi_2 = 0.08$

b.   Without component: Expected Cost = 0.25 ($500) = $125

With component: Expected Cost = 0.08 ($500) = $ 40

Breakeven Cost = $125 - $40 = $85 per hour.

5.

	No Traffic Delay	Traffic Delay
No Traffic Delay	0.85	0.15
Traffic Delay	0.25	0.75

a.

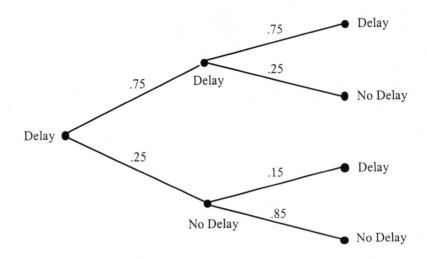

$$P \text{ (Delay 60 minutes)} = (0.75)(0.75) = 0.5625$$

b. $\pi_1 = 0.85\, \pi_1 + 0.25\, \pi_2$

$\pi_2 = 0.15\, \pi_1 + 0.75\, \pi_2$

$\pi_1 + \pi_2 = 1$

Solve for $\pi_1 = 0.625$ and $\pi_2 = 0.375$

c.   This assumption may not be valid. The transition probabilities of moving to delay and no delay states may actually change with the time of day.

6.   a.

	City	Suburbs
City	0.98	0.02
Suburbs	0.01	0.99

b. $\pi_1 = 0.98\, \pi_1 + 0.01\, \pi_2$ (1)

$\pi_2 = 0.02\, \pi_1 + 0.99\, \pi_2$ (2)

$\pi_1 + \pi_2 = 1$ (3)

Solving equations (1) and (3) provides

$$0.02\, \pi_1 - 0.01\, \pi_2 = 0$$
$$\pi_2 = 1 - \pi_1$$

Thus, $0.02 \pi - 0.01 (1 - \pi_1) = 0$

$0.03 \pi_1 - 0.01 = 0$

$\pi_1 = 0.333$

and $\pi_2 = 1 - 0.333 = 0.667$

c. The area will show increases in the suburb population and decreases in the city population. The current 40% in the city is expected to drop to around 33%.

7. a. Let π_1 = Murphy's steady-state probability
       π_2 = Ashley's steady-state probability
       π_3 = Quick Stop's steady-state probability

$\pi_1 = 0.85 \pi_1 + 0.20 \pi_2 + 0.15 \pi_3$ (1)

$\pi_2 = 0.10 \pi_1 + 0.75 \pi_2 + 0.10 \pi_3$ (2)

$\pi_3 = 0.05 \pi_1 + 0.05 \pi_2 + 0.75 \pi_3$ (3)

$\pi_1 + \pi_2 + \pi_3 = 1$

Using 1, 2, and 4 we have

$0.15 \pi_1 - 0.20 \pi_2 - 0.15 \pi_3 = 0$

$-0.10 \pi_1 - 0.25 \pi_2 - 0.10 \pi_3 = 0$

$\pi_1 + \pi_2 + \pi_3 = 1$

Solving three equations and three unknowns gives $\pi_1 = 0.548$, $\pi_2 = 0.286$, and $\pi_3 = 0.166$

b. 16.6%

c. Murphy's 548, Ashley's 286, and Quick Stop's 166. Quick Stop should take 667 - 548 = 119 Murphy's customers and 33 - 286 = 47 Ashley's customers.

8. a. Only 5% of MDA customers switch to Special B while 10% of Special B customers switch to MDA

b. $\pi_1 = 0.333$, $\pi_2 = 0.667$

9.

π_1	=	$0.80\pi_1$	+	$0.05\pi_2$	+	$0.40\pi_3$	[1]
π_2	=	$0.10\pi_1$	+	$0.75\pi_2$	+	$0.30\pi_3$	[2]
π_3	=	$0.10\pi_1$	+	$0.20\pi_2$	+	$0.30\pi_3$	[3]

also

$\pi_1 + \pi_2 + \pi_3 = 1$ [4]

Using equations 1,2 and 4, we have $\pi_1 = 0.442$, $\pi_2 = 0.385$, and $\pi_3 = 0.173$.

The Markov analysis shows that Special B now has the largest market share. In fact, its market share has increased by almost 11%. The MDA brand will be hurt most by the introduction of the new brand, T-White. People who switch from MDA to T-White are more likely to make a second switch back to MDA.

10.

$$(I-Q) = \begin{bmatrix} 1 & 0 \\ 0 & 1 \end{bmatrix} - \begin{bmatrix} 0.4 & 0.3 \\ 0.1 & 0.5 \end{bmatrix} = \begin{bmatrix} 0.6 & -0.3 \\ -0.1 & 0.5 \end{bmatrix}$$

$$N = (I-Q)^{-1} = \begin{bmatrix} 1.85 & 1.11 \\ 0.37 & 2.22 \end{bmatrix}$$

$$NR = \begin{bmatrix} 1.85 & 1.11 \\ 0.37 & 2.22 \end{bmatrix} \begin{bmatrix} 0.2 & 0.1 \\ 0.2 & 0.2 \end{bmatrix} = \begin{bmatrix} 0.59 & 0.41 \\ 0.52 & 0.48 \end{bmatrix}$$

0.59 probability state 3 units end up in state 1;
0.52 probability state 4 units end up in state 1.

11.

$$(I-Q) = \begin{bmatrix} 0.75 & -0.25 \\ -0.05 & 0.75 \end{bmatrix}$$

$$N = \begin{bmatrix} 1.36 & 0.45 \\ 0.09 & 1.36 \end{bmatrix}$$

$$NR = \begin{bmatrix} 0.909 & 0.091 \\ 0.727 & 0.273 \end{bmatrix}$$

$$BNR = [4000, 5000] \, NR = [7271, 1729]$$

$1729 in bad debts.

12.

$$(I-Q) = \begin{bmatrix} 0.5 & -0.2 \\ 0.0 & 0.5 \end{bmatrix}$$

$$N = (I-Q)^{-1} = \begin{bmatrix} 2 & 0.8 \\ 0 & 2.0 \end{bmatrix}$$

$$NR = \begin{bmatrix} 0.52 & 0.48 \\ 0.80 & 0.20 \end{bmatrix}$$

$$BNR = \begin{bmatrix} 1500 & 3500 \end{bmatrix} \begin{bmatrix} 0.52 & 0.48 \\ 0.80 & 0.20 \end{bmatrix} = \begin{bmatrix} 3580 & 1420 \end{bmatrix}$$

13. a. Retirement and leaves for personal reasons are the two absorbing states since both result in the manager leaving the company.

b. Middle Managers:

Probability of retirement = 0.03
Probability of leaving (personal) = 0.07
Probability of staying middle manager = 0.80
Probability of promotion to senior manager = 0.10

c. Senior Managers:

Probability of retirement = 0.08
Probability of leaving (personal) = 0.01
Probability of staying middle manager = 0.03
Probability of promotion to senior manager = 0.88

d.

$$(I\text{-}Q) = \begin{bmatrix} 1 & 0 \\ 0 & 1 \end{bmatrix} - \begin{bmatrix} 0.80 & 0.10 \\ 0.03 & 0.88 \end{bmatrix} = \begin{bmatrix} 0.20 & -0.10 \\ -0.03 & 0.12 \end{bmatrix}$$

$$N = (I\text{-}Q)^{-1} = \begin{bmatrix} 5.714 & 4.762 \\ 1.429 & 9.524 \end{bmatrix}$$

$$NR = \begin{bmatrix} 0.552 & 0.448 \\ 0.805 & 0.195 \end{bmatrix}$$

55.2% will retire and 44.8% will leave for personal reasons.

e.

$$BNR = \begin{bmatrix} 640 & 280 \end{bmatrix} \begin{bmatrix} 0.552 & 0.448 \\ 0.805 & 0.195 \end{bmatrix} = \begin{bmatrix} 579 & 341 \end{bmatrix}$$

579 will retire (63%) and 341 will leave (37%).

14. a. Graduating and dropping out are the two absorbing states.

b. Probability of dropping out = 0.15
Probability of staying a sophomore next year = 0.10
Probability of becoming a junior next year = 0.75

All other transition probabilities are zero.

c. Due to the size of the problem, The Management Scientist software was used to make the Markov process calculations.

P (Graduate) = 0.706   P (Drop Out) = 0.294

d. Yes; for freshman, P (Graduate) = 0.54 and P (Drop Out) = 0.46. Thus about half of the freshman will not make graduation day.

e.

$$\begin{bmatrix} 600, 520, 460, 420 \end{bmatrix} \begin{bmatrix} 0.540 & 0.460 \\ 0.706 & 0.294 \\ 0.848 & 0.152 \\ 0.947 & 0.053 \end{bmatrix} = \begin{bmatrix} 1479 & 521 \end{bmatrix}$$

1479 students (74%) will eventually graduate.

Chapter 18
Dynamic Programming

Learning Objectives

1. Understand the basics of dynamic programming and its approach to problem solving.

2. Learn the general dynamic programming notation.

3. Be able to use the dynamic programming approach to solve problems such as the shortest route problem, the knapsack problem and production and inventory control problems.

4. Understand the following terms:

   stages
   state variables
   principle of optimality
   stage transformation function
   return function
   knapsack problem

Solutions:

1.

Route	Value	Route	Value
(1-2-5-8-10)	22	(1-3-6-8-10)	26
(1-2-5-9-10)	25	(1-3-6-9-10)	22
(1-2-6-8-10)	24	(1-3-7-8-10)	22
(1-2-6-9-10)	20	(1-3-7-9-10)	21
(1-2-7-8-10)	25	(1-4-5-8-10)	22
(1-2-7-9-10)	24	(1-4-5-9-10)	25
(1-3-5-8-10)	19	(1-4-6-8-10)	27
(1-3-5-9-10)	22	(1-4-6-9-10)	23

The route (1-3-5-8-10) has the smallest value and is thus the solution to the problem.

The dynamic programming approach results in fewer computations because all 16 paths from node 1 to node 10 need not be computed. For example, at node 1 we considered only 3 paths: the one from 1-2 plus the shortest path from node 2 to node 10, the one from 1-3 plus the shortest path from node 3 to node 10, and the one from 1-4 plus the shortest path from node 4 to node 10.

2.   a.   The numbers in the squares above each node represent the shortest route from that node to node 10.

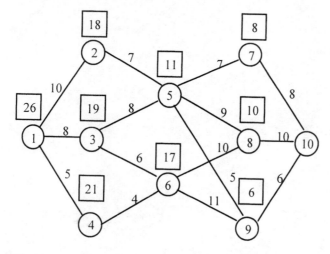

The shortest route is given by the sequence of nodes (1-4-6-9-10).

b.   The shortest route from node 4 to node 10 is given by (4-6-9-10).

c.

Route	Value	Route	Value
(1-2-5-7-10)	32	(1-3-6-8-10)	34
(1-2-5-8-10)	36	(1-3-6-9-10)	31
(1-2-5-9-10)	28	(1-4-6-8-10)	29
(1-3-5-7-10)	31	(1-4-6-9-10)	26
(1-3-5-8-10)	35		
(1-3-5-9-10)	27		

See 1 above for an explanation of how the computations are reduced.

3.	Use 4 stages; one for each type of cargo.

Let the state variable represent the amount of cargo space remaining.

a.	In hundreds of pounds we have up to 20 units of capacity available.

Stage 1 (Cargo Type 1)

x_1	0	1	2	d_1^*	$f_1(x_1)$	x_0
0-7	0	–	–	0	0	0-7
8-15	0	22	–	1	22	0-7
16-20	0	22	44	2	44	0-4

Stage 2 (Cargo Type 2)

x_2	0	1	2	d_2^*	$f_2(x_2)$	x_1
0-4	0	–	–	0	0	0-4
5-7	0	12	–	1	12	0-2
8-9	22	12	–	0	22	8-9
10-12	22	12	24	2	24	0-2
13-15	22	34	24	1	34	8-10
16-17	44	34	24	0	44	16-17
18-20	44	34	46	2	46	8-10

Stage 3 (Cargo Type 3)

x_3	0	1	2	3	4	d_3^*	$f_3(x_3)$	x_2
0-2	0	–	–	–	–	0	0	0-2
3-4	0	7	–	–	–	1	7	0-1
5	12	7	–	–	–	0	12	5
6-7	12	7	14	–	–	2	14	0-1
8	22	19	14	–	–	0	22	8
9	22	19	14	21	–	0	22	9
10	24	19	14	21	–	0	24	10
11	22	29	26	21	–	1	29	8
12	24	29	26	21	28	1	29	9
13	34	31	26	21	28	0	34	13
14-15	34	31	36	33	28	2	36	8-9
16	44	41	38	33	28	0	44	16
17	44	41	38	43	40	0	44	17
18	46	41	38	43	40	0	46	18
19	46	51	48	45	40	1	51	16
20	46	51	48	45	50	1	51	17

Stage 4 (Cargo Type 4)

x_4	0	1	2	3	d_4^*	$f_4(x_4)$	x_3
20	51	49	50	45	0	51	20

Tracing back through the tables we find

Stage	State Variable Entering	Optimal Decision	State Variable Leaving
4	20	0	20
3	20	1	17
2	17	0	17
1	17	2	1

Load 1 unit of cargo type 3 and 2 units of cargo type 1 for a total return of $5100.

b. Only the calculations for stage 4 need to be repeated; the entering value for the state variable is 18.

x_4	0	1	2	3	d_4^*	$f_4(x_4)$	x_3
18	46	47	42	38	1	47	16

Optimal solution: $d_4 = 1, d_3 = 0, d_2 = 0, d_1 = 2$

Value $= 47$

4. a. There are two optimal solutions each yielding a total profit of 186.

	# of Employees	Return
Activity 1	3	44
Activity 2	2	48
Activity 3	0	46
Activity 4	3	48
		186

	# of Employees	Return
Activity 1	2	37
Activity 2	3	55
Activity 3	0	46
Activity 4	3	48
		186

b.

	# of Employees	Return
Activity 1	1	30
Activity 2	2	48
Activity 3	0	46
Activity 4	3	48
		172

5. a. Set up a stage for each possible length the log can be cut into: Stage 1 - 16 foot lengths, Stage 2 - 11 foot lengths , Stage 3 - 7 foot lengths, and Stage 4 - 3 foot lengths.

Stage 1

x_1	d_1 0	1	d_1^*	$f_1(x_1)$	x_0
0-15	0	–	0	0	x_1
16-20	0	8	1	8	x_1-16

Stage 2

x_2	d_2 0	1	d_2^*	$f_2(x_2)$	x_1
0-10	0	–	0	0	x_2
11-15	0	5	1	5	x_2-11
16-20	8	5	0	8	x_2

Stage 3

x_3	d_3 0	1	2	d_3^*	$f_3(x_3)$	x_2
0-6	0	–	–	0	0	x_3
7-10	0	3	–	1	3	x_3-7
11-13	5	3	–	0	5	x_3
14-15	5	3	6	2	6	x_3-14
16-17	8	3	6	0	8	x_3
18-20	8	8	8	1	8	x_3-7

Stage 4

x_4	d_4 0	1	2	3	4	5	6	d_4^*	$f_4(x_4)$	x_3
20	8	9	8	8	7	5	6	1	9	17

Tracing back through the tableau, we see that our optimal decisions are

$$d_4^* = 1, \ d_3^* = 0,$$

$$d_2^* = 0, \ d_1^* = 1.$$

The total return per log when this pattern is used is $9.

b. We simply create a stage for every length.

6. a. In the network representation below each node represents the completion of an assignment. The numbers above the arcs coming into the node represent the time it takes to carry out the assignment.

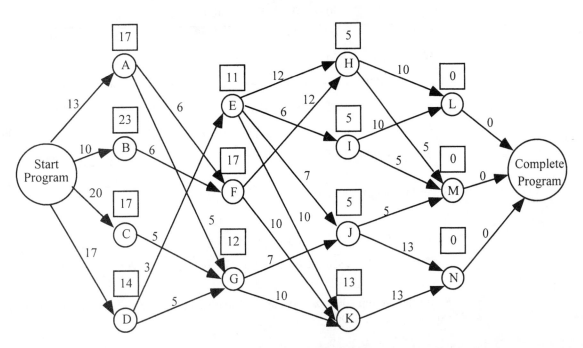

Once the network is set up we can solve as we did in section 18.1 for the shortest route problem. The optimal sequence of assignments is A-G-J-M. The total training period for this solution is 30 months.

   b. He should choose H. The training program can then be completed in 17 months.

7. Let each stage correspond to a store. Let the state variable x_n represent the number of golf balls remaining to allocate at store n and d_n represent the number allocated to store n.

Stage 1 (Store 1)

				d_1					
x_1	0	100	200	300	400	500	d_1^*	$f_1(x_1)$	x_0
0	0	–	–	–	–	–	0	0	0
100	0	600	–	–	–	–	100	600	0
200	0	600	1100	–	–	–	200	1100	0
300	0	600	1100	1550	–	–	300	1550	0
400	0	600	1100	1550	1700	–	400	1700	0
500	0	600	1100	1550	1700	1800	500	1800	0

Stage 2 (Store 2)

x_2	d_2 0	100	200	300	400	500	d_2^*	$f_2(x_2)$	x_1
0	0	–	–	–	–	–	0	0	0
100	600	500	–	–	–	–	100	600	100
200	1100	1100	1200	–	–	–	200	1200	0
300	1550	1600	1800	1700	–	–	200	1800	100
400	1700	2050	2300	2300	2000	–	200 or 300	2300	200 or 100
500	1800	2200	2750	2800	2600	2100	300	2800	200

Stage 3 (Store 3)

x_3	d_3 0	100	200	300	400	500	d_3^*	$f_3(x_3)$	x_2
500	2800	2850	2900	2700	2450	1950	200	2900	300

Robin should ship 200 dozen to store 3, 200 dozen to store 2 and 100 dozen to store 1. He can expect a profit of $2900.

8. a. Let each of the media represent a stage in the dynamic programming formulation. Further, let the state variable, x_n, represent the amount of budget remaining with n stages to go and the decision variable, d_n, the amount of the budget allocated to media n.

Stage 1 (Daily Newspaper)

x_1	d_1 0	1	2	3	4	5	6	7	8	d_1^*	$f_1(x_1)$	x_0
0	0	–	–	–	–	–	–	–	–	0	0	0
1	0	24	–	–	–	–	–	–	–	1	24	0
2	0	24	37	–	–	–	–	–	–	2	37	0
3	0	24	37	46	–	–	–	–	–	3	46	0
4	0	24	37	46	59	–	–	–	–	4	59	0
5	0	24	37	46	59	72	–	–	–	5	72	0
6	0	24	37	46	59	72	80	–	–	6	80	0
7	0	24	37	46	59	72	80	82	–	7	82	0
8	0	24	37	46	59	72	80	82	82	7 or 8	82	0 or 1

Stage 2 (Sunday Newspaper)

x_2	0	1	2	3	d_2 4	5	6	7	8	d_2^*	$f_2(x_2)$	x_1
0	0	–	–	–	–	–	–	–	–	0	0	0
1	24	15	–	–	–	–	–	–	–	0	24	1
2	37	39	55	–	–	–	–	–	–	2	55	0
3	46	52	79	70	–	–	–	–	–	2	79	1
4	59	61	92	94	75	–	–	–	–	3	94	1
5	72	74	101	107	99	90	–	–	–	3	107	2
6	80	87	114	116	112	114	95	–	–	3	116	3
7	82	95	127	129	121	127	119	95	–	3	129	4
8	82	97	135	142	134	136	132	119	95	3	142	5

Stage 3 (Radio)

x_3	0	1	2	3	d_3 4	5	6	7	8	d_3^*	$f_3(x_3)$	x_2
0	0	–	–	–	–	–	–	–	–	0	0	0
1	24	20	–	–	–	–	–	–	–	0	24	1
2	55	44	30	–	–	–	–	–	–	0	55	2
3	79	75	54	45	–	–	–	–	–	0	79	3
4	94	99	85	69	55	–	–	–	–	1	99	3
5	107	114	109	100	79	60	–	–	–	1	114	4
6	116	127	124	124	110	84	62	–	–	1	127	5
7	129	136	137	139	134	115	86	63	–	3	139	4
8	142	149	146	152	149	139	117	87	63	3	152	5

Stage 4 (Television)

x_4	0	1	2	3	d_4 4	5	6	7	8	d_4^*	$f_4(x_4)$	x_3
8	152	159	167	169	164	149	125	94	70	3	169	5

Tracing back through the tables, we find the optimal decision is

$$d_4 = 3 \qquad x_3 = x_4 - d_4 = 8 - 3 = 5$$
$$d_3 = 1 \qquad x_2 = x_3 - d_3 = 5 - 1 = 4$$
$$d_2 = 3 \qquad x_1 = x_2 - d_2 = 4 - 3 = 1$$
$$d_1 = 1 \qquad x_0 = x_1 - d_1 = 1 - 1 = 0$$

This gives the agency a maximum exposure of 169.

b.   We simply redo the calculations for stage 4 with $x_4 = 6$.

x_4	d_4 0	1	2	3	4	5	6	d_4^*	$f_4(x_4)$	x_3
6	127	134	139	134	120	94	70	2	139	4

Tracing back through the tables, we find a new optimal solution of

$$d_4 = 2 \qquad x_3 = x_4 - d_4 = 6 - 2 = 4$$
$$d_3 = 1 \qquad x_2 = x_3 - d_3 = 4 - 1 = 3$$
$$d_2 = 2 \qquad x_1 = x_2 - d_2 = 3 - 2 = 1$$
$$d_1 = 1 \qquad x_0 = x_1 - d_1 = 1 - 1 = 0$$

This gives the agency a maximum value of 139.

c.   We can simply return to the stage 3 table and read off the answers.

If $8,000 was available, the optimal decisions are

$$d_3 = 3$$
$$d_2 = 3$$
$$d_1 = 2.$$

The maximum exposure value is 152.

If $6,000 was available, the optimal decisions are

$$d_3 = 1$$
$$d_2 = 3$$
$$d_1 = 2.$$

The maximum exposure is 127.

9. a.

d_3	d_2	d_1	$r_1(d_1) + r_2(d_2) + r_3(d_3)$
100	100	0	295
100	100	100	405
100	100	200	595
100	100	300	695
100	100	400	720
100	300	0	575
100	300	100	685
100	300	200	875
100	300	300	975
100	300	400	1000
100	500	0	825
100	500	100	935
100	500	200	1125
100	500	300	1225
100	500	400	1250
100	600	0	875
100	600	100	985
100	600	200	1175
100	600	300	1275
100	800	0	1150
100	800	100	1260
500	100	0	820
500	100	100	930
500	100	200	1120
500	100	300	1220
500	100	400	1245
500	300	0	1100
500	300	100	1210
500	300	200	1400
500	500	0	1350

The optimal solution is $d_1 = 200$, $d_2 = 300$, $d_3 = 500$.

b. Stage 1

x_1	0	100	d_1 200	300	400	d_1^*	$f_1(x_1)$	x_0
0	0	–	–	–	–	0	0	0
100	0	110	–	–	–	100	110	0
200	0	110	300	–	–	200	300	0
300	0	110	300	400	–	300	400	0

Stage 2

| | d_2 | | | | | | | |
x_2	0	300	500	600	800	d_2^*	$f_2(x_2)$	x_1
500	545	700	650	–	–	300	700	200
900	545	825	1075	1100	1085	600	1100	300

Stage 3

| | d_3 | | | | |
x_3	100	500	d_3^*	$f_3(x_3)$	x_2
1000	1275	1400	500	1400	500

Tracing back through the tableaus, we see we get the same solution as in (a) with much less effort.

10.   The optimal production schedule is given below.

Month	Beginning Inventory	Production	Ending Inventory
1	10	20	10
2	10	20	0
3	0	30	0